Construction and Engineering Law:
A Guide for Project Managers

Construction and Engineering Law:
A Guide for Project Managers

Sally Marsden and Pauline Makepeace

General Editors

LexisNexis™ UK

Members of the LexisNexis Group worldwide

United Kingdom	LexisNexis UK, a Division of Reed Elsevier (UK) Ltd, Halsbury House, 35 Chancery Lane, LONDON, WC2A 1EL, and 4 Hill Street, EDINBURGH EH2 3JZ
Argentina	LexisNexis Argentina, BUENOS AIRES
Australia	LexisNexis Butterworths, CHATSWOOD, New South Wales
Austria	LexisNexis Verlag ARD Orac GmbH & Co KG, VIENNA
Canada	LexisNexis Butterworths, MARKHAM, Ontario
Chile	LexisNexis Chile Ltda, SANTIAGO DE CHILE
Czech Republic	Nakladatelství Orac sro, PRAGUE
France	Editions du Juris-Classeur SA, PARIS
Germany	LexisNexis Deutschland GmbH, FRANKFURT, MUNSTER
Hong Kong	LexisNexis Butterworths, HONG KONG
Hungary	HVG-Orac, BUDAPEST
India	LexisNexis Butterworths, NEW DELHI
Ireland	Butterworths (Ireland) Ltd, DUBLIN
Italy	Giuffrè Editore, MILAN
Malaysia	Malayan Law Journal Sdn Bhd, KUALA LUMPUR
New Zealand	LexisNexis Butterworths, WELLINGTON
Poland	Wydawnictwo Prawnicze LexisNexis, WARSAW
Singapore	LexisNexis Butterworths, SINGAPORE
South Africa	LexisNexis Butterworths, DURBAN
Switzerland	Stämpfli Verlag AG, BERNE
USA	LexisNexis, DAYTON, Ohio

© Reed Elsevier (UK) Ltd 2003.

A CIP Catalogue record for this book is available from the British Library.

ISBN 0 406 96508 0

Typeset by Doyle & Co, Colchester
Printed and bound in Great Britain by Hobbs the Printers Ltd, Totton, Hampshire

Visit LexisNexis UK at www.lexisnexis.co.uk

Foreword

There have been projects from time immemorial. Egyptian and Chaldean hieroglyphs reveal that, even eight thousand years ago, there were people charged with the management of major projects. If one switches to the twenty-first century, project management as an independent facet of control of developments has emerged or re-emerged. Whereas, up to forty years ago, projects were generally managed by the primary designer, such as the architect or the engineer on construction projects, the job of Project Manager has become recognised as a key feature in a world where life has become more busy and has been made more complex than before. In complex developments, the client often wishes to have their own eyes and ears, the Project Manager, not only keeping an eye on the project but also controlling the project.

The office of Project Manager can be filled by a wide range of disciplines and of experience. In construction projects, building and quantity surveyors are the most popular but they have included architects, engineers, planners, in-house lawyers, client staff and wholly unqualified people, to mention only a few.

Given the substantially increased use and popularity of Project Managers, it is vital that, even though they are not recognised (yet) as an independent profession, they are educated or educate themselves for what are in many instances extremely complicated developments. Such projects demand a great number of skills and knowledge which include but go beyond the control and management of people, important though that is.

A good working knowledge of the law and of the relevant statutory framework is vital. To understand how the many contracts can come into being and how they can and should be operated is critical. The inter-relationship between the client, the other professionals and the contractor is one that needs to be operated at a practical level but also in the legal framework of the contracts entered into and the statutes applicable to the development in question.

The responsibilities of Project Managers have inevitably attracted the attention of the courts and arbitrators, with Project Managers being sued for negligence. Because there is no separate recognised profession of 'Project Manager' as such (there is no chartered institute), it is important that Project Managers understand not only what they should or should not do but also what may happen to them if they do not perform as they should.

This is the first book published in this country which gives guidance to people who practise and wish to practise as Project Managers in relation to construction and engineering law. It is intended to, and does, provide a thorough, comprehensive but practical, guide to actual or would-be Project Managers in the principal legal areas in which they are likely to find themselves in the very real world of managing projects.

It is obviously important that Project Managers understand how and when their contracts of engagement come into being and the circumstances in which they can be enforced by or against them. In this book their liabilities are considered along with practical advice as to how those liabilities can be limited. The standard (and not so standard) forms are considered, as are the duties imposed upon Project Managers by their contracts of engagement and by the related construction and professional contracts in relation to which the Project Managers must usually operate. The statutory framework in which the Project Manager must work is considered: environmental, building control, European procurement rules, third party rights, limitation, and health and safety are just the main areas of legislation which the average Project Manager will encounter upon a regular basis; these are reviewed in detail.

Finally, in our increasingly litigious society, the Project Manager needs to know how to handle disputes and not only those which arise between the project manger and the client. There is a large variety of dispute resolution methods, some of which are relatively new in this country, such as mediation, conciliation, adjudication and neutral evaluation, which the Project Manager needs to know of and understand because disputes are such a common feature in building and engineering contracts. Two chapters in this book address this important area.

I have absolutely no hesitation in recommending this book not only to actual and would-be Project Managers but also to legal and other construction professionals. It is important that with thousands of people, in the United Kingdom and elsewhere, acting as Project Managers there is a book specifically written for them, which can be used by them as a textbook when they are learning the ropes and as a practitioner's guide when they are actually running projects. The book is split into all the relevant sections which will in practice arise on projects. The authors can and do speak with authority and experience. Dechert and the College of Estate Management are to be commended for filling a previously unfilled gap in the continuing education of construction professionals in this crucial area.

This book should help Project Managers to anticipate and avoid the legal pitfalls which inevitably exist on most projects.

Robert Akenhead QC
Atkin Chambers
Atkin Building
Gray's Inn
London
June 2003

Preface

The inspiration for this book

Between 1994 and 1996 Sally Marsden undertook the RICS Diploma in Project Management Course through distance learning with the College of Estate Management. Pauline Makepeace was one of her lecturers on that course. Since undertaking the course there have been a number of notable cases on the liability of Project Managers, in particular *Chesham Properties Ltd v Bucknall Austin Project Management Services Ltd*, *Pride Valley Foods Ltd v Hall & Partners* and *Copthorne Hotel (Newcastle) Ltd v Arup Associates and Others*. A review of Dechert's Construction Unit workload over the last two years suggests that 50% of the disputes have involved project management in some guise. During 2002, Dechert, and in particular Sally, were asked to carry out a number of lectures on the liabilities of Project Managers covering the recent case law.

The College of Estate Management, in conjunction with RICS, launched a Diploma in Project Management in 1982 and since 1994 has offered an MBA in Construction Real Estate. Owing to the College's experience in Project Management, the College was invited to undertake some research for the RICS Project Management Faculty, which included carrying out a survey of its members. The survey asked which professional development topics would interest members most. At the top of the list 53% of respondents said they would like to know more about legal issues in order to improve their knowledge. Sally concluded that there was a need for a law book aimed specifically at Project Managers and she approached Pauline and The College of Estate Management to co-edit the book.

Writing a textbook from scratch can be quite a daunting task if only one or two people are to write it. Sally therefore asked a number of people to contribute. Each chapter has been written by one or two authors who have a particular knowledge of the aspect on which they are writing.

The Editors (both female) decided for stylistic reasons that, throughout, the Project Manager should be referred to as 'he'. No discourtesy is intended to the many very able female Project Managers who are currently practising in the profession.

Who is the book aimed at?

The book is aimed at Project Managers in the construction and engineering fields, whether surveyors, architects, engineers or from other construction professional backgrounds. The book is based on the law of England and Wales, although the principles are relevant to other common law jurisdictions.

How to use this book

We have tried to make this book as reader-friendly as possible for a book covering legal issues! Each chapter to a certain extent is self-contained, which means that you can either read the book from cover to cover or dip into particular chapters you feel are relevant. You will find at the start of each chapter (with the exception of Chapter 1) a brief summary of what the chapter contains. To assist the reader, not all of whom will be interested in the details of individual cases, we have provided case summaries in boxes to allow the reader to skip over the details of the case unless they are particularly interested. Chapter 9, however, is an in-depth study of those cases which have touched upon the liabilities of Project Managers.

Acknowledgments

There are a number of people who have assisted the authors of our various chapters and they are listed below.

RICS: Brian Berry, Martin Russell-Croucher.

The College of Estate Management: Roger Waterhouse, Gaye Pottinger, Patricia Brown, James Pinder.

British Property Federation: Anthony Britten.

Dechert: Sarah Pritchard, James Pearson.

E & O Professional: Michael Earp.

Others: Keating Chambers, Mark Siddle, James Maw, Tamara Suaris, Anne-Sophie Julienne, Matthew Holt, Peter Madden and Bernard Ainsworth.

We are indebted to all the above for the assistance given.

Sally Marsden
Pauline Makepeace

Contents

Contributors

Keith Andrews

Keith Andrews is a Partner of EC Harris, responsible for a number of client accounts and management of capital projects throughout the UK and in Europe. He provides the lead role in the strategic planning of a number of significant single location projects and multi-site projects, providing advice from inception, through feasibility and design, to construction and delivery of end product to the client. He is a specialist in the commercial office, office fit-out, refurbishment and shopping centre development markets. Many of his clients are developers and office owner occupiers/tenants. He has a particular expertise in fund surveying/tenants' representative, and acts for a number of European Funds on an ongoing basis.

Keith holds a BSc(Hons) in Quantity Surveying and is a Fellow of the RICS.

Charles Brown

Charles Brown is a partner at Dechert and head of the construction unit. He has 25 years of construction experience including 15 years as a partner in a specialist construction practice in London. He deals with all aspects of construction, including drafting national and international construction contracts, appointment of consultants and amendments to standard terms and conditions.

Charles has extensive litigation experience in the UK and overseas, including arbitrations conducted under ICC and domestic UK jurisdiction involving claims of up to £150m. He is a Fellow of the Chartered Institute of Arbitrators, an accredited Arbitrator in the GCC states and a TeCSA accredited Adjudicator in the UK. He has been instructed on projects for a range of clients, including government agencies, contractors, design consultants and developers. For ten years he advised a division of one of the top ten UK contractors. His overseas experience includes projects throughout Europe, the USA, Southeast Asia and the Gulf.

Andrew Davies

Andrew Davies is a solicitor at Dechert in the firm's construction team. He graduated from the University College of Wales in 1997 and qualified as a solicitor in 2000.

Andrew specialises in the resolution of construction disputes by litigation, arbitration, adjudication and ADR. He has experience of working for employers and contractors on commercial and retail developments.

Frances Fowler

Frances Fowler is an assistant solicitor at Dechert in the firm's construction team. She is a graduate of the University of Newcastle upon Tyne and qualified in March 2000.

Frances has acted on behalf of employers, contractors and sub-contractors. She has experience of all forms of dispute resolution, including litigation, arbitration and mediation. She has been instructed on a number of successful adjudications.

Kathryn Gilbertson

Kathryn Gilbertson is a partner at Dechert and heads up the Corporate Safety Group, advising leading companies on all aspects of regulatory law, including corporate manslaughter and health and safety issues, with particular emphasis on director liability and corporate governance. A recognised leader in her field since 1997, she has a reputation for an innovative approach to regulatory compliance issues and for her astute commercial awareness.

Dual-qualified as both as an environmental health officer (1984) with extensive enforcement experience, and as a solicitor, Kathryn has a unique insight into enforcement strategies and policies. In addition to her extensive defence work for leading companies, she has been called to advise Government agencies on the practical aspects of regulatory enforcement matters.

Sarah Hannaford

Sarah Hannaford was called to the Bar in 1989 and has been a tenant of Keating Chambers since 1990, specialising in construction law. Her fields of practice include litigation and arbitration (domestic and international) in the fields of construction and engineering, involving all major Standard Forms of Contract including JCT, ICE, FCEC, FIDIC and NEC/ECC, professional negligence actions, party wall disputes, and jurisdictional disputes. She is a member of TECBAR and COMBAR, and her publications include *Current Law Annotations Party Walls (etc) Act 1996*.

Pauline Makepeace

Pauline Makepeace is a tutor in law at The College of Estate Management and course director of the CEM Postgraduate Diploma in Arbitration. After obtaining her law degree she spent five years in the construction industry dealing with contract administration. In 1985 she qualified as a teacher in further and higher education. She initially worked for the College on a part-time basis but became a full-time tutor in January 1989. She deals with all aspects of law teaching at the College, but specialises in contract, tort and dispute resolution.

Sally Marsden

Sally Marsden is an assistant solicitor with Curtis Davis Garrard. She was previously at Dechert in the construction team. She is a graduate of the University of Newcastle upon Tyne and is admitted to practice in England and Wales and Hong Kong. Prior to joining Dechert she spent three and a half years in Hong Kong dealing with large project disputes, and prior to that was a partner in a practice in Manchester.

She has been involved in a wide variety of construction projects, covering buildings from housing to bus stations, power stations and tunnels. She has had experience of technical contracts, including mechanical, plant and process engineering, telecommunications, project structuring and project management.

She has been involved in a number of international arbitrations and has acted for a wide variety of clients, including government agencies, professionals, contractors and developers.

She is a member of the Chartered Institute of Arbitrators and holds the RICS Postgraduate Diploma in Project Management.

Andrew McCormack

Andrew McCormack is an assistant solicitor in Dechert's construction unit. Andrew graduated in law from the University of Manchester and undertook his legal training with Dechert where he qualified as a solicitor in 2001. Andrew acts for a number of developer clients involved in the construction of large UK office and retail developments.

Kevin Quinn

Kevin Quinn was made a Director of Barrie Tankel Partnership (Chartered Quantity Surveyors and Project Managers) in 1995. Kevin qualified as a Chartered Surveyor in 1989 and obtained a Diploma in Project Management in 1998 and an MBA in Construction and Real Estate also in 1998.

He achieved Fellowship of the RICS in 1996 and has been an APC doctor since 1996 and APC Assessor since 2002. He also serves as a member of the Advisory Board for the RICS Postgraduate Diploma in Project Management. Kevin acts principally as a Project Manager for commercial clients. The majority of these appointments are for developers on a wide range of projects.

Adrian Smith

Adrian Smith is a tutor in construction management at The College of Estate Management, where he specialises in professional practice, project management and construction law. He is also a senior consultant with Knowles Management, a subsidiary of James R Knowles Ltd, where he advises a wide range of public and private sector clients on the avoidance of disputes and strategic procurement issues in construction. Adrian holds a Masters' degree in Education from the University of Sheffield, and is a Fellow of both the Royal Institution of Chartered Surveyors and the Hong Kong Institute of Surveyors.

Following almost 20 years in practice as a Chartered Quantity Surveyor in the public and private sectors in the UK, Adrian took up a teaching post at the Nottingham Trent Polytechnic in 1984. He subsequently moved to the City University of Hong Kong in 1991, where he took up a post as Associate Professor in Surveying, returning to the UK in 1998.

Adrian is an established researcher, and has published academic papers on a range of construction management related issues. He has also published four books on subjects as diverse as computers in quantity surveying, tendering for construction work, and privately financed infrastructure.

Samuel Townend

Samuel Townend was called to the Bar in 1999 and has been a member of Keating Chambers, specialising in construction law, since October 2000. His fields of practice include all aspects of construction and engineering litigation and arbitration, professional negligence and adjudication. He has advised and represented a number of managing contractors, sub-contractors, employers, architects and other specialities within the construction field and appeared before various tribunals, domestic (as sole and junior counsel) and international (as junior counsel). A speciality is the drafting of documents to adjudicators, and all matters concerned with the enforcement of adjudication decisions.

Table of Statutes

Table of Statutory Instruments

Table of EU Legislation

Table of Cases

CHAPTER I

Introduction to the discipline of project management

By Kevin Quinn

I Background to professional disciplines of Project Managers in the construction industry

The management of construction projects has traditionally been the remit of the Architect as leader of the design team – the Structural Engineer, Service Engineer and Quantity Surveyor following the lead of, and being co-ordinated by, the Architect. Having managed and co-ordinated the design, the Architect was also traditionally responsible for appointing a building contractor to carry out the construction project works, drawing up terms of contract with the builder, administering the contract, instructing other consultants and co-ordinating all works to the client's satisfaction to the completion of the project. This has been the case for hundreds of years.

Over the last 20–30 years, however, there has been a growing trend amongst clients to appoint Project Managers rather than Architects to lead and manage their construction projects. Many construction clients have criticised Architects for focusing solely upon their design ideals to the detriment of other factors such as cost, time and the functionality of the end building product. Today's clients do not wish to add costs to their construction projects unless they will add value to the end product, which they can then justify to an end user customer. There is little value in specifying gold-plated taps if there is no demand for those high quality fittings and the cost will not simply be recouped from the sale price or rental income. Conversely, individualistic architectural design flair can add substantial value to a project when focused in the right areas.

Some designers feel inhibited by working within a budget. This is acceptable at the inception or feasibility stages of a project, when lateral thinking and ideas are important. It is not, however, helpful to proceed to the detailed design stage of the project until the cost budget and scheme design are agreed and fully signed off by the client. A £20m complex may satisfy a whole number of client requirements, wishes and wants, but is not of much use if the client only has a £5m budget.

Clients are now demanding greater accountability in respect of the design of their building. They want to know that they are obtaining maximum value and getting what *they* want, not just what their designers want.

The functionality of a building is an extremely important factor which needs to be weighed against the design put forward by the architect. For example, a fully glazed façade on a south-facing elevation may be aesthetically pleasing, but at the same time may cause extreme discomfort to the occupants of the building due to temperature gains throughout the day, glare from the sun, increased running costs due to cooling to offset heat gains, and additional heating throughout the night due to heat loss. Costs in use and life-cycle costing are now key considerations fundamental to most clients' requirements.

The key driving force that has led to the increase in the use of Project Managers is the fact that construction projects are now becoming far more complex than ever before and are also required to be carried out within much shorter timescales. The challenges of these projects have demanded a separate role and discipline of project management in addition to the traditional design team arrangement. The Project Manager is responsible for establishing clear lines of communication and management of the project; setting programmes and monitoring performance; co-ordinating the design team members; fully involving the contractor with buildability studies; setting the project brief and agreeing it with the client; introducing new construction techniques where beneficial to a project; promoting the use of standardisation where it is economical and sensible to do so; supporting and motivating the design team; managing the financial aspects of the project; and, most of all, managing the client's expectations.

Good Project Managers have a holistic understanding of the project. They realise that an inadequate project brief is the single most common reason for project failure, and strive to set a clear brief at the earliest opportunity. They realise that clients do not always say what they want at the outset of a project and that an essential skill of the Project Manager is to draw this information out of the client so that all of the client's wants and conflicts of interest are identified as early as possible in order to enable clear decisions to be made from the outset.

Most construction projects are unique, and as a result there are always new problems to be dealt with. Spotting these problems and overcoming them at the earliest opportunity is fundamental to the success of the project. The Project Manager has a key role in achieving and facilitating this. Problems can be compared to ships spotted on the horizon. While they are small and distant something can be done about them, but as they come closer they get bigger and bigger until they knock straight into you, and there is then nothing you can do to overcome them. By spotting the Armada early, Drake was able to prepare to defend England, finish his game of bowls, and still gain a famous victory.

2

Project Managers are constantly required to programme and plan into the future in order to ensure a successful outcome. Spotting the problems and overcoming them early is essential, because if a problem is allowed to come too close it can totally knock the Project Manager over and take control of the project. What can then happen is that the Project Manager becomes so absorbed with solving the immediate problem that other small but potentially nasty problems lurking on the horizon are not dealt with and are allowed to sail closer. If left unchecked, the Armada will sail right up to the face of the Project Manager and little can be done other than be overwhelmed.

A good Project Manager tries to deal with these problems while they are small and far away. By spending much time worrying about the future, the good Project Manager spots these minor irritants while there is still plenty of time to find eloquent solutions. There is even time for a good Project Manager to pat himself on the back. The trouble then is, however, that the more successful the Project Manager is in solving the minor irritants before they are problems, the less visible he becomes. Ironically, the totally successful Project Manager is often invisible to the lay client. It is only when the client decides to proceed with another project without using his invisible Project Manager that problems arise and the client's projects become a huge mess. By this time the successful Project Manager can do little about the problems which are now pushing hard against the project's face, many irresolvable without substantial extra time and cost penalties being incurred by the client.

Following the growth of project management as a discipline and its use by NASA as a method for managing projects during the Cold War, a number of institutions have formed to support Project Managers. The Project Management Institute (PMI) was founded in 1969 and has now grown in such a way that it supports some 95,000 members in 125 countries worldwide. The Chartered Institute of Building published a seminal work on Project Management in 1979. The RICS Project Management Association was formed in 1982 and has now been recreated as the RICS Project Management Faculty, which has some 29,000 members. It currently supports the work of surveyors involved in project management in the property and construction industry throughout the UK, through a programme of research and by focusing upon improved education for its members. The Association of Project Managers (APM) has some 12,000 members, comprising PM representatives from all sections of industry, commerce, the arts and education, irrespective of professional discipline. It also organises training seminars and workshops to support its members.

2 The role of project management

Project management may be defined as 'the overall planning, control and co-ordination of a project from inception to completion aimed at meeting a client's requirements in order that the project will be completed on time within authorised cost and to the required quality standards'.

The Project Manager acts on behalf of and represents the client. He has the duty of providing a cost effective and independent service correlating, integrating and managing different disciplines and expertise to satisfy the objectives and visions of the project brief from inception to completion. The service provided must be to the client's satisfaction, safeguard his interests at all times, and, where possible, give consideration to the needs of the eventual user of the facility.

The Project Manager plays a key co-ordinating role in assisting his clients to realise their project objectives. The right appointment may make the difference between success and failure. Because of the important role assumed by the Project Manager, it is recommended that he be appointed at the outset to enable him to understand and influence the client's objectives and establish a successful project strategy. Having had powers delegated to him by the client at the inception, the Project Manager will exercise an executive role within the project team throughout the project.

The Project Manager does not normally undertake an entrepreneurial role in the project, and this distinction should be clearly made. The Project Manager's fee is normally based upon either a pre-agreed lump sum, or calculated on a percentage basis of the contract value, or an hourly time charge basis, depending upon the scope of his duties. The fee is not dependent upon the success or failure of the project. However, sometimes bonus arrangements are applicable on certain key objectives being obtained. These arrangements will differ for Project Managers who work in-house within client organisations rather than as external consultants.

The term 'Project Co-ordinator' is also sometimes used where the responsibility and authority of a Project Manager embraces only part of a project, such as the reconstruction or fitting out stages.

Project Managers must at all times fully embrace all provisions of quality assurance and health, safety and environmental protection throughout the various stages of the project.

Sally Marsden, Frances Fowler and Keith Andrews review a typical job specification for a Project Manager and review some of the standard forms of appointment for Project Managers in Chapter 4.

3 Inter-relationship between Project Managers and other professionals on the construction project

The most important aspect of project management today is managing the people side and the differing relationships between the various project stakeholders. The Project Manager has to get all of these parties to work together for the benefit of the project, much as a conductor conducts an orchestra. Most people claim to be good team players. The Project Manager's role (to change the metaphor) is to make sure that the team are all wearing the same shirts and kicking in the same direction.

Doing this successfully starts with establishing a clear project brief and agreeing it as much as possible with all parties. Inadequate project definition from the outset is the single most likely cause of project failure. Obtaining the agreement and buy-in of all parties to the same project objectives and goals is not an easy task. It is not uncommon for differing project stakeholders never to agree on certain aspects of the project brief. Clients generally want the largest amount of saleable or useable area and wish to minimise circulation areas in order to maximise returns. Letting Agents want the largest, grandest reception area in order to make the building easier to let. Architects want the building to act as an expression of their design philosophy and reflect their architectural trademark. Services Engineers want space for their services installations.

Typically the project brief is established, developed and reissued to all parties during and at the conclusion of each of the stages A to D of the RIBA Plan of Work. These stages are Inception (stage A), Feasibility (stage B), Outline Proposals (stage C) and Scheme Design (stage D). During stages B and C the Quantity Surveyor costs out alternative design options and issues cost plans to the Project Manager against which the project construction costs can be evaluated and monitored.

Alternatively, or in addition to the above, Value Management (VM) workshops and techniques are sometimes used to assist project teams in establishing and agreeing the project brief. These workshops generally involve:

- issuing a pack of all relevant project information to all project stakeholders in advance of the VM workshop;

- ensuring that all project stakeholders attend the VM workshop, and stating the proposed project objectives at the start of the workshop;

- drawing up 'How–Why' diagrams which set out why the project's objectives are what they are and how the objectives are to be achieved: these diagrams are also known as FAST (functional analysis systems technique) diagrams;

- evaluating each project objective and establishing a value hierarchy ranking against each one;

- holding a brainstorming session in order to generate alternative ideas and allow creativity;

- evaluating new ideas and selecting those to be considered for further development;

- presenting a revised project brief to the VM workshop for agreement with all parties;

- reviewing feedback from VM workshop and issuing a clear project brief.

Precisely how the project brief is established does not necessarily matter. The most important factor is that it is agreed and effectively communicated in writing to all parties at the earliest possible stage.

The Project Manager should also ensure that consultants' appointments are properly drafted and agreed at the earliest possible stage and that they include reference to the project brief. This promotes effective communication within the project team. One of the most common reasons for disputes in the construction industry is where consultants are sued for not carrying out a service which they believed they were never obliged to do. These misunderstandings are commonplace, and it is the Project Manager's job to ensure that they do not occur. The Project Manager must ensure that there are no gaps in design responsibility within the appointments. This means, for example, that he must define which parties are responsible for below and above ground drainage, and whether the services engineer will undertake full design of the services installations or prepare performance specifications and schematic designs only, with the detailed design being done by the specialist mechanical and electrical sub-contractor.

The Project Manager must set up the project structure and establish clear lines of communication between the project team by defining who reports to whom, who is lead design consultant, the various project meetings which are required to be held, who will chair these meetings, and who should attend which meetings. The Project Manager should facilitate clear communication between the project team.

Project Managers should have a structured method for what they do and set out milestones against which the project is monitored, together with gates through which the project has to pass. Sign-off is then required against a number of items at each milestone gate, and the project cannot pass to the next phase until this is done. These gates are normally set out against RIBA Plan of Work Stages and are back-to-back with consultants' appointments. The Project Manager should ensure that the architect does not move to preparing outline design proposals (stage C) until the client signs off the feasibility stage (B) and confirms that he is happy to proceed to this next stage. The Project Manager should ensure that the consultants do not proceed to detailed design (stage E) until the scheme design (stage D) is prepared and signed off by the client. Moving to the next stage in the design development process before fully completing the stage before and obtaining sign-off to that stage is another very common cause for project failure and dispute between clients and consultants.

As well as managing the project team, the Project Manager is often the lynchpin between the team and end user tenants. He should establish suitable meetings with tenants and end users and try to obtain their involvement and input at the earliest stage possible. The Project Manager needs to communicate obligations contained within Agreements to Lease to the project design team and the building contractor and ensure that contract documentation is back to back with these obligations.

The Project Manager needs to be aware of the differing requirements of any funders to the construction project, and ensure that they are invited to attend relevant meetings and are provided with suitable reports and correspondence.

Leadership is a key quality. The good Project Manager normally does this by personally establishing a leadership dynamic without actually stating that he is the leader of the project team.

4 The role of Project Manager as it fits within standard forms – or doesn't!

The most common form of building contract is from the JCT 98 range of publications. The JCT98 with or without quantities contracts refer to the contractor, the employer, the architect (or contract administrator), the quantity surveyor, the structural engineer and the services engineer. No reference, however, is made to the Project Manager. The Project Manager's role is therefore substantially limited under this standard form. The Project Manager generally assumes the role of the employer in many respects. Where appropriate he will issue instructions to the architect, who in turn will issue formal contract instructions to the building contractor. The Project Manager will also normally monitor and log payments to be made under the contract and agree or comment upon dates for valuations between the quantity surveyor and the contractor.

The Standard Form of Architect's Appointment also makes reference only to the employer, the contractor and the architect. Again, no reference is made to the Project Manager, and again the Project Manager generally assumes the role of the employer in terms of instructing the architect to undertake the services as set out within his appointment.

The Project Manager is responsible for reviewing and commenting upon the architect's design in order to ensure that the project's objectives are met. The Project Manager does not approve the architect's design.

Under the JCT 98 with contractor's design form of contract, reference is made to the Employer's Agent, and it is normal for the Project Manager to undertake this role of issuing instructions, notices and certificates under the contract. The Project Manager has a duty to review the designs put forward by the design and build contractor and check their compliance with the employer's requirements. Again, the Project Manager should comment upon, rather than approve, the contractor's designs.

Adrian Smith looks in detail at how the role of the Project Manager fits in with the more common standard forms of building and engineering contracts in Chapter 5.

5 What is the future for Project Managers?

As construction projects become more and more complex, are required in shorter timescales, and tend to involve more and more project stakeholders than ever before, there is a growing demand for Project Managers. The trend towards clients employing Project Managers to manage their projects is set to increase further.

Clients will, however, only employ a Project Manager if they perceive that the value being added by utilising this consultant is greater than the cost of the fee payable. Project Managers will need to demonstrate that they do add value to their client's businesses by eliciting the client's value drivers, analysing the suppliers and subcontractors who currently work for the client, building the optimum project supply chain and driving it, and then implementing effective management procedures.

Project size is a determining factor. There is little point in employing a Project Manager to manage the project team for a small house extension, as the value–cost equation is unlikely to work and the level of project complexity does not demand it. Conversely, some projects may have a relatively small construction cost but be so sensitive to the client's business that the cost of employing a Project Manager is an essential investment when set against the potential business losses if the project is not successful.

The Wembley football stadium project illustrates the complexities introduced by the involvement of numerous client bodies and the changing ways in which Project Managers are now required to operate. One Project Manager is quoted as saying: 'Building Wembley is going to be easy compared to managing the many parties providing funding, establishing the needs of these differing project stakeholders, and managing each of their needs, whilst always considering the overall effect on the whole project.' Different funders have different layers of debt. Some will care about life-cycle costs over the whole building life; others will require the construction to be completed as swiftly as possible, as this is the trigger for their funds being returned; others may have finite budgetary controls for construction; and all these requirements may be in slight conflict with the requirements of end users. Managing these conflicting requirements is a difficult but absolutely essential task vital for the success of the project, and is best done by an independent Project Manager who has both the time and the skills available to achieve consensus between the project stakeholders as to the project development brief.

In the Millennium Dome project, managing the physical construction of the dome was relatively simple compared with establishing the ever-changing briefs for each of the zones within the dome and how they impacted upon each other. Co-ordination of the conflicting requirements of the zones and managing their interfaces and the many different parties involved illustrates some of the mammoth challenges faced by today's Project Managers.

Project Managers today are expanding their areas of expertise in order to cover the full effect of a project upon a client's business. One Project Manager advised that managing the media was the most complicated aspect of carrying out engineering works on the District Line. The project involved closing the District Line for 14 weeks in order to carry out engineering works. To do this required a nine-month plan to manage the media and organise the necessary shutdowns. Future Project Managers will continue to need to understand their clients' business requirements and apply their skills to add maximum value, in addition to giving purely construction advice.

6 Practical difficulties faced by the profession

Project Managers undertake a diverse range of activities and work upon a wide range of projects. They need to apply a standard method on each project so that a consistent project management service is offered. Although various codes are in publication, greater industry-wide knowledge with regard to project management techniques and best practice should be more widely available. Research sponsored by the RICS Project Management Faculty and other bodies is currently being undertaken in these areas in order to promote a better understanding and cohesive view amongst Project Managers as to best practice in the industry.

The RICS Guidance Notes publication, 'Selection and Appointment of the Project Manager', recommends that clients should request '... previous experience, particularly of comparable projects with a summary of the Consultant's performance for each project'; and that 'Details concerning completion dates, target costs achieved and employer's satisfaction ...' should be provided.

Difficulties sometimes arise, however, because there are no recognised qualifications for Project Managers that are universally accepted, other than experience and track record. In addition to experience, a formal academic training in project management is a requirement of today's Project Manager. This is being addressed by a number of universities and other educational establishments which now run courses specifically designed to promote the techniques and skills required of today's Project Managers. The University of Reading's MSc in Project Management and its MBA in Construction and Real Estate (the latter provided through The College of Estate Management) are two examples of courses currently being run in this fashion. The aim is to provide training in management issues which supports the professional training already gained by individuals who have qualified in disciplines such as architecture, quantity surveying, building surveying or engineering.

These courses are designed to plug the gap that previously existed in the training of architects who wished to manage projects as well as design, since traditional architectural courses devoted 90% of their academic time to learning about design and less than 10% to management. This meant that the qualified architect straight out of university had great theoretical knowledge of all the different types of Georgian, Tudor or gothic design principles, but little training in or understanding of the immediate requirements of administering building contracts and communicating effectively with the construction personnel dependent upon their instructions.

The one quality that is always required and sought from today's Project Manager on any project is 'leadership'. Some people are born leaders and others gradually grow into the role over a period of time. Leadership is hard to teach effectively other than through project case studies and academic training, mixed with practical experience over a period of time. As this skill is rarely effectively taught and is difficult to gain over a short period, this will have a limiting effect upon the number of Project Managers available for managing high profile construction projects.

The Project Manager's role and authority is sometimes not fully accepted or understood by all parties, due to the lack of a formal reference to it within standard building contracts. Whilst this is usually overcome by the client formally communicating the Project Manager's involvement to all parties by letter or within the tender documents, there is no reason why this should not also be done within the standard forms of building contracts. Again, it is understood that the RICS PM faculty has instructed research in this area and hopefully recommendations will be put forward to the JCT Board so that the situation will be resolved in the not too distant future.

7 Why knowledge of the law is important

It is absolutely essential that Project Managers have an understanding of the law in order that they can safeguard their clients' interests and grasp the legal issues at stake on the project. In particular, the Project Manager needs a basic knowledge and understanding of contract law, tort and statute law in relation to the project.

Initially, the Project Manager must both oversee and delegate the drafting of the building contracts and consultants' appointments to ensure that obligations are imposed upon third parties, such as the building contractor and architect, to comply with various statutes and requirements of development agreements. If this is not done, the client may be unable to recoup his losses in the event of a breach by the builder not complying with the requirements of a development agreement or agreement to lease, etc. Alternatively, the client may find that although he requires the project to be completed by a certain date, the building contract imparts a different obligation and the builder has no incentive to work to the same timescales. The Project Manager must therefore ensure that all contracts are properly prepared to reflect the client's full requirements and are in place from the earliest possible date prior to work starting on site.

The Project Manager has a duty to check that relevant insurances are taken out by the builder and design team so that there is financial backing in the event of a claim being made. This takes the form of public liability insurances, insurance against damage to property, designer's professional indemnity insurance, etc. If these are not properly in place, the client could be adversely affected in the event of a breach by the builder or another member of the project team. Insurance issues are covered by Sarah Hannaford in Chapter 8.

The Project Manager should liaise with the client and his legal advisers in order to ensure that all necessary collateral warranties are obtained and provided. Again, if these are not in place the client may find that he is unable to recover a claim against a third party who has carried out work on the project. Although the Contracts (Rights of Third Parties) Act 1999, which came into force in May 2000, potentially avoids the need for collateral warranties, in the vast majority of cases the Act is expressly excluded by agreement between the parties. Andrew McCormack looks at these issues in Chapter 3.

The Project Manager should be familiar with the Housing Grants, Construction and Regeneration Act 1996 ('the Construction Act'). This Act applies to all construction contracts and has led to the introduction of adjudication as the preferred form of dispute resolution. It also provides for the referral of a dispute to a person (adjudicator), acting impartially, who should form a decision with regard to the dispute within a set timetable. Andrew Davies explains in Chapter 10 how adjudication works.

The Construction Act also imposes stringent requirements in relation to payment, including the need to give notice in writing within a specified number of days of payment falling due if a payment is to be withheld for any reason. The Project Manager should ensure that the proper procedure is followed and keep his client fully informed of his obligations under the Act. Samuel Townend looks at some of the key provisions of the Act in Chapter 6.

The Project Manager should be aware of the Construction (Design and Management) Regulations 1994 (CDM Regulations 1994). The Regulations apply to most construction projects and the client has an obligation to appoint a Planning Supervisor and a Principal Contractor. The Project Manager should ensure that the Health and Safety Executive (HSE) is notified prior to construction work starting on site, that the design gives consideration to health and safety issues, and that a comprehensive health and safety file is kept. As alleged breaches of CDM Regulations 1994 are currently investigated and, if serious, prosecuted by the HSE with convictions which can lead to an unlimited fine and/or up to a two-year prison sentence, the Project Manager should take the duties imposed by these regulations very seriously. Kathryn Gilbertson gives an essential overview of some key health and safety legislation in Chapter 7.

The Project Manager should have a good understanding of the current Building Regulations and the Building Act 1984. If a construction project is completed which does not comply with the building regulations, it cannot be properly used, occupied, let out or sold. This would obviously have serious consequences for the client, the Project Manager and the project team. Chapter 6 also contains a review of the legislation and regulations in practice.

The Project Manager also needs to be aware of the Control of Pollution Act 1974, the Environmental Protection Act 1990, the Limitation Act 1980, the Latent Damage Act 1986 and any other legislation relevant to the construction project such as the Disability Discrimination Act 1995.

Dealing with construction disputes is a large part of any Project Manager's role. These can relate to claims for delay from the builder, valuations of variations under the contract, poor quality materials, poor quality workmanship, poor supervision, communication problems or increased construction costs. If a problem occurs on the construction project, the Project Manager should deal with this on the client's behalf. This may involve enforcing the terms of a contract in order to obtain a suitable remedy, or taking matters further to adjudication, arbitration or litigation.

The Project Manager needs to be able to negotiate a successful outcome to construction disputes and engender a win–win philosophy, as this avoids the expensive scenario whereby projects end up in the hands of the courts. To do this he needs a good understanding of the legal aspects of project management and must know how to properly set up and administer projects from the outset.

Bibliography

Reiss, Geoff *Project Management Demystified – Today's Tools and Techniques* (2nd edn), EFN Spon.

CHAPTER 2

Liability of the Project Manager

By Pauline Makepeace and Adrian Smith

Summary

This chapter gives an overview of the basis legal principles which give rise to the Project Manager's liability. For those who have some knowledge of contract and tort, this is a good revision chapter. For those with little or no knowledge of contract and tort law, this is a good introduction. The chapter covers:

- Potential areas of liability.

- Liability in contract.

- What is a contract?

- How to form a valid contract, including:
  - the battle of the forms (your terms or theirs)
  - obligations at tender stage
  - letters of intent.

- What can affect the formation of contract:
  - mistake
  - misrepresentation.

- What is meant by 'due skill and care'.

- What remedies are available if there is a breach of contract:
  - damages and an explanation of unliquidated and liquidated damages
  - specific performance.

- Liability in tort:
  - your duty of care
  - the loss arising from the breach of that duty and what loss can be claimed.

- Limitation periods in contract and tort – liability does not last forever.

1 Introduction

The major problems to be faced in considering the legal liability of Project Managers are, first, defining the precise nature and extent of 'project management services', and secondly establishing whether or not 'good practice models' of 'standard' project management services exist. These problems arise because the discipline of project management is not a primary qualification in the same way as architecture, surveying or the various branches of engineering. Project management is in essence a secondary profession frequently adopted by professionals from a wide range of primary disciplines.

In addition, project management is a relatively new discipline, and few cases involving the legal liability of Project Managers have so far been brought to court.

These difficulties are compounded by the fact that project management also spans a broad range of industries, and a wide spectrum of management tasks. At one extreme, project management has simply been described as 'the management of change'[1], but others define the task in a variety of different ways. One commentator, for example, sees the task as primarily one of co-ordination:

> ... the art and science of co-ordinating people, equipment, materials, money and schedules to complete a specified project on time and within approved cost[2];

whereas another equally prominent authority sees the task as predominantly one of motivation and leadership:

> 'The Project Manager is ultimately responsible for the productivity of the people in the project team; it is therefore the Project Manager's job to maintain cohesion and co-operation among all of those involved in the project. The Project Manager must be a leader, one who can inspire and motivate people who have ties to the project[3]...

Perhaps the most comprehensive definition comes from the Chartered Institute of Building (CIOB) in the UK, which defines project management as:

> The overall planning, co-ordination and control of a project from inception to completion aimed at meeting the Client's requirements in order to produce a functionally and financially viable project that will be completed on time within an authorised cost and to the required quality standards[4].

1   W J Day Project Management and Control (1994).
2   G D Oberlender Project Management for Engineering and Construction (1993).
3   H N Ahuja, S P Dozzi and S M Abourizk Project Management: Techniques in planning and controlling construction projects (1994).
4   CIOB Code of Practice for Project Management for Construction and Development (2002).

The difficulties arising from this broad diversity of project management activities and client expectations were highlighted in *Pride Valley Foods v Hall and Partners*[5]. Here, despite his being presented with a *Code of Practice for Project Management*, the trial judge commented that the bespoke nature of the project management services required on this particular project meant that there was no established professional procedure that could be used as an exemplar. He therefore rejected substantial parts of the expert evidence submitted by both sides from other Project Managers as to how they would have approached the commission in question, on the grounds that it amounted to no more than an expression of opinion of what different experts would have done in similar circumstances. He even went so far as to comment that he doubted whether it would ever be possible to accept expert opinion evidence as to the nature of project management.

In view of the uncertainty surrounding the nature of project management services, it is plain that we need to consider the legal liability of the Project Manager in the broadest possible light.

2 Potential areas of liability

It is clear from the definitions set out above that in many, perhaps most, cases consultant Project Managers act as the employer's agent with, in the most extreme case, virtually total responsibility for both identifying and satisfying the client's needs.

This agency relationship has significant legal consequences, in that an agent is bound to his principal in a number of ways, as set out below. The employer may sue if the agent fails to comply with these duties:

- To act as required by the terms of his engagement and/or his contract of employment. The principal may sue if an agent either acts outside his terms of reference or alternatively fails to act effectively at an appropriate time.

- To obey his principal's instructions provided that they are both legal and reasonable.

- To declare any conflicts of interest to his principal.

- To keep proper accounts.

- Not to take secret payments, bribes or secret profits. Failure to comply will give the principal grounds to sue for damages, and the measure of damages will typically be the amount of the secret payment.

- Not to delegate without authority. This is very significant in the light of the contractual duties assigned to the Project Manager under some standard forms of contract.

5   [2001] EWCA Civ 1001, 76 Con LR 1.

In a construction project the scope of the Project Manager's work may range from, at one extreme, assisting the client to determine the need for the project and presenting the outline business case, to post-occupancy analysis and the establishment of facilities management processes at the other. In addition to the obligations arising from the general law relating to agency, the consultant Project Manager will therefore incur liabilities to his employer both in contract and in tort under the specific terms of his consultancy agreement. Project Managers who are employees of the client will incur liability to their employer in accordance with the terms of their contract of employment.

In addition to these general obligations, Project Managers may also incur liabilities through their duties on specific projects. Some of the standard form contracts commonly used in construction require the Project Manager to fulfil certain duties in the administration of the contract, and even where this is not the case the Project Manager may still be named in the contract as the contract administrator (see Chapter 5).

It is also necessary to consider the potential statutory liabilities of the Project Manager. These may arise under a number of different pieces of legislation, but major liabilities may arise under:

- Health and safety legislation, principally the Health and Safety at Work etc Act 1974 and the Construction (Design and Management) Regulations 1994.

- Construction legislation, including the current Building Regulations, the Defective Premises Act 1972 and the Housing Grants, Construction and Regeneration Act 1996 ('the Construction Act').

- The Supply of Goods and Services Act 1982.

- European Community Public Procurement legislation as embodied in the various European Community Directives[6] which are given effect in British law through the Public Works Contracts Regulations 1991, 1993, 1995 and 1996, as amended[7].

Statutory liability is considered in detail in Chapter 6.

The remaining potential areas of liability are considered here under two separate headings:

6   General public sector Directives comprise:
  - The Works Directive originally published 1971. Consolidated text published as Directive 93/37 (amended by Directive 97/52)
  - The Supplies Directive originally published 1977. Consolidated text published as Directive 93/36 (amended by Directive 97/52)
  - The Services Directive 92/50 (amended by Directive 97/52)
  - The Utilities (Water, Energy, Transport and Telecommunications) Directive originally published 1990. Consolidated text published as Directive 93/38 (amended by Directive 98/4)
  Also relevant are the Enforcement Directives 89/665 (general public sector works) and 92/13 (utilities).
7   SI 1991/2680; SI 1993/3228; SI 1995/201; SI 1996/2911.

- Liability in contract.

- Liability in the tort of negligence.

3 Liability in contract

It has already been shown that contractual obligations may arise under the Project Manager's consultancy agreement (or his contract of employment), and under specific project contracts. This chapter examines the first of these areas, while the second is examined in some detail in Chapter 5.

(a) The consultancy agreement

Many project management appointments are made using one of the standard consultancy agreements (see Chapter 4). Should this not be the case, then it is plainly in both parties' interests for the terms of the agreement to be specifically agreed and clearly expressed in the consultancy appointment documentation. It is also plainly desirable for the avoidance of future disputes for the Project Manager to have a clear and unambiguous brief detailing:

- what is to be achieved;

- how success or failure of the end result will be assessed;

- the scope of his duties and the extent of his authority together with any constraints and/or limits.

Experience shows that many appointments are made either on the basis of a letter or even a simple oral agreement, or as an addition to another appointment, for example as Engineer, Architect or Quantity Surveyor. In these cases the extent of the Project Manager's liability will depend upon the terms of the consultancy appointment (either express or implied), but is typically expressed in broad overall terms. Such appointments are frequently so vague that the first major question may be whether or not a contract actually exists, and if so what the terms of that contract are.

(b) What is a contract?

A contract is a legally binding agreement between two or more parties, under which one party promises to do something, in return for which the second and subsequent parties promise to do something else. In project management a typical contract will consist of the parties agreeing that certain goods and/or services will be supplied and executed for a certain price (i e one party agrees to sell, the other to purchase for an agreed price). The execution of these tasks will be conducted according to a number of pre-determined rules, these being the terms of the contract. These rules may be specifically agreed by the parties, or may in some cases be prescribed by law (e g Sale of Goods Act 1979, Supply of Goods and Services Act 1982), or they may occasionally be implied either by custom and practice or to give the contract business efficacy.

It is a general legal principle that neither the agreement nor the terms under which the parties trade need necessarily be in writing. The contract may be oral or may in some cases arise by implication through the actions of the parties. There are, however, some contracts which may not be purely oral. They fall into two groups:

1 **Contracts which must be in writing**. Important construction-related contracts in this category include contracts for the sale of land (Law of Property (Miscellaneous Provisions) Act 1989, s 2).

2 **Contracts which must be 'evidenced in writing'**. Such contracts need not be completely in writing but the material terms of the contract must be recorded on at least one note or memorandum. The most important in this group are contracts of guarantee (Statute of Frauds 1677, s 4).

Note, however, that the Construction Act, s 105 states that to be covered by the Act the contract must be in writing. The definition of writing is, however, very wide. 'Writing' in this case means recorded by any means and also covers something evidenced in writing.

Formation of a valid contract

The essence of agreement is the *consensus ad idem* (consent to the same thing). It should be obvious that important contracts ought to be in writing if only to ensure that both parties are aware of what has been agreed. A written contract also is much more reliable as evidence in the event of a dispute, to facilitate proof in a court of law, and for general commercial reasons of good practice. It is therefore essential that the written form (the terms) should truly and accurately record the agreement made, with a clear definition of what each unique agreement contains – for example, who the parties are, what is being bought and sold, when, where and how much is to be paid.

Particular difficulties may arise here in the case of international projects where contracts are translated into other languages, or where agreements are made in jurisdictions where there is more than one official language. In Hong Kong, for example, where Chinese and English are the official languages, disagreements occasionally occur because ideas and concepts cannot be translated accurately from one language to the other.

There are six essential points which must be satisfied for a contract to be valid and enforceable at law:

I **Agreement**. There must be a clear offer matched by a clear acceptance.

2 **Intention**. There must be the intention on the part of both parties to create a legally binding relationship.

3 **Consideration**. There must be mutual exchange of valuable promises.

4 **Capacity**. Both parties must be legally able to enter into a binding contract.

5. **Legality**. The contract must be for a legal purpose.

6. **Consent**. There must be nothing which vitiates consent.

I AGREEMENT

An agreement is made up of an offer and an acceptance. An offer is a statement of the terms by which the offeror intends to be bound and an acceptance is the unconditional assent to those terms. There is no requirement for the offer and acceptance to be in writing, and again both may, in some cases, be inferred from the parties' conduct (*Brogden v Metropolitan Rail Co*[8]). In many cases there is a stage before the offer and acceptance known as an invitation to treat. This is an invitation to someone to make an offer.

These principles are readily translated into the construction scenario – the request for tenders to be submitted is the invitation to treat; the submission of the tender is the offer, and the awarding of the work is the acceptance.

Under the common law an offer may be withdrawn at any time prior to acceptance, and the withdrawal becomes effective as soon as the offeree receives the notice. Support for the traditional view has historically been drawn from *Routledge v Grant*[9]. Here the defendant offered to buy a house, giving Routledge six weeks to give an answer. It was held that Grant could withdraw the offer at any time before acceptance, even though the six-week period had not expired, on the grounds that the promise was unsupported by consideration.

However, this fundamental principle has now been refined, particularly where the terms of the tender require that tenders remain open for acceptance for a specified period. In *City Polytechnic of Hong Kong v Blue Cross (Asia Pacific) Insurance*[10]. City Polytechnic invited tenders for a medical insurance scheme for its staff, and the tender form included a requirement that tenders remain open for acceptance for three months. Blue Cross submitted the lowest tender, but wrote to withdraw it before

---

8 (1877) 2 App Cas 666, HL.
9 (1828) 4 Bing 653.
10 [1994] HKCFI 273.

expiry of the three-month period. City Polytechnic none the less wrote to accept the tender, but Blue Cross refused to issue the policy.

The court initially held that the law of contract could accept that, in a tendering situation, an implied contract could come into existence binding the tenderer to keep his tender open for the specified period of time. The consideration for such a promise was the express or implied agreement of the person inviting the tenders (following *Blackpool and Fylde Aero Club v Blackpool Borough Council*[11]) that he would consider all compliant tenders before awarding the contract. Blue Cross were therefore at first instance held to be in breach of that implied contract and were liable to pay damages assessed as the difference between the Blue Cross tender and the next lowest tender.

The case was subsequently reviewed on appeal and the decision overturned on the basis of other wording in the tender document, but the basic legal analysis regarding the possible existence of an implied contract during the tender period was not challenged.

When a tender is accepted, the acceptance must be unequivocal, i e it must relate specifically to the other party's offer. In *Peter Lind & Co v Mersey Docks and Harbour Board*[12], Lind submitted two alternative tenders, one on a fixed price basis and one on a fluctuating basis. The Board purported to accept 'your tender' without specifying which alternative. It was held that there was no contract because it was impossible to state to which offer the acceptance referred.

The offer must also be accepted within a 'reasonable' time. There is no fixed definition of reasonable, but most invitations to tender for construction work will specify the length of time for which the offer must remain open for acceptance.

While the acceptance does not have to be in writing, good business practice would require that it should be so, and when the offer is accepted by post the contract will come into force as soon as the acceptance is posted (*Adams v Lindsell*[13]).

Problems sometimes arise where the acceptance is made 'subject to formal contract'. While the use of this phrase generally means that the purported contract will not be treated as binding, the courts will consider all of the accompanying documentation in order to decide whether the conclusion of a formal agreement is a necessary pre-requisite to the contract coming into being, or whether the statement is merely an expression of desire that the agreement made should be recorded in some particular form. In *Lewis v Brass*[14], for example, Brass's tender was accepted by Lewis's architect

11   [1990] 3 All ER 25.
12   [1972] 2 Lloyd's Rep 234.
13   (1818) 1 B & Ald 681.
14   (1877) 3 QBD 667.

with the words: 'The contract will be ready for signature in the course of a few days.' Brass discovered a mistake in his tender and sought to withdraw the offer. It was held that he was too late – there was already a binding contract. The wording of the supporting letters and other documentation is plainly of great importance here.

If the acceptance is not unequivocal (i e if it suggests different terms and conditions from those suggested by the offer) it will be construed as a counter offer which destroys the original offer (*Hyde v Wrench*[15]). Thus the counter-offer must then be accepted before the contract comes into being. This state of affairs arises frequently where contracts are negotiated over a lengthy period of time, often on the basis of an exchange of letters. In this case the courts will examine the whole of the correspondence in order to determine when the *consensus ad idem* was achieved, and this will be the point at which the contract will be held to come into existence.

A further twist to this tale occurs during what has become known as the 'battle of the forms'. This is the situation where the parties communicate by letters which attempt to incorporate their own standard terms and conditions into the contract. Here, where the work has been carried out, the courts may well be able to rule that the conduct of the parties has brought a contract into being even though there may be no formal acceptance.

CASE LAW

The 'Battle of the Forms'

Sauter Automation Ltd v Goodman (Mechanical Services) Ltd[16]

A Sub-contractor's quotation was expressed as 'subject to our standard terms and conditions' which included a retention of title clause. The main Contractor sent an order stating 'terms and conditions in accordance with the main contract'. The Sub-contractor, without further communication, delivered the goods.

Held that this amounted to an acceptance by them of the main contractor's counter offer.

Davies and Co (Shopfitters) Ltd v William Old Ltd[17]

A nominated Sub-contractor submitted a tender which was accepted by the Architect. The Architect instructed the main Contractor to order work. The

15   (1840) 3 Beav 334.
16   (1986) 34 BLR 81.
17   (1969) 67 LGR 395.

main Contractor placed the order in accordance with his standard terms and conditions, which were different from those quoted in the earlier documentation.

Held that although the main Contractor's order was a counter offer which was never formally accepted, nonetheless the Sub-contractor's starting work was sufficient to constitute acceptance.

Chichester Joinery Ltd v John Mowlem & Co plc[18]

A quotation submitted by a Sub-contractor was accompanied by their standard terms and conditions. The main Contractor sent a purchase order containing their own standard terms which stated that 'any delivery made will constitute an acceptance of this order'. Sub-contractors delivered the work, but not until after they sent the main Contractor a printed acknowledgment of order, which stated that the order was accepted 'subject to the conditions overleaf'.

Held that by accepting the joinery the main Contractor had accepted the Sub-contractor's conditions.

(i) Obligations at tender stage

Consultants are frequently required to compete for work through some form of tender process, and we might therefore consider in outline the obligations which might arise as a result of a tender process.

As has been stated, an employer's request for tenders is an invitation to treat, and the tenders themselves comprise offers to do the work. It follows, then, that the employer is under no general legal obligation, in the absence of any promises to the contrary, to accept any of the tenders submitted (*Spencer v Harding*[19]).

The costs of tendering are therefore borne by the tenderer, unless the employer has made a promise to pay, or such a promise can be implied from the tender documents or from the employer's conduct. Such a promise might be implied where the preliminary work goes beyond what would normally be expected, or where the employer can secure some benefit from the tender itself (*William Lacey (Hounslow) Ltd v Davis*[20]).

---

18 (1987) 42 BLR 100.
19 (1870) LR 5 CP 561.
20 [1957] 1 WLR 932.

CASE LAW

Payment for preparation of tender

William Lacey (Hounslow) Ltd v Davis[21]

A Contractor tendered for reconstruction of war-damaged property and was led to believe that they would receive the contract. WL then prepared, at Davis's request, calculations and estimates which Davis used to negotiate a claim with the War Damage Commission. Davis then sold the property without concluding a contract for the reconstruction.

Held that a promise by the defendant to pay a reasonable sum for these services could be implied.

Note that the claim in this case was founded upon a profit which had already been realised, but the courts also reached a similar decision in *Marston Construction v Kigass* (1989) 46 BLR 109 where the client had only requested the work by implication and the potential profit was still largely theoretical.

The employer's discretion in respect of acceptance of tenders is therefore subject to the following qualifications:

(1) A person who invites tenders with no intention whatsoever of accepting any of the tenders will be liable for any expenses incurred. The action would be brought for fraudulent misrepresentation (*Richardson v Silvester*[22]).

(2) A person who expressly promises to accept the lowest tender will be bound by that promise provided that a compliant tender is submitted (*Harvela Investments Ltd v Royal Trust Co of Canada (CI) Ltd*[23]).

(3) In some circumstances where public bodies are concerned the employer may be under a n implied obligation to fairly consider any compliant tender submitted (*Blackpool and Fylde Aero Club v Blackpool Borough Council*[24]).

(4) Where public sector work is concerned, European Community Directives place considerable restrictions on an employer's powers of discretion (*Harmon CFEM Façades (UK) Ltd v Corporate Officer of the House of Commons*[25]). As stated earlier,

---

21   [1957] 2 All ER 712.
22   (1873) LR 9 QB 34.
23   [1985] 2 All ER 966, HL.
24   [1990] I WLR 1195.
25   (1999) 67 Con LR I.

the European regulations are given effect in British law through the Public Works Contracts Regulations.

CASE LAW

EC Directives

Harmon CFEM Façades (UK) Ltd v Corporate Officer of the House of Commons[26]

The case concerned the procurement of the external cladding to Portcullis House, London. The facts of the case are as follows.

In late 1993 an OJEC notice was published seeking expressions of interest in the work. Only one truly British firm responded, and the Project Manager instructed the managing contractor to seek other British companies prepared to tender. A number of companies, including Harmon (an American company), were subsequently pre-qualified and briefed. The Project Manager stated that the final choice would be based on lowest price unless there were good reasons otherwise. The Alvis/Seele consortium (a British/German joint venture) was added to the tender list.

Tenders opened in mid-1995. Harmon bid £40m, Alvis/Seele bid £41m, against a budget of £22m. Subsequent negotiation reduced Harmon's bid to £35m. The design was then revised. Harmon bid £31.4m, Alvis/Seele bid £37.2m.

Alvis/Seele were chosen as the 'best value' bid, citing better long-term maintenance, better factory, better welding and better staff.

In August 1996 Harmon sued, alleging a failure to observe the Public Works Regulations, breach of articles of the Treaty of Rome and obligations arising from European Directives concerning the procurement of public works, and unfair treatment of its tender amounting to misfeasance in public office.

Held that the case was proved, and Harmon were awarded legal costs, damages and loss of profit amounting to some £6.5m.

The in-house Project Manager was severely criticised for his conduct of the procurement exercise, Other important issues from the judgment are as follows:

- 'I consider that it is now clear in English law that in the public sector where competitive tenders are sought and responded to, a contract

26   (1999) 67 Con LR 1.

comes into existence whereby the prospective employer impliedly agrees to consider all tenders fairly.'

- In respect of 'most economically advantageous tenders', the tender selection criteria must be explicit.

- 'Overall value for money' and 'most economically advantageous tender' are not in themselves sufficient.

- 'Overall value' implies that the value will be assessed in a number of different ways, all of which would need to be taken into account. 'Most economically advantageous to the contracting authority' requires even more information to be given, since the tenderer has no idea what this is likely to mean. This must therefore be explained in the request for tenders.

LETTERS OF INTENT

Many contracts are begun before completion of the formal documentation, on the basis of a simple exchange of letters usually termed 'letters of intent'. Such letters are conventionally given to provide some comfort to tenderers that there will eventually be a contract for the work under which they will be paid.

The question of whether or not a contract can come into being purely on the basis of a letter of intent is frequently a difficult one. When correctly worded, letters of intent do not create a contractual relationship between the parties. They are not intended to. They are merely intended to convey the intention that a contract will eventually be put in place. In the words of Fay J in *Turriff Construction Ltd v Regalia Knitting Mills Ltd*[27]:

> A letter of intent would ordinarily have two characteristics: one, that it will express an intention to enter into a contract in the future, and, two, it will itself create no liability in regard to that future contract.

Letters of interim agreement, however, do create a binding contract between the parties, although the aim is not to form a relationship for the whole of the works, merely for that portion that needs to be put in hand before the larger contract can be finalised.

Another definition of a letter of intent was given by Judge Thornton QC in the case of *Hall & Tawse South Ltd v Ivory Gate Ltd*[28]:

27   (1971) 222 Estates Gazette 169.
28   (1997) 62 Con LR 117.

A letter of intent is usually a unilateral assurance intended to have contractual effect if acted upon, whereby reasonable expenditure reasonably incurred in reliance upon such a letter will be reimbursed. Such a letter places no obligation on the recipient to act upon it and there is usually no obligation to continue with the work or to undertake any defined parcel of work, the recipient being free to stop work at any time. The effect of such a letter is to promise reasonable reimbursement if the recipient does act upon it.

In that case, since the letter in question imposed obligations on both parties, it was held by the judge to constitute a 'provisional contract' which remained in effect until the parties completed their negotiations as to the terms of the main, or 'permanent', contract.

The judge in that case believed that the recipient, if he chose to act on the letter, would create a contractual relationship between the parties.

Another view is that if the recipient so acts, there is no contract, but he is entitled to be reimbursed his reasonable expenditure under the legal doctrine of restitution, which prevents unjust enrichment of the employer by having work done for which he is not obliged to pay. On this view, in the absence of any specific facts, a letter of intent does not have any contractual significance. It is merely an expression of an intention to do something, not a promise to create a contractual relationship.

The problems really arise because no two letters are likely to be the same and each can only be assessed on its own contents. It is therefore of critical importance to determine whether the letter confers on the recipient some authority to take action.

The leading case on the subject is *British Steel Corporation v Cleveland Bridge and Engineering Co Ltd*[29]. Other cases of interest are *Kitsons Insulation Contractors Ltd v Balfour Beatty Buildings Ltd* (1990) unreported, *Turriff Construction Ltd v Regalia Knitting Mills Ltd*[30], and *C J Sims v Shaftsbury plc*[31].

The key as to whether or not a contract exists would appear to be certainty. As long as there is an offer which is matched by an acceptance, and no doubt that the parties intended to create legal relations (for example there may be a reference to drawing up formal documentation at a later date), the letter itself can be regarded as an ancillary contract, and a legal relationship will exist.

---

29   [1984] 1 All ER 504.
30   (1971) 222 Estates Gazette 169.
31   (1991) 25 Con LR 72.

CASE LAW

Letters of intent

British Steel Corporation v Cleveland Bridge and Engineering Co Ltd[32]

CB were Sub-contractors involved in the construction of a bank. They approached BS with a view to their fabricating components for the steel frame. The negotiations were complex and time-consuming, but a letter was sent to BS which said:

> We are pleased to advise you that it is our intention to enter into a subcontract with your company for the supply and delivery of the steel castings which form the roof nodes on this project. ... We request you to proceed immediately with the works pending the preparation and issuing to you of the official form of subcontract.

The letter referred to a price that had been telexed to CB by BS, and also referred to the CB's standard terms. BS made it clear that they were unwilling to contract on those terms, but none the less commenced the work. Negotiations continued throughout this time. Delivery was made, but part was late due to a national steel strike.

BS sued for payment and CB counter-claimed for damages due to delays caused by late delivery.

Held that there was no contract because there was no *consensus ad idem*. There was no agreement on staged payments or liability for late delivery. BS were therefore entitled to payment on a *quantum meruit* basis and CB were unable to claim for the late delivery.

Kitsons Insulation Contractors Ltd v Balfour Beatty Buildings Ltd[33]

A letter of intent was sent by BBB which included the following:

> We confirm that it is our intention to enter into a subcontract with you to provide all labour, plant and supervision necessary to carry out and complete

---

32   [1984] I All ER 504.
33   (1990) unreported.

the design, fabrication, supply, transportation, installation and testing of the [components] in accordance with the documentation listed hereto.

The documentation stated a lesser contract sum than the letter of intent, and K refused to sign the sub-contract. None the less work was undertaken and six payments were made. A dispute then arose about the total amount payable to K. K said that there was no contract and that payment should be made on a *quantum meruit* basis. BBB said that there was a fixed price contract at the amount stated in the letter of intent.

Held that there was no contract. As in *British Steel Corporation v Cleveland Bridge* there were a number of issues that were not agreed, such as method of payment and amount of payment.

Turriff Construction Ltd v Regalia Knitting Mills Ltd[34]

T tendered for the design and construction of a factory, and when told that their tender was successful asked for a letter of intent 'to cover us for the work we will now be undertaking'. The letter was issued stating that it was subject to agreement on an acceptable contract. T began design work, and six months later R abandoned the project.

Held that T's request for a letter of intent made it clear that they required reassurance that they would be paid, and the letter contained that assurance. There was therefore *consensus ad idem* and a contract was found to exist.

C J Sims v Shaftsbury plc[35]

A letter of intent stated that:

In the unlikely event of the contract not proceeding, [the plaintiffs] will be reimbursed their reasonable costs which have been and will be incurred and costs for which they are liable including those of sub-contractors and suppliers, such costs to include loss of profit and contributions to overheads, all of which must be substantiated in full to the reasonable satisfaction of our quantity surveyor.

---

34   (1971) 222 Estates Gazette 169.
35   (1991) 25 Con LR 72.

No contract was concluded but considerable work was done.

Held that a contract arose on the terms of the letter of intent, and that the whole terms of the contract were set out in that letter. The contractor was therefore entitled to payment on a 'cost plus' basis.

(ii) Use of letters of interim agreement

Letters of interim agreement may be used, generally on the grounds of convenience, in any of the following circumstances:

- when one party requires certain work to be put in hand immediately;

- where there may be some delay before the formal documentation can be put in order;

- where there is a nominated sub-contractor that is required to commence work in advance of the appointment of a main contractor;

- where there is concern that a tenderer may withdraw his tender before the final documentation can be prepared.

The term 'interim agreement' may give rise to some confusion. Such a letter will in fact amount to an interim *contract*, so that all the parties will have rights and obligations under that contract. It is for this reason that such letters usually contain limits either in terms of time or finance. If they do not contain such limits, they will amount to contracts for the whole work.

In the case of *Monk Construction Ltd v Norwich Union Life Assurance Society*,[36] Monk were sent a letter authorising them to carry out certain preliminary works up to a limit of £100,000 and stating that, if no contract was entered into, they would be limited to their 'proven costs'. Monk subsequently carried out all the work, but no contract was ever signed. Monk claimed to be entitled to payment for all the work on a *quantum meruit* basis. The Society argued that the letter covered all the work and that therefore the 'proven costs' ceiling applied. The court found in favour of Monk. The letter was only intended to cover the preliminary works in circumstances where no further work was carried out by Monk.

As with any document, the courts are not influenced by what the parties call 'the letter'. They will look at its contents to determine whether it is a letter of intent or

36   (1992) 62 BLR 107, CA.

a letter of interim agreement. Thus in *Hall & Tawse*[37] the fact that the crucial letter referred to itself as being a letter of intent did not prevent the court from finding that it was in fact a provisional contract.

2   INTENTION

There must be genuine agreement. Both parties must intend that the agreement will be legally binding, and both must be willing to suffer the legal consequences (usually to pay damages) if they breach the agreed terms. The presumption is that such an intention exists in any commercial arrangement unless the parties clearly indicate otherwise (*Rose and Frank Co v J R Crompton and Bros*[38]).

In general the parties are free to decide the terms of the contract, provided they are not illegal, and the courts will not normally intervene in contracts between commercial organisations. It is therefore important that contracts are worded precisely, since the courts have no power to amend the terms of commercial contracts even if they are manifestly unfair, and their duty will be limited to interpreting the terms the parties have agreed in order to make the contract workable.

3   CONSIDERATION

Consideration is perhaps the most difficult concept to grasp. It is often taken to mean money, but there is no legal reason why consideration should not take some other form. The law of contract accepts that many kinds of promise have economic 'value', and the primary rule is simply that the contract must make demands on both parties. There is no general legal requirement for the 'values' of the promises the parties make to each other to be equal, but consumer protection legislation does prescribe some limits in contracts between private individuals and trading organisations. Where contracts between commercial bodies are concerned, however, the courts will generally not interfere, believing that commercial organisations ought to be capable of protecting themselves. A consultant's price for providing services or a contractor's price for carrying out work, even if it is not high enough for him to make a profit, will still constitute a legal consideration, provided it is freely given and properly accepted. Note that if the contract is solely one-sided (i e there is no consideration at all), then it is not enforceable unless it is made by deed.

37   (1997) 62 Con LR 117.
38   [1925] AC 445.

Privity of contract

As a general rule, a contract is a private arrangement made between the parties to it, i e those who give consideration under the contract. This being the case, only the parties to the contract may take action in the event of a breach (*Tweddle v Atkinson*,[39] *Dunlop Pneumatic Tyre Co v Selfridge & Co*[40]).

This fundamental principle has recently been amended by legislation, such that in certain circumstances 'third parties' (i e people other than the parties to the contract) may be granted some contractual rights, and may also take action in the event of a breach of contract which fundamentally affects them. The legislation, the Contracts (Rights of Third Parties) Act 1999, came into force in May 2000.

Briefly, the Act allows the parties to a contract to provide that certain terms of that contract are intended to benefit third parties, and if this is the case then the third parties will be able to take legal action to secure their rights in the event that those terms are breached. This is groundbreaking legislation. In the past, even if the contract clearly benefited a third party then that third party would have no right to enforce the contract in the event of a breach. With a few exceptions unrelated to construction, the Act applies to all contracts. It therefore includes all construction and consultancy contracts, agreements for sale and lease, etc. The Act has clear implications for the construction industry, where the contractual web may be extremely complex.

It should be remembered that the Act is specifically intended to allow the parties to a contract to grant third party rights *if they so wish*, and there is a provision permitting the parties to a contract specifically to exclude the Act from their contractual arrangements.

The Act is discussed in more detail in Chapter 3.

4 CAPACITY

The parties must be legally able to enter into a contractual relationship. Examples of people who are legally incapable of entering into a contract include minors and those certified insane.

Organisations can also have limits placed upon their contracting ability. Local authorities, for example, usually have the power to contract for the construction of things like roads, schools and houses, but their legal authority may not extend to, for example, building public houses or bingo halls. National Health Trusts initially

39   (1861) 1 B & S 393.
40   [1915] AC 847.

encountered problems in entering into PFI contracts until their contracting powers were amended by government to specifically empower them to do so. Authorities who act beyond their powers are said to be acting 'ultra vires' and the contract will as a result be void, i e of no legal standing, although Companies Act 1985, s 35B offers protection to parties who enter such contracts unaware of the limited powers of the organisation.

It is also important to establish that the person signing any document has the authority to do so.

5 LEGALITY

To be legally enforceable the contract must be for a purpose which is itself legal. A contract in Britain to build, for example, a brothel or a centre for the manufacture, storage and distribution of illegal drugs would therefore itself be illegal, and promises made under it would not be legally enforceable.

6 CONSENT

There are a number of things which can destroy the true consent of the parties to the contract.

(i) Mistake

Mistakes may arise from a mutual misconception of the material facts, or from a unilateral mistake made by one of the parties. The general position is as follows:

Common mistake

(1) A common mistake as to existence of subject matter arises where, for example, a contract is signed for the refurbishment of an existing building, but unbeknown to the parties the building has already been destroyed by fire. In this case the contract is void. If the building is destroyed after the contract has been signed but prior to the work commencing, the contract would still be valid but might be discharged due to frustration (*Taylor v Caldwell*[41]).

(2) A mistake as to expression of true intention arises where, for example, if the parties were in complete agreement on the terms of the contract but in error wrote them down incorrectly. In this case the contract could be rectified to represent the true intention of the parties.

41   (1863) 3 B & S 826.

Mutual and unilateral mistake

A mutual mistake occurs when the parties are at cross purposes – each is mistaken as to the intention of the other. A unilateral mistake occurs where only one party makes a mistake and the other party is aware of that mistake.

So in the case of a unilateral mistake the important issue is whether the other party is aware of the mistake at the time of agreement (*Roberts and Co Ltd v Leicestershire County Council*[42]). If, as in this case, the mistake is not only known but has also been induced by the other party, the case is even stronger. Where the mistake is not known to other party at the time of agreement (e g pricing errors made by the contractor), rectification will not normally be granted (*W Higgins v Northampton Corporation*[43]).

CASE LAW

Mistake

Roberts and Co Ltd v Leicestershire County Council[44]

The Contractor submitted a tender which specified completion in 18 months. The County Architect decided that the period should be 30 months and, unbeknown to the Contractor, entered this period in the formal contract. Before the sealing of the contract, there were two meetings at which the Contractor referred to their plans to complete in 18 months and produced a progress schedule on that basis. Held that the Contractor was entitled to rectification.

W Higgins v Northampton Corporation[45]

The Contractor made an error in pricing in a tender for 58 houses. As a result of the error, the price quoted was £1,613 per pair instead of £1,670 per pair. On discovering the error, the Contractor sought to be released from the contract. Held that they were bound by the terms of the contract as signed.

---

42   [1961] Ch 555.
43   [1927] 1 Ch 128.
44   [1961] Ch 555.
45   [1927] 1 Ch 128.

It is an established principle that employers may not take advantage of errors in a tender of which they are aware without the consent of the other party. However, an employer advised of a mistake who then asked the tenderer to confirm their tender may be able to rely upon the terms in the event that the tender is subsequently withdrawn. In *City University of Hong Kong (formerly City Poytechnic) v Blue Cross Insurance*[46], previously mentioned, the tender document stated that if City Polytechnic became aware of any error in the tenders submitted they were required to notify the tenderer and ask them to confirm their tender. City Polytechnic were aware, but failed to refer the matter back to Blue Cross. Blue Cross were therefore not bound by their tender due to City Polytechnic not abiding by its own tender conditions.

It is interesting to note that had City Polytechnic complied with the requirement in the tender conditions and referred the matter to Blue Cross, they may have been able to rely on the collateral contract requiring the tenderer to keep the tender open for a period of three months. Withdrawal of their tender within this time limit, notwithstanding the mistake, would have been breach of this collateral contract.

Non est factum

Non est factum is where a party signs a contract under a mistake as to its essential nature. This only applies in very rare cases (for example, believing the contract was for the erection of a house whereas in fact it was for the purchase of a house).

(ii) Misrepresentation

A misrepresentation is an untrue statement of fact which induces a party to enter into a contract. If the statement becomes a term of the contract, the injured party can sue for breach of contract.

It is therefore important to identify what is a statement of fact and what is a mere opinion or tradesman's puff. The court must decide as to whether the statement is so important that it can be considered to be a term in the contract (*Bacal Construction v Northampton Development Corporation*[47]).

46   [2001] HKCFI 214.
47   (1975) 8 BLR 88.

CASE LAW

Representation/term

Bacal Construction v Northampton Development Corporation[48]

The contract concerned a local authority housing development. As part of their tender, the Bacal submitted sub-structure designs based on borehole data supplied by the NDC. During the course of the work, 'tufa' was discovered in various areas, necessitating the redesign of the foundations.

Held that there should be an implied term that the ground conditions would accord with the hypotheses upon which the contractor had been instructed to design the foundations and, accordingly, the risk of the ground conditions differing from those postulated was to be borne by the employer.

In cases where the misrepresentation has influenced a tenderer in entering into a contract, the aggrieved party may be entitled to rescission and/or damages. The remedy will depend on the status of the misrepresentation, that is, whether it was fraudulent, negligent or innocent.

The Project Manager should be careful not to overstate his own skills and capabilities, as these might well influence his own appointment and lay him open to an action in misrepresentation if he proved not to have those skills or capabilities.

(iii) Economic duress

As has been seen, for there to be a valid contract there must be an agreement, and it is essential that the agreement is freely made. If there is any coercion in the formation of the agreement it will be voidable on the grounds of duress. The traditional view of duress has been the threat or use of actual physical force. However, matters have moved on, and now the courts recognise the concept of economic duress, where a threat is made to a party's economic wellbeing (*North Ocean Shipping Co v Hyundai Construction Co, The Atlantic Baron*[49]). What amounts to economic distress was closely examined in *DSND Subsea Ltd v Petroleum Geo-Services ASA*[50]. Important issues are:

---

48   (1975) 8 BLR 88.
49   [1979] QB 705.
50   [2000] BLR 530.

- there must be pressure,

- whose practical effect is that there is compulsion on, or a lack of practical choice for, the victim,

- which is illegitimate, and

- is a significant cause inducing the victim to enter the contract.

In deciding what is illegitimate it is necessary to consider whether:

- there was an actual or threatened breach of contract;

- the person exerting the pressure acted in good or bad faith;

- the victim protested at the time;

- the victim affirmed or sought to rely on the contract.

It has been pointed out that illegitimate pressure must be distinguished from 'the rough and tumble of the pressures of normal commercial bargaining'.

These factors were applied to the settlement of a construction final account in *Carillion Construction Limited v Felix (UK) Ltd*[51].

CASE LAW

Economic duress

Carillion Construction Limited v Felix (UK) Ltd[52]

C was the main Contractor, F the cladding Sub-contractor. F started work in September 1998; the contract was concluded in December 1999. The final account was agreed in March 2000. The settlement agreement was followed until F made their final delivery, after which C reverted to the original sub-contract. C then commenced proceedings in June 2000. They contended that the only reason that they agreed the final account was that F were refusing to complete the outstanding work.

Held that F's threat to withhold deliveries was a threat to breach their contract and so illegitimate pressure. The cladding was non-standard and an alternative supplier was not a practical possibility. Adjudication was not a practical alternative, as six weeks was too long to wait, and a mandatory injunction would be too difficult to obtain. There was no affirmation of the contract as proceedings were commenced immediately following the final delivery.

---

51   [2001] BLR 1.
52   [2001] BLR 1.

(d) Formalities

1 FORM

There is no requirement for a construction contract to be in any particular form, although it should be remembered that the Housing Grants, Construction and Regeneration Act 1996 only applies to contracts in writing.

As a result, a contract may be entered into as a deed (referred to as specialty contracts or contracts under seal) or in writing, orally or by implication (a simple contract). The usual reason for requiring a contract to be contained in a deed is to take advantage of the longer limitation period (see below).

2 CONTENT

The formalities refer to the words of the contract agreement. It defines the basis of the agreement, the obligations of the parties, and the duties to be undertaken by any other persons involved. In the case of poorly documented or oral contracts, determining the terms of the contract is often a major difficulty in the event of a dispute.

It is plainly important that the terms of the contract should be agreed before the contract is signed, but it is commonly the case, particularly with negotiated contracts, that the precise terms are not finally agreed. In this case the courts will attempt to construe the expressed and implied intentions of the parties in such a way as to make the contract work. In some cases terms will be implied by the courts. For example, in construction contracts, regardless of the express terms of the contract, certain basic conditions must be fulfilled if the contract is to be carried out at all, The courts will therefore imply the following terms:

- The employer and his agent will do all that is reasonably necessary to enable the contractor to carry out and complete the works in accordance with the contract (*Luxor (Eastbourne) Ltd v Cooper*[53]).

- Neither the employer nor his agent must hinder or prevent the contractor from carrying out and completing the works in accordance with the contract (*William Cory & Sons v City of London Corporation*[54]).

In cases where the existence of a contract can be established but it is silent as to time, then the normal rule will be that the work must be completed within a reasonable

---

53 [1941] AC 108.
54 [1951] 2 KB 476.

time. In terms of payment, where work is ordered there is an implied promise to pay, and where the contract is silent as to price then the normal rule will be for payment to be made on a *quantum meruit* (i e fair value) basis.

As far as the supply of goods is concerned, s 14 of the Sale of Goods Act 1989 requires that materials supplied under a commercial arrangement should be of satisfactory quality and also fit for their intended purpose. The Supply of Goods and Services Act 1982 requires that people offering services on a commercial basis will exercise all due skill and care in the performance of their duties.

In contracts for project management services, it would therefore be at least arguable that, in the absence of express terms to the contrary, the following terms could be implied:

(1) That the employer will provide the Project Manager, within a reasonable time, with all necessary information, access to land and buildings etc required for the Project Manager to carry out the required work; that he will not obstruct the Project Manager in the performance of the work; and that he will pay a reasonable price for the work done.

(2) That the Project Manager will do the work in a workmanlike manner, that he will exercise all due skill and care in the performance of his duties, and that he will complete the work within a reasonable time.

(3) That the Project Manager warrants that any materials he supplies are reasonably fit for the purpose for which they are to be used, and are of satisfactory quality.

These warranties may, however, be excluded, either expressly or by the actions of the parties (*Young & Marten v McManus Childs Ltd*[55]).

CASE LAW

Fit for purpose

Young & Marten v McManus Childs Ltd[56]

A Contractor was ordered to tile a roof with 'Somerset 13 tiles'. The tiles were apparently perfect on delivery but weathering defects developed later, requiring replacement of the tiles.

Held that the Contractor would not have been responsible if tiles of good quality had been supplied which proved unfit for their purpose because they

---

55 [1969] 1 AC 454.
56 [1969] 1 AC 454.

had been chosen by the employer, but he was liable for the fact that the tiles were defective even though the defect was latent and could not have been discovered through the use of proper skill and care.

Rotherham Metropolitan Borough Council v Frank Haslam Milan & Co[57]

The employer invited tenders for an office block. Specification for hardcore stated that it should be '... gravel, stone, rock fill, crushed concrete or slag or natural sand'. The Contractor provided samples for approval. Approved hardcore as supplied included steel slag which expanded and damaged the ground floor.

Held that the employer did not rely on the Contractor's skill and care, that the Contractor provided material in accordance with the specification, and that the material was of merchantable quality.

The need to ensure that all of the fundamental terms are agreed before the contract comes into existence is clearly shown in *Courtney and Fairbairn Ltd v Tolaini Bros (Hotels) Ltd*[58]. This case should be contrasted with *ATC Construction v Clarke & Sons (Coaches) Ltd*[59] where, in the Court of Appeal, Ward LJ stated that:

Provided there is an instruction to do work and an acceptance of the instruction, then there is a contract and the law will imply into it an obligation to pay a reasonable sum for that work.

57 (1996) 78 BLR 1.
58 [1975] 1 All ER 716.
59 [2002] CILL 1897.

CASE LAW

Agreement to negotiate

Courtney and Fairbairn Ltd v Tolaini Bros (Hotels) Ltd and Another[60]

In 1969 Mr Tolaini decided to develop a site. He contacted Mr Courtney, who was a property developer and a building contractor. C wrote to T suggesting that he (C) should act as a broker in attempting to find financial sponsors for the scheme. The suggested arrangement was that if those sponsors then subsequently reached a satisfactory financial arrangement with T, then T would instruct his quantity surveyor to negotiate a building contract for the project with C based on 'fair and reasonable sums in respect of ... the projects ... based on agreed estimates of net cost and general overheads with a margin for profit of 5%'.

T replied in writing agreeing to this arrangement. Financial sponsors were found, satisfactory financial arrangements were concluded and T appointed a Quantity Surveyor. Negotiations, however, broke down over the agreement of the estimates of net costs, and T let the contract to another Contractor.

C sued T for breach of contract.

Held on appeal that the exchange of letters did not constitute a contract. In a building contract, the price was of fundamental importance and was so essential a term that there was no contract unless a price was agreed, or there was an agreed method of ascertaining it. The method agreed here was not considered to be certain enough to satisfy the test.

The difference between the two appears to be that, in the former, the price still had to be *negotiated* and therefore there was no enforceable contract, whilst in the latter there was an agreement, albeit silent as to price, and therefore the doctrine of restitution dictates that a reasonable sum must be paid.

In attempting to interpret the terms of the contract, the courts will examine the contract documents as a whole and will restrict their interpretation to the information contained in them. Where standard forms of contract are used, the documents which comprise 'the contract documents' will be explicitly identified in the contract conditions. Where standard forms are not used, the contract documents will be

---

60 [1975] 1 All ER 716.

those documents expressly referred to in the contract agreement. It is therefore of fundamental importance to know what the contract documents comprise for any specific project.

Additional information contained in other documents will not normally be admissible in resolving contractual disputes. The point is well demonstrated by the case of *Davis Contractors v Fareham UDC*[61], where a Contractor agreed to build 78 houses for a fixed price in eight months. Attached to the tender was a letter stating that the tender was subject to adequate supplies of labour being available, but the letter was not incorporated in the contract documents. Unanticipated shortages of labour increased the contract period to 22 months and the cost to about £17,000 more than the contract price. It was held that the Contractors had to bear the cost themselves. The letter was not incorporated in the contract and, therefore, had no effect.

Finally, particularly in the case of negotiated contracts, it is not uncommon for the formal contract to be signed some time after the commencement of the work. A valid acceptance can require the contract itself to be signed at a later date (*Lewis v Brass*[62]), but a further question arises as to the method of payment for any work done after the contract is accepted but before the contract is signed. In other words, can the contract conditions be retrospective, or is the contractor entitled to payment on a *quantum meruit* basis until the contract is actually signed?

This situation was considered in *Trollope & Colls Ltd and Holland, Hannen and Cubitts Ltd v Atomic Power Construction Ltd*[63].

CASE LAW

Retrospective acceptance

Trollope & Colls Ltd and Holland, Hannen and Cubitts Ltd v Atomic Power Construction Ltd[64]

The Contractors tendered for work under a contract with provision for variations and fluctuations. After four months the Contractors received a letter of intent requesting that the work be started subject to a formal contract when the terms had been settled. The formal contract was entered into ten months later following substantial changes to the scheme.

---

61   [1956] AC 696.
62   (1877) 3 QBD 667.
63   [1962] 3 All ER 1035.
64   [1962] 3 All ER 1035.

> The Contractor claimed payment on a *quantum meruit* basis for work carried out before entering into the formal agreement, rather than on the basis of the original tender adjusted for variations.
>
> Held that as the parties had always contemplated entering into a contract which would govern work done before as well as after the agreement, the contract had retrospective effect and the Contractor's claim failed.

(e) The meaning of 'due skill and care'

It has already been established that, as a matter of principle, all Contractors must carry out their work with proper professional skill and care, and this applies just as much to Project Managers as to anyone else. The question which then arises is what does this phrase actually mean?

In this context it must be remembered that, in general, professional consultants are not legally required to warrant the success of what they do. A doctor, for example, does not guarantee to cure the patient, and neither does a barrister guarantee to win a case. They merely warrant that they will employ a generally acceptable level of professional skill and care. Consequently, a Project Manager charged with procuring construction work does not, under normal circumstances, guarantee that the completed building will be fit for its purpose. In the absence of any specific requirements from the employer, it will be sufficient if he can show that in procuring the work he employed a legally acceptable degree of professional expertise.

The level of professional skill and care which users of professional services are entitled to expect was established in *Bolam v Friern Hospital Management Committee*[65] in these terms:

> Where you get a situation which involves the use of some special skill or competence, then the test as to whether there has been negligence or not ... is the standard of the ordinary skilled man exercising and professing to have that special skill.... it is well established law that it is sufficient if he exercises the ordinary skill of an ordinary competent man exercising that particular art.

So in *William Tomkinson and Sons Ltd v Parochial Church Council of St Michael in the Hamlet*[66], the Architect was found to have been negligent where he failed to advise

65   [1957] 2 All ER 118.
66   (1990) 6 Const LJ 814.

his employer of the need to take out appropriate insurance under the construction contract (see also *Pozzolonic Lytag v Bryan Hobson Associates*[67], discussed in Chapter 9).

It has even been held that this general duty of care obligation still applies even where one has paid extra to obtain the services of the best in the field (*Wimpey Construction v Poole*[68]). However, the dividing line as to what constitutes an unacceptable level of skill and care is very narrow (*Greaves & Co v Baynham Meikle & Partners*[69]).

CASE LAW
Acceptable levels of skill and care

Wimpey Construction v Poole[70]

The case concerned a Wimpey design and build scheme where a number of design defects had arisen. Wimpey made good the defects and subsequently attempted to claim the cost back from their Professional Indemnity Insurers. They argued that they had special skills which were not available from 'ordinary' consultants, and that they had been professionally negligent in this particular area and should therefore be entitled to claim the cost of the repairs back from their own insurers under their professional negligence policy.

Held that there was no legal obligation to provide anything other than the 'normal' standard of skill and care as established in *Bolam*.

Greaves & Co v Baynham Meikle & Partners[71]

An oil company contracted with Greaves for them to design and construct a multi-storey warehouse for the storage of oil drums, the drums to be moved around with fork-lift trucks. Greaves subcontracted with Baynham Meikle, Consulting Engineers, to design the structure. Shortly after the building was handed over, the floors began to crack and within a short time the building became unusable.

The cause of the failure was found to be vibration caused by the stacker trucks. The building was constructed using the then relatively new technique of concrete beam and infill floors on a steel frame.

---

67   [1999] BLR 267.
68   (1984) 27 BLR 58.
69   [1975] 3 All ER 99.
70   (1984) 27 BLR 58.
71   [1975] 3 All ER 99.

> The Contractors, while accepting their own liability to the oil company, successfully sued their Engineers for negligence in the design despite the fact that, at the time, little was known of the effects of vibration on such a structure, and independent experts testified that they would have designed the building in the same way.

The issue of the use of 'new' techniques was specifically addressed in *Victoria University, Manchester v Hugh Wilson and Lewis Womersley*[72], when Newey J said:

> For architects to use untried or relatively untried materials or techniques could not in itself be wrong, as otherwise the construction industry would never make any progress. However, architects venturing into the untried or little tried were wise to warn their clients specifically of what they were doing and to obtain their express approval.

The line between what constitutes the use of reasonable skill and care and what could constitute professional negligence in any particular situation is therefore a very fine one. It has caused some designers to retreat into what has been called 'defensive design', where modern and comparatively untried methods and materials are set aside in favour of the use of well-established and well-tried methods and solutions.

It should also be pointed out that, under the rules for agency set out above, consultants who effectively attempt to pass some part of the work on to others, either directly or indirectly, may still be responsible to the client for the work as a whole unless the client's express approval has previously been obtained (*Moresk Cleaners v Hicks*[73]).

CASE LAW

Delegation of duties

Moresk Cleaners v Hicks[74]

An Architect was engaged to design an extension to a laundry. He subsequently arranged for a specialist Sub-contractor to design and build

---

72   (1984) 2 Con LR 43.
73   [1966] 2 Lloyd's Rep 338.
74   (1966) 2 Lloyd's Rep 338.

the reinforced concrete portal frame. Two years after completion, the structure became defective because of negligent design by the Sub-contractor.

The Architect argued that, as the employer's agent, he was entitled to delegate some design works if he did not have the skills to do it himself.

Held that the Architect was liable. Acceptable courses of action would be to:

- tell the client he was not competent to do the work and seek his instructions;

- ask the client to employ a specialist;

- employ and pay a specialist himself (in this case, while he would still be liable, he would be able to step down the responsibility for the defective design to his own Sub-contractor).

However, this obligation may not apply in cases where a reasonably competent consultant could not be expected to possess the relevant specialist technical knowledge to pass judgment, but even in this situation the consultant would still have a duty to warn his client about the possible consequences of failure (*Pozzolonic Lytag v Bryan Hobson Associates*[75], discussed in Chapter 9.

The extent of the professional skill and care required in the case of project management is still a largely unexplored area, and the problems which beset litigants are well illustrated by the comments made in *Pride Valley Foods v Hall and Partners*[76] cited above. Any consultant entering into a contract for the provision of services gives an implied undertaking under the Supply of Goods and Services Act 1982 that the person providing the service will be appropriately qualified so to do. Assuming that this essential pre-condition is met, and in the absence of a substantial body of case law or a generally accepted standard model of project management services, it is believed that the Project Manager's exposure to claims of failing to provide proper services of an appropriate standard can best be limited by ensuring that the consultancy agreement includes a precise description of the services required.

It is therefore glaringly obvious that the terms of the consultancy appointment must be explicit, and that the Project Manager must satisfy himself before entering into the contract that he has the necessary skills and knowledge to carry out his contractual obligations. Vaguely worded and imprecise contractual documentation which does not adequately specify what is required of the Project Manager, or how the results of his efforts will be measured, will potentially leave him open to very wide-ranging allegations of negligent conduct, and may result in his being cited as a

75   [1999] BLR 267.
76   [2001] EWCA Civ 1001, (2001) 76 Con LR 1.

co-defendant in negligence claims made against other professional members of the project team.

Note that it has also been held that a Project Manager has a duty to monitor the actions of other consultants in the team, and to report any deficiencies in their performance to the employer (*Chesham Properties v Bucknall Austin*[77] – discussed in Chapter 8).

I   DESIGN AND BUILD CONTRACTS AND A FITNESS FOR PURPOSE LIABILITY

Particular problems could potentially arise for Project Managers acting for clients in the procurement of work through a design and build route.

We have already seen that consultant professionals have only a general obligation to exercise ordinary skill and care, but in the case of a Builder providing a complete product there may well be an implied term in the contract that the building supplied will be fit for its purpose.

While the fitness for purpose obligation can be expressly excluded in the construction contract (for example, the Joint Contracts Tribunal Standard Form of Building Contract with Contractor's Design (JCT CD 98) does not make reference to fitness for purpose), many clients are now specifically requesting buildings which are fit for their intended purpose. Similar issues of fitness for purpose may arise on more traditionally designed schemes in the event of design by nominated Sub-contractors, particularly where selection of materials or components is left to the nominated Sub-contractor under the provisions of a performance specification.

Project Managers responsible for procuring work through this route, particularly those where the client has specifically made the Project Manager aware of his wish for a building which is fit for its purpose, may therefore have a significantly greater level of exposure to the employer than under a conventionally designed project. There may also be difficulties in arranging cost-effective insurance cover against failure to satisfy a fitness for purpose obligation.

Project Managers should also be aware that, whilst design professionals acting as consultants are often required by their own professional bodies to carry mandatory professional indemnity insurance (PII), design and build contractors in general have no such obligation.

77   (1996) 82 BLR 92.

CASE LAW

Design and build and fitness for purpose

Development has taken place by extension from statutory obligations under the Sale of Goods Act 1979.

IBA v EMI and BICC[78]

The case concerned the design and construction of an aerial mast for the IBA. BICC were nominated Sub-contractors to EMI and were responsible for the design of the mast. Following construction the mast collapsed in severe weather.

Held that BICC were negligent in the design, and that EMI were liable for not providing a mast fit for its purpose.

London Borough of Newham v Taylow Woodrow (Anglian)[79]

A package deal contract for the construction of a 22-storey block of flats at Ronan Point, London. A gas explosion on the 18th floor caused collapse of the south east corner of the block. N claimed the cost of repair and of strengthening other blocks, alleging negligence and/or breach of contract.

Held that TWA were not guilty of negligence, but that they were in breach of contract in that the flats were not fit for purpose.

Viking Grain Storage v T H White Installations[80]

The contract concerned the supply of grain silos. The grain developed mould whilst stored, due to inadequate ventilation.

Held that the defendants were liable for not providing goods fit for their purpose.

---

78 (1980) 14 BLR 1.
79 (1981) 19 BLR 99.
80 (1985) 33 BLR 103.

(f) Remedies for breach of contract

I DAMAGES

The usual remedy for breach of contract is damages. The purpose of damages is to put the claimant 'so far as money can do it … in the same situation … as if the contract had been performed' (*Robinson v Harman*[81]). Under the common law damages are a right if there has been a breach of contract; the only question once a breach has been proved is the amount to be paid.

Damages may be unliquidated or liquidated (often referred to as liquidated and ascertained damages (LADs).

(i) Unliquidated damages

These are assessed by the courts. First the courts will look at causation, that is, the loss must be a direct result of the breach of contract.

The second thing that they will examine is remoteness. Not every loss which occurs as a result of a breach will be recoverable. The loss is said not to be too remote if, at the time the parties entered the contract, they ought reasonably to have contemplated that a loss of that type was a serious possibility. The leading case is *Hadley v Baxendale*[82], where Alderson B held that:

> Where two parties have made a contract which one of them has broken, the damages which the other party ought to receive in respect of such breach of contract should be such as may fairly and reasonably be considered either arising naturally, i e according to the usual course of things, from such breach of contract itself or such as may reasonably be supposed to have been in the contemplation of both parties, at the time they made the contract, as the probable result of the breach of it.

Thus we can see the two grounds for recovery, known as the two limbs:

- Losses which arise naturally or in the usual course of events – each party is deemed to be aware of such losses.

- Losses which arise as additional or special consequences of the breach – it must be shown that the parties were or ought to have been aware of such losses.

81 (1848) I Exch 850.
82 (1854) 9 Exch 341.

The case of *Victoria Laundry (Windsor) Ltd v Newman Industries Ltd*[83] clearly illustrates the operation of the second limb. Here the laundry ordered a new boiler from Newman. They intended to take on additional work which was potentially extremely profitable. Newman was not made aware of this additional work. The boiler was not delivered in time and the additional work was lost. Held that the laundry could only recover for the normal loss of profit, as Newman had no actual knowledge at the time that the contract was entered of the additional work.

The measure of damages is set so as to restore the injured party to the position that they would have been in had the other party performed their obligations.

The normal measure where there has been defective workmanship is the actual or estimated cost of reinstatement. Where there has been a total failure to carry out work, then the measure will be the additional cost of carrying out that work. Two cases worthy of examination here are *Ruxley Electronics and Construction Ltd v Forsyth*[84] and *Harbutts Plasticine Ltd v Wayne Tank & Pump Co Ltd*[85].

CASE LAW

Assessment of damages

Ruxley Electronics and Construction Ltd v Forsyth[86]

The plaintiff built the defendant a swimming pool. The contract stated that the diving area should be 7ft 6in deep, but on completion it was found to be only 6ft deep. This had no direct effect on the cost of the property or the ability to use the pool for diving. The estimated cost of rebuilding to the required depth was £21,560.

At first instance the court awarded £2,500 for loss of amenity, holding that the cost of reinstatement was an unreasonable claim.

Court of Appeal awarded the cost of reinstatement, but the House of Lords upheld the original judgment on the basis that the cost of reinstatement was out of all proportion to the benefit that would be obtained.

83   [1949] 2 KB 528.
84   [1996] AC 344.
85   [1970] 1 QB 447.
86   [1996] AC 344.

Harbutts Plasticine Ltd v Wayne Tank & Pump Co Ltd[87]

The plaintiff's factory was burnt down as a result of a breach of contract by the defendants.

The plaintiff recovered the full cost of rebuilding the factory as there was no reasonable alternative to rebuilding.

It must not, however, be forgotten that the claimant has a obligation to mitigate his loss, that is, he has an obligation to keep his loss to a minimum and not sit back and watch them mount up. However, it is for the defendant to prove that the loss has not been mitigated, but all that is really required is to show that the claimant has acted reasonably in the circumstances.

(ii) Liquidated damages

It is common, but not essential, for construction contracts to include a liquidated damages clause. Liquidated damages is a sum of money agreed as a term of the contract to be payable in the event of a specific breach.

In order to be valid, the sum included must be a genuine pre-estimate of the party's anticipated loss and not a sum designed to act as a penalty on the other party. It does not matter that it is difficult to arrive at a genuine pre-estimate as long as the methodology used is reasonable (*Philips v A-G of Hong Kong*[88]).

The leading case on the differentiation between liquidated damages and penalty is *Dunlop Pneumatic Tyre Co Ltd v New Garage & Motor Co Ltd,*[89] where Lord Dunedin set out four rules of construction:

1 It will be a penalty if the sum is for an extravagant and unconscionable amount in comparison with the greatest loss that could be anticipated.

2 It will be a penalty if the breach of contract arises because a sum of money has not been paid and the sum stipulated as liquidated damages is greater than the sum that ought to have been paid.

3 It is presumed to be a penalty when a single lump sum is payable however long the delay occurs. This is only a presumption and could be set aside on specific evidence.

87 [1970] 1 QB 447.
88 (1993) 61 BLR 41.
89 [1915] AC 79.

4   It is not an obstacle to the sum being a genuine pre-estimate that it is difficult to
    arrive at a precise figure.

If the sum is found to be a penalty then the clause will be void and the defendant
will only be entitled to unliquidated damages. However, if the stipulated sum conforms
with the requirement but is nevertheless in excess of the sum actually lost, the
liquidated damages will still stand. In *BFI Group of Companies Ltd v DCB Integration
Systems Ltd*[90], on the completion date of warehouse the doors still had not arrived
from the manufacturer. The contractor gave the employer possession of the building
so that they could carry out the fit-out, thus ensuring that the employer lost no
time. It was nevertheless held that the employer could claim liquidated damages.

If the actual loss is far in excess of the liquidated damages, the clause will still be
upheld. In *Cellulose Acetate Silk Co Ltd v Widnes Foundry (1925) Ltd*[91] the clause stated
'£20 per working week'. The plant was 30 weeks late and the actual losses were
£5,850. It was held that only £600 was recoverable.

A salutary lesson can be learnt from *Temloc Ltd v Errill Properties Ltd*[92], where, in an
attempt to void the contractual liquidated damages provision, thus leaving himself
free to claim for unliquidated damages on the basis of his actual loss, the employer
inserted '£nil' in the contract particulars as the amount of liquidated damages. It was
held that the fact that the damages provision was set as £nil did not invalidate the
contractual liquidated damages provision, and the employer was therefore entitled
to nothing at all for the delay in completion.

2   EQUITABLE REMEDIES

(i) Specific performance

In a construction scenario it is unlikely that specific performance would be awarded,
as the courts are not in a position to ensure that someone carries work out or carries
it out to the required standard. However, if the breach of contract concerns the
refusal to convey a piece of land for which a valid contract of sale exists, then specific
performance will be available. The courts take the view that they will exercise their
discretion where the situation cannot be remedied by the paying of money. If the
piece of land is an integral part of the development and the owner is reluctant to
complete, then no amount of money can compensate the developer.

90   [1987] CILL 348.
91   [1933] AC 20.
92   (1987) 39 BLR 30.

4 The tort of negligence

Liability in contract arises through the agreement that the parties have reached. Liability in tort is independent of any contractual relationship and arises from the status of parties. Parties have the option as to whether or not they enter into a contractual relationship. Liability in tort is imposed, there is no choice in the matter. Therefore, it follows that a party may have a concurrent liability in contract and in tort (*Esso Petroleum Co Ltd v Mardon*[93]).

The most important tort in this context is the tort of negligence. It is therefore important to understand its basic principles. According to the *Oxford English Dictionary*, negligence is 'want of proper care, disregard of precision'. In *Blyth v Birmingham Waterworks Co*[94] Alderson B stated:

> Negligence is the omission to do something which a reasonable man guided upon those considerations which ordinarily regulate the conduct of human affairs would do, or doing something which a prudent and reasonable man would not do.

A more useful definition for our purposes comes from Lord Wright in *Lochgelly Iron & Coal Co v McMullan*[95]:

> In strict legal analysis, negligence means more than heedless or careless conduct, whether in omission or commission. It properly connotes the complex concept of duty, breach, and damage thereby suffered by the person to whom the duty was owing.

Therefore we can conclude that an action in negligence will lie where:

- the defendant owes the claimant a *duty* of care, and

- the defendant is in *breach* of that duty, and as a result

- the claimant suffers *loss/damage*.

The standard against which the defendant will be judged is that of the *reasonable man*.

(a) Duty of care

We have already examined the level of skill and care required by a professional man, but to whom is this duty of care owed? Under contract obviously to the other contractual parties, but the obligation in negligence is wider, in that a duty of care is owed to:

93   [1976] QB 801.
94   (1856) 11 Exch 781.
95   [1934] AC 1.

... persons who are so closely and directly affected by my act that I ought reasonably to have them in contemplation (Lord Atkin in *Donoghue v Stevenson*[96]).

This doctrine has been extended over the years to cover construction cases, and is of obvious interest, for example, to people who might have bought a building which is suffering from undiscovered latent defects. Such purchasers would normally have no right of action in contract (unless granted by virtue of the Contracts (Rights of Third Parties) Act 1999 or by an assignment of contractual rights/collateral warranty: see Chapter 3) against either the original contractor or the architect. An action in tort might therefore be their only hope of compensation.

As has already been pointed out, it has long been a basic principle that there may be a concurrent liability in contract and in tort for the same act. This issue has been one of great concern to consultants, and it was for many years believed that, where the parties were in contract for professional services, there could not as a matter of law be a concurrent liability in tort. The basis of this belief arose from the views of the Privy Council in *Tai Hing Cotton Mill v Liu Chong Bank*[97], where Lord Scarman said that:

... their Lordships do not believe that there is anything to be gained in the law's development in searching for a liability in tort where the parties are in a contractual relationship. This is particularly so in a commercial relationship.

The issue was raised in the case of a construction contract in *Lancashire and Cheshire Associations of Baptist Churches Inc v Howard and Seddon Partnership*[98]. Here, the Partnership designed a new sanctuary for a church and acted as construction managers. The Association was dissatisfied, alleging defects in the design and construction. By the time the writ was issued the action was statute-barred in contract because more than six years had passed from the date of the alleged breach, but the limitation period for tort was still current. Kershaw J held, following *Midland Bank Trust v Hett, Stubbs and Kent*[99], that:

There can in law be a duty of care actionable in the tort of negligence where the parties are in a contractual professional relationship. It would be illogical if a negligent act performed on or for a person who was by contract a client was not actionable.

A further twist to this story concerns the liability of contract administrators. A basic principle that the Contract Administrator could not be sued in negligence was laid down by the Court of Appeal in *Chambers v Goldthorpe*[100], on the grounds that the

96   [1932] AC 562.
97   [1986] AC 80.
98   [1993] 3 All ER 467.
99   [1979] Ch 384.
100 [1901] 1 KB 624.

Contract Administrator was acting in a quasi-judicial capacity and therefore enjoyed immunity from actions in negligence. This principle was, however, overturned by the House of Lords in *Sutcliffe v Thakrah*[101], where an Architect was liable to his employer for over-certifying payments to a Contractor who subsequently went into liquidation.

There have also been a large number of cases brought in the tort of negligence where owners of defective buildings have attempted, sometimes successfully, to take action against local authority inspectors alleging breach of their duty of care to inspect buildings under construction.

It is therefore necessary to consider the nature of the duty of care imposed in tort, since it is only breach of this duty of care which will give rise to a claim for negligence. The law does not proceed from the assumption that, just because someone suffers a loss, someone else must have legal liability for that loss. Nor do the courts necessarily hold someone to be legally liable even if they are proved to have fallen below the required standard. Liability in tort does not exist without proof of a legally recoverable type of loss. The claimant must therefore show not only that the defendant owed him a duty of care and was in breach of that duty, but also that he, the claimant, suffered a loss/damage which is legally recoverable.

(b) Loss/damage

Loss/damage can be classified in a number of ways:

* personal injury;

* damage to other property;

* damage to the product itself (pure economic loss).

This classification is very important, as the law readily accepts the first two but severely limits recovery of the last one. The leading case is *Hedley Byrne & Co Ltd v Heller & Partners Ltd*[102], where it was established that a successful action could be brought where there was pure financial loss as a result of reliance on a financial reference provided negligently.

The principle of reimbursement for pure economic loss was extended to construction cases over a number of years. The high water mark was *Junior Books v Veitchi Co*[103]. Veitchi were a specialist flooring company acting as a nominated Sub-contractor

101 [1974] AC 727.
102 [1964] AC 465.
103 [1983] 1 AC 520.

without a form of warranty. Their specialist advice was negligent, but Junior Books was unable to claim in contract due to insolvency of the main Contractor. It was therefore held that it could recover the loss suffered from the Sub-contractor in negligence. Subsequent cases have made it very clear that this case turned upon a special series of facts and that it would not constitute a precedent for more general actions in this area.

The courts have now, however, clearly indicated that where there is no negligent misstatement damages for economic loss will not be awarded (*D&F Estates v Church Comrs for England*[104]. In *Murphy v Brentwood District Council*[105], which followed *D&F Estates*, some of their Lordships suggested that, in exceptional cases, a subsequent owner might still be permitted to recover damages from a negligent designer or contractor. This has subsequently been confirmed in *Baxall Securities Ltd v Sheard Walshaw Partnership*[106], where it was stated that a duty of care was owed to a later owner of a building in respect of latent defects which could not be discovered through reasonable inspection.

CASE LAW

Economic loss

D&F Estates v Church Comrs for England[107]

The case concerned a claim by the tenant of a block of flats built by Wates in a joint venture with the Church Commissioners. Due to the negligence of a Sub-contractor (described as 'not worth suing') the walls and ceiling needed to be completely replastered. The plaintiffs therefore sued Wates in tort claiming the cost of work already carried out, cost of future work (estimated at £50,000) and prospective loss of rent.

Held by the House of Lords that a builder's liability in tort is limited to defects which cause either injury to persons or physical damage to property other than the building itself. Damage to the building was regarded as purely economic loss and was not recoverable.

104 [1989] AC 177.
105 [1991] 1 AC 398.
106 [2002] EWCA Civ 09, [2002] BLR 100.
107 [1989] AC 177.

Two potential cases were foreseen:

- Where defects in the building created a danger to adjoining property and the owner incurred expense in averting that danger. This doctrine was followed in *Morse v Barratt (Leeds) Ltd*[108], where a retaining wall was constructed fronting a row of houses constructed on a slope. The wall was in danger of falling outwards on to the road, and the local authority served a dangerous structures notice on the householders, causing them to pay for remedial work. Held that they were entitled to recover the cost from the builders whose negligence had created the problem.

- Where different parts of the building were constructed by different people, and the negligence of one caused damage to another part (the so-called 'complex structure theory'). It was, for example, suggested that subsequent owners might be able to recover damages from a central heating Sub-contractor whose negligent installation of a boiler caused an explosion, damaging the rest of the building (*Nitrigin Eirean Teoranta v Inco Alloys Ltd*[109]).

It may not be necessary for owners to wait until damage has actually occurred: it may only be necessary to show that the potential danger exists. In *Portsea Island Mutual Co-operative Society v Michael Brashier Associates*[110], Brashier was the Architect for a building clad with brick slips erected by a private developer and let to Portsea under a fully repairing lease. After completion, some of the brick slips began to fall off, posing a danger to the public. Portsea sued the Architects for negligence. Held that they were entitled to recover the cost of making the building safe by removing the defective tiles, but they were not able to recover the cost of re-cladding the wall.

A similar principle was applied in *Department of the Environment (DoE) v Thomas Bates*[111], where the DoE leased an office block and it was subsequently found that the concrete in the columns was defective. DoE undertook repair work and sued for negligence. Held that the defects in the columns were not sufficient to pose a danger to the structural integrity of the building, and that the repairs were only required so that DoE could maximise its use of the building. The loss was therefore judged purely economic and not recoverable.

Although the courts have apparently retreated wholesale from the recovery of economic loss in negligence, the recovery of loss as a result of negligent *misstatement* remains unchallenged and has even been extended. In *Nye, Saunders and Partners v Bristow*[112], Bristow appointed Nye to design the refurbishment of a house. Nye estimated the costs at £238,000, but immediately before tenders were due the quantity

108   (1992) 9 Const LJ 158.
109   [1992] 1 All ER 854.
110   (1990) 6 PN 43.
111   [1990] 2 All ER 943.
112   (1987) 37 BLR 92.

surveyor informed Bristow that there was no possibility of carrying out the work within the approved budget and that the true cost was likely to exceed £300,000. Bristow terminated Nye's contract and refused to pay its fees. Held that the Architect misled his client in respect of the costs involved, that this was a breach of the *Hedley Byrne* type of duty of care, and that Bristow's action in refusing to pay the architect's fees was justified.

Similar principles were applied in *Wessex Regional Health Authority v HLM Design and John H Webb & Associates*[113]), where an Architect negligently issued extensions of time to which the Contractor was not entitled, thus removing from the employer the right to deduct liquidated damages; and also in *Royal Brompton Hospital v Hammond*[114], where an Architect was found to have been negligent in granting unauthorised extensions of time and in the ascertainment of additional loss and expense. In this latter case the employer was rendered unable to deduct liquidated damages, amounting to some £2.1m, and was obliged to pay the Contractor a further £2.3m for ascertained additional loss and expense.

In *Barclays Bank v Fairclough Building and Carne (Structural Repairs) and Trendleway*[115], the negligent misstatement doctrine was extended to cover Contractors and Sub-contractors. In this case the Bank's premises were damaged during cleaning of an asbestos roof. Fairclough sub-contracted to Carne, who further sub-contracted to Trendleway. The problem arose because Trendleway and Carne between them were allegedly negligent in cleaning the roof. Held that the principle of negligent misstatements covers not only statements by professional consultants but also by Contractors and Sub-contractors. If, therefore, contractors provide advice which is in itself negligent, then economic loss may be recoverable against them.

(c) Compensation

The calculation of damages in contract and tort differ. In contract damages will be assessed so as to place the injured party in the same position that they would have been in had the breach of contract not occurred. The purpose of damages in the law of tort is to put the claimant in the position that they would have been had the tort not occurred, in so far as this can be achieved by the payment of money (*Livingstone v Rawyards Coal Co*[116]).

---

113   (1994) 40 Con LR 1.
114   [2001] EWCA Civ 778, [2001] BLR 317.
115   [1995] 1 All ER 289.
116   (1880) 5 App Cas 25.

5 Limitation periods

So liability may arise in either contract or tort. However, liability does not last forever – it is subject to the provisions of the Limitation Act 1980 ('LA 1980') as amended.

(a) Contract

Under s 5, LA 1980, liability under a simple contract lasts for six years from the date on which the cause of action accrued. Under LA 1980, s 8 liability under a specialty contract lasts for twelve years. The cause of action accrues on the date of the breach. This may not be as straightforward as it seems when considering a construction contract. Defective work will create a cause of action when it is done; a further breach will occur if the work is not rectified once an instruction to do so has been issued; a further breach may occur at the end of the maintenance period.

(b) Tort

Under LA 1980, s 2, liability in tort lasts for six years from the date on which the cause of action accrued.

There is a marked difference between contract and tort, in that in the latter the action accrues only when damage is suffered. This means that time may not begin to run until long after a breach has occurred.

Following the case of *Pirelli General Cable Works v Oscar Faber & Partners*[117], the Limitation Act 1980 was amended by the Latent Damage Act 1986 to take into account situations where damage occurs but its nature is such that it cannot be discovered. An action may now therefore be brought within three years of the date upon which a reasonable person could have realised that a right of action existed (LA 1980, s 14A). The amendment also introduced a 15-year long stop so that any action would have to be instigated within 15 years of the actual breach of duty (LA 1980, s 14B).

Under s 3 of the Latent Damage Act 1986 where property suffering from a latent defect changes hands before the defect is discoverable the purchaser acquires a right of action. That cause of action will run from the original dates, as the defendant cannot be put in a worse position than they would have been to the original owner. This section has had little impact because of the development of the law through *Murphy v Brentwood District Council*[118] and the restrictions on the recovery of damages for pure economic loss.

117 [1983] 2 AC 1.
118 [1991] 1 AC 398.

It is possible for the court to postpone the limitation period where there has been fraud, deliberate concealment or mistake (LA 1980, s 32). Where this has occurred, the period will not begin to run until the claimant has, or ought to have, been able to discover the concealment.

This issue takes on a greater significance in the construction context, as it can be readily imagined that it is all too easy for a contractor to cover up works which he knows to be defective. Deliberate concealment was considered in *British Steel plc v Wyvern Structures Ltd*[119], where it was found that it was not sufficient for British Steel to show that there had been shoddy or incompetent work which happened to be covered up in the course of manufacture. They would be required to prove that Wyvern's conscience had been affected. The court here found against British Steel, stating:

> Having heard the evidence in this case, it seems to me that where there are errors, they are much more likely to have been committed through boredom or other neglect rather than as a result of some deliberate conspiracy to cover bad work. In any event, even assuming that there had been a breach of contract or a tort by welding over excessively large fit-up gaps without the agreement of the other contracting party, it would be a matter of degree whether that should have affected the welder's conscience.

The matter was looked at again in *Cave v Robinson Jarvis & Roff*[120]. Here the House of Lords emphasised that a breach of duty cannot be regarded as deliberate unless the person concerned is aware that what he is doing is a breach of duty. So where a breach is negligent but inadvertent LA 1980, s 32 does not operate to postpone the limitation period.

Bibliography

Day W J *Project Management and Control* (1994) Macmillan.

Oberander G D *Project Management for Engineering and Construction* (1993) McGraw-Hill.

Ahuja H N, Dozzi S P and Abourizk S M *Project Management: Techniques in planning and controlling construction projects* (1994) John Wiley and Sons.

CIOB *Code of Practice for Project Management for Construction and Development* (2002) Longman.

119 (1997) 52 Con LR 67.
120 [2002] UKHL 18, [2002] 2 All ER 641.

CHAPTER 3

Extending and limiting liability

By Andrew McCormack

Summary

In the last chapter we looked at how the Project Manager's liability arises. In this chapter we look at how that liability can be extended or limited.

The chapter covers:

- What contractual limitations there are to extending or limiting liability.

- What statutory limitations there are on extending or limiting liability:
  - the Unfair Contract Terms Act 1977
  - the Unfair Terms in Consumer Regulations 1999.

- How liability can be limited:
  - signing the contract as a simple contract not as a deed
  - excluding or placing a cap on consequential losses
  - when and how to use a net contribution clause.

- How to construe contractual documents – how the parole evidence and contra proferentum rules work.

- How liability can be extended:
  - collateral warranties: what are they, who wants the benefit of them and what clauses as a minimum they should contain
  - the effect of the Contract (Rights of Third Parties) Act 1999 and how to exclude it.

1 Introduction

When a Project Manager is considering the relative merits of a contract document, it is important to keep in mind the reason for entering into that (or indeed any) contract. A contract creates a series of binding rights and obligations between the contracting parties. If one party fails to perform any of its obligations under the contract, the other party has a right of action against it.

Although a contract may be created orally, or even by conduct, most contracts are recorded in writing, as a written contract will – or, perhaps more accurately, should – leave no room for doubt as to the nature of the performance owed by each contracting party to the other. Experience, as well as the wealth of case law in the field of contract, tells us that this is not always so!

A written contract such as that between a client and a Project Manager should always aim to set out, as clearly and concisely as possible, the precise nature of the rights enjoyed and obligations owed by the parties to that agreement. For a Project Manager, it is important to establish the extent of his potential liability under a particular contract. To name but a few examples, it will affect his ability to obtain (and the premium he is charged for) his professional indemnity insurance; it may affect his ability to obtain finance such as loans; and it will also have a bearing on his internal projections of profit and growth. The Project Manager will therefore be keen to limit his potential liability as far as possible.

However, the Project Manager will need to strike a balance between his desire to limit his liability and his client's wish for that same liability to be as wide as possible. Clearly, a client will want to ensure that, in the event of a breach of contract, he has as wide a scope as possible for recovering his losses from his professional team, including the Project Manager. Furthermore, a client will often require the Project Manager to extend his liability by entering into agreements with third parties (known as collateral warranties), to whom the Project Manager will also then have a potential liability.

In this chapter we will first examine the various ways in which a Project Manager's liability under his contract of appointment can be limited. We will then go on to consider the subject of collateral warranties – the reasons they are required and the content of a typical collateral warranty. Finally we will examine what alternatives are available in place of collateral warranties, their relative merits and the construction industry's apparent reluctance to embrace them.

2 Contractual limitations

Although, as a general proposition, parties are free to negotiate and agree the terms of their contract, there are a number of factors that constrain the parties' freedom to agree terms. Chief amongst these are the requirements of the Project Manager's professional indemnity insurer. Insurers will simply refuse to provide cover where certain terms (incorporating risk which is not palatable to the insurer) are included in a Project Manager's contract of appointment with his client (the appointment). Other clauses are resisted whenever possible and accepted only grudgingly – more often than not in return for an increase in the insurance premium. Insurance is discussed in more detail in Chapter 7, but it is an issue that, as we shall see, is inextricably entwined with questions of liability – or, in the language of insurers, questions of risk.

Parliament too has stepped in and legislated on certain aspects of the contractual relationship. The Unfair Contract Terms Act 1977 (UCTA 1977) was introduced in order to protect those in a weak bargaining position where Parliament considered it just to do so.

(a) The Unfair Contract Terms Act 1977

The provisions of UCTA 1977 apply to the treatment of clauses where one contracting party is seeking to exclude or restrict his liability to the other. As we shall see, consideration of UCTA 1977 is extremely important where a Project Manager enters into a contract with a 'consumer'.

UCTA 1977, s 12 states that a party to a contract 'deals as a consumer' if he does not make the contract in the course of his business and the other party does make the contract in the course of his business. Perhaps surprisingly, the courts have held that in certain circumstances a company can deal as a consumer. This will occur where it can be shown that a company has entered into a transaction that is not in the regular course of its business[1].

Although, in practice, Project Managers may rarely contract with a 'consumer', UCTA 1977 also has implications for 'business to business' transactions, in particular where one party deals on the other party's standard written terms of business.

It should be noted that UCTA 1977 does not apply to contracts relating to land, contracts relating to intellectual property rights, or international supply contracts. Where UCTA 1977 does apply, there are two main thrusts to its treatment of contractual exclusion clauses:

1 CLAUSES WHICH ARE UNENFORCEABLE

UCTA 1977 identifies certain matters for which liability cannot be excluded or restricted. Although UCTA does not expressly state so, such exclusion clauses are effectively void and will be unenforceable. The sections, and the issues they address, are:

* UCTA 1977, s 2(1) – a party cannot exclude liability for personal injury or death resulting from negligence;

1 R and B Customs Brokers Co Ltd v United Dominions Trust [1988] 1 All ER 847.

- UCTA 1977, s 6(1) – a party cannot exclude or restrict liability for breach of the implied condition of title (i e that a seller has title to the goods it is intending to sell) pursuant to Sale of Goods Act 1979, s 12 or the Supply of Goods (Implied Terms) Act 1973, s 8;

- UCTA 1977, s 6(2) – against any person who is dealing as a *consumer*, a party cannot exclude or restrict liability for breach of the implied conditions set out in the Sale of Goods Act 1979, ss 13–15 or the Supply of Goods (Implied Terms) Act 1973, ss 9–11. (Detailed consideration of these sections is beyond the scope of this book.)

It should be noted that UCTA 1977, s 7 concerns miscellaneous contracts under which goods pass (e g work and materials contracts). UCTA 1977, s 7 contains similar provisions to those contained in s 6.

2 REASONABLENESS TEST

UCTA 1977 provides that, in certain circumstances, any exclusion clause in a contract will be subject to a 'reasonableness test'. If a clause is deemed by a court to be 'unreasonable', it will be unenforceable. By virtue of UCTA 1977, s 3, there are two circumstances where the 'reasonableness test' will apply:

(1) where one party deals as a consumer; and

(2) where one party deals on the other party's standard written terms of business.

It should be noted that any attempt to exclude the liability referred to in UCTA 1977, s 6(2) (*see above*) against a person who does not deal as a consumer will also be subject to the reasonableness test.

As to the 'reasonableness test' itself, UCTA 1977, s 11 states that:

> In relation to a contract term, the requirement of reasonableness ... is that the term shall have been a fair and reasonable one to be included having regard to the circumstances which were, or ought reasonably to have been, known to or in the contemplation of the parties when the contract was made.

It is important to appreciate that the reasonableness test is not an attempt to assess whether it is reasonable for a party to rely on a particular exclusion clause in the light of events that actually transpired. When assessing the reasonableness of a particular exclusion clause, the court should consider whether, given the parties' knowledge (both actual and constructive) at the time the contract was entered into, it was reasonable for that exclusion clause to be included. 'Constructive knowledge' is knowledge of those things which the parties *ought* to have known as well as those of which they had actual knowledge. If the answer to this question is Yes, then the clause is deemed to be reasonable and the test is satisfied.

Schedule 2 of UCTA 1977 sets out various guidelines for applying the reasonableness test. Strictly, these only apply to UCTA, ss 6 and 7. However, it is fair to say that the courts will, by analogy, apply these guidelines when considering whether any clause caught by UCTA satisfies the reasonableness test. The list at Sch 2 is not exhaustive and a court is free to take into account any relevant factor it deems fit to decide reasonableness. That said, Sch 2 provides useful guidance. The most pertinent factors are summarised below:

- the relative bargaining strengths of the parties.

- whether one party received an inducement for agreeing the term.

- whether the party against whom the clause operates knew or ought to have known that the clause existed and what it covered.

(b) The Unfair Terms in Consumer Contracts Regulations 1999[2]

The Unfair Terms in Consumer Contracts Regulations 1999 ('UTCCR 1999') apply in addition to UCTA 1977. As the title of the regulations implies, they do not apply to contracts between two commercial parties, and consideration of the regulations is only necessary where a Project Manager (as a commercial party) enters into a contract with a 'consumer'. For the purpose of the regulations, a 'consumer' is a natural person (i e not a company) acting for purposes outside his business.

Pursuant to UTCCR 1999, reg 5(1), any 'unfair term' in a contract between a commercial party and a consumer shall not be binding upon the consumer. UTCCR 1999, reg 4(1) defines an unfair term as one which '... *contrary to the requirement of good faith causes a significant imbalance in the parties' rights and obligations under the contract to the detriment of the consumer.*' The regulations also contain a list of examples of terms that may be regarded as 'unfair'.

Furthermore, UTCCR 1999, reg 7 requires that a consumer contract be expressed in plain, intelligible language. The regulations do not elaborate further on the concept of plain, intelligible language, nor do they state what will happen if the contract is not expressed in plain, intelligible language. Presumably any clause that is not in plain, intelligible language will be deemed unfair. Regulation 7 does state, however, that where there is some doubt as to the meaning of a written term, the interpretation most favourable to the consumer will prevail.

2 SI 1999/2083.

CHECKLIST

In summary, when considering the effect of legislation on his contractual arrangements, a Project Manger will look to address the following questions:

- Does UCTA 1977 apply?

- Are there any clauses which are unenforceable?

- Does the reasonableness test apply?

  - does one party deal as a consumer; or

  - does one party deal on the other party's standard written terms of business?

- Do the UTCCR 1999 apply?

---

3 Imposing limitations on liability – the Project Manager's appointment

As discussed in the introduction to this chapter, a Project Manager will seek to limit his potential liability to his client under his appointment as far as he is able. As mentioned, his success in doing so will enable him perhaps to secure a reduced professional indemnity insurance premium, as his Insurer's potential exposure will be reduced. This is a particularly important consideration given the premium hikes that have been experienced across insurance market generally as a result of the September 11 terrorist attacks. Indeed, negotiating the terms of a Project Manager's appointment will be of equal (if not more) importance to his Professional Indemnity Insurers, as it is they who will bear the cost of covering any claim against the Project Manager. As a result, Insurers will often require the Project Manager to consult with them on the terms of each and every appointment they enter into.

We will now examine in more detail the provisions one might find in an appointment that enable liability to be reduced or extended.

(a) Limitation period

As we saw in Chapter 2, the key issue for a Project Manager is whether his Appointment is executed as a simple contract or as a deed. As we saw, an action founded on a simple contract has a limitation period of six years, whereas an action founded on a contract executed as a deed has a limitation period of twelve years from the date on which the cause of action accrued. As one would expect, a client will always seek to have the appointment executed as a deed in order to take advantage of the extended limitation period.

The statutory limitation period for an action founded in tort is six years from the date on which the cause of action accrued[3]. In negligence claims (which almost all tortious claims under an appointment will be), the cause of action does not accrue until the damage to the claimant occurs. This can occur some time after the negligent act is committed. The result is that time may start to run for an action brought in negligence *after* time starts to run for an action in contract.

The Latent Damage Act 1986 made certain amendments to the Limitation Act 1980[4] and extended the limitation period for claims in tort (but not in contract) by three years, starting from the date when the claimant both had the knowledge required for bringing an action and the damage had occurred. The Act also imposes a long-stop date for commencing any action of fifteen years from the date on which the negligent act which caused the damage occurred.

(b) Exclusion/cap on consequential loss

It is not unusual for a Project Manager to request a clause which seeks to exclude or places a cap on his liability for what is often referred to as 'economic and consequential loss'. Such a clause might exclude entirely, or limit to a specified amount (for example, to the value of his professional indemnity insurance), the Project Manager's liability for such losses.

Parties to construction contracts commonly refer to 'consequential and indirect loss' in clauses limiting their liability. Parties use this as shorthand for their own commercial understanding of this liability, often taken to be liability for loss of profit or revenue or loss of use. The English courts, however, do not give these words the same effect as the parties might have expected. Indeed, recent judicial decisions of the High Court and the Court of Appeal have made it clear that parties should refer expressly, and in greater detail, to those categories of loss that they intend to exclude/limit.

The losses that parties have in mind when they refer to 'consequential loss' are usually expressed as losses going beyond repair or reconstruction of the property. Obvious examples include loss of rent and business relocation costs.

The cornerstone of the case law relating to the recoverability of losses is the nineteenth century case of *Hadley v Baxendale*[5] that still stands as good law to this

3 Limitation Act 1980, s 2.
4 Limitation Act 1980, ss 14A and 14B.
5 (1854) 9 Exch 341.

day. The decision in this case split damages recoverable for breach of contract into two limbs:

(1) those damages that arise naturally (i e in the usual course of things) from the breach of contract; and

(2) those damages which may reasonably be supposed to have been in the contemplation of the parties at the time the contract was made as being the probable result of a breach.

The first limb refers to consequences of a breach of contract which any person could expect to arise without needing any special knowledge of the circumstances. The second limb refers to losses which could only be foreseen if one had knowledge of facts peculiar to the injured party.

It can now be said with some certainty that the English courts, when considering an attempt by a party to exclude for 'consequential and indirect loss', will still find the excluding party to be liable for ordinary loss of profit, loss of revenue and such like which arise 'naturally' from the breach. The lesson to be learnt is that a party wanting to exclude liability for 'naturally arising' (i e limb 1) loss of profit and the like should expressly refer to those losses they wish to exclude.

By way of example, let us consider the case of *Hotel Services Ltd v Hilton International Hotels (UK) Ltd*[6], which involved a contract for the installation of mini-bars by HSL in rooms of hotels owned by Hilton. The mini-bars proved to be defective, and Hilton brought an action for the cost of removal and storage of the chillers and cabinets and loss of profit on the mini-bars. HSL, in their defence, relied on a clause in the contract that stated that:

> ... the company [HSL] will not in any circumstance be liable for any indirect or consequential loss damage or liability....

The court held that both the cost of removal/storage and the loss of profit were recoverable, as both were a direct consequence of the defective minibars (i e limb 1) and therefore not excluded by the clause referred to above.

(c) Net contribution clauses

The net contribution clause is a fairly recent phenomenon. It is worth noting that, to date, no net contribution clause has been the subject of judicial scrutiny before a court. The effect of a net contribution clause is to limit the Project Manager's liability to that proportion of the client's loss that is attributable to his default.

6 [2000] BLR 235.

For example, if a client suffers a loss of £100,000 due to a defect for which the Project Manager was 40% responsible and other parties were 60% responsible, the net contribution clause limits the Project Manager's liability to £40,000 of that £100,000 loss. This ousts the common law position that all parties responsible for a loss (even if their liability is minimal) are jointly and severally liable for the whole of that loss. This means that an injured party can (if he chooses) sue any one of those responsible for his loss for the full amount of that loss and leave it to that party to seek a contribution from any other culpable parties.

An example of a typical net contribution clause is set out below:

> The Project Manager's liability under this Appointment shall be limited to that proportion of such costs which it would be just and equitable to require the Project Manager to pay having regard to the extent of the Project Manager's responsibility for the same and on the basis that [insert names of design team] shall be deemed to have provided contractual undertakings on terms no less onerous than this Appointment to the Client in respect of the performance of their Services in connection with the Project and shall be deemed to have paid to the Client such proportion which it would be just and equitable for them to pay having regard to the extent of their responsibility.

While a net contribution clause is seemingly equitable on its face (why should a party be liable for a loss for which he is not responsible?), the ousting of the common law position of joint and several liability is, perhaps not surprisingly, not terribly attractive to clients. Those clients with sufficient bargaining strength will always seek to resist the inclusion of such a clause. Although net contribution clauses are becoming increasingly common in collateral warranties, they are still rare in Appointment documents. This position may change as a result of a recent decision of the House of Lords, *Co-operative Retail Services Ltd v Taylor Young Partnership*[7].

The law relating to contribution is governed by the Contribution Act 1978. In short, this Act provides that any person liable in respect of any damage suffered by another person may recover a contribution from any other person liable in respect of the same damage.

The ramifications of this decision are that a third party who may also be responsible for causing damage can be excluded from contribution proceedings. This can result in one professional (in the case of *Co-op v Taylor Young*, the Architect) being held liable for something for which he was only in part to blame. This makes the inclusion of a net contribution clause in the appointment (which would have protected the architect in the *Co-op* case from exposure to the liability ultimately imposed upon him) all the more attractive.

7 [2002] UKHL 17, [2002] 1 WLR 1419.

CASE LAW

When a party may be excluded from contribution proceedings

Co-operative Retail Services Ltd v Taylor Young Partnership[8]

The case concerned a claim by an Architect (A) seeking a contribution from a Building Contractor (B). A was being sued (in the name of the owner of the building, C) by an Insurer who had paid out monies to C under a joint names insurance policy following fire damage to a property during building works. It was alleged that A and B were both in part responsible for the fire. The parties named in the joint names insurance policy were C, B and a Sub-contractor of B.

The House of Lords held that the contributing party (B) must have been liable, or must have been capable of being liable to the victim (C). As B and C were both parties to the joint names insurance policy, there was no liability between them as there cannot be any liability between co-insured[9]. Therefore A could not claim a contribution from B in respect of the claim brought against it by C.

(d) Questions of construction

Two further areas which are worthy of consideration as regards the extent of a party's liability are two rules of contractual construction (i e how contractual terms are to be interpreted): the *parol evidence rule* and the rule of *contra proferentem*.

1 PAROL EVIDENCE RULE

The *parol evidence rule* provides that where contractual terms are contained in a written document, the contracting parties are prevented from relying upon extrinsic evidence to add to, vary or amend the terms of that written agreement. The parol evidence rule applies to both oral and documentary evidence outside of the written agreement, for example letters and minutes of meetings.

The rule is, however, not an absolute one and there are a number of exceptions to it. If there is some uncertainty or ambiguity as to the intentions of the contracting

---

8 [2002] UKHL 17, [2002] 1 WLR 1419.
9 *Petrofina (UK) Ltd v Magnaload Ltd* [1984] QB 127.

parties, the courts have been willing to examine what Lord Wilberforce referred to[10] as the 'matrix of fact', i e the background and surrounding circumstances of a particular contract. It is a risky business to throw oneself at the mercy of the court's view of the parties' intentions. The golden rule, once again, is to set out clearly what you mean.

2 *CONTRA PROFERENTEM*

The expression *contra proferentem* essentially means 'against the party who drafted the document'. This rule states that when the wording of a clause in a written agreement is uncertain or ambiguous (but not otherwise), that wording should be construed more strongly against the person whose words they are (i e the party who drafted it) than against the other party.

Consequently, an exclusion clause (which will clearly be in favour of one party and likely to have been drafted by that party) will more often than not be subject to the rule of *contra proferentem*. An important point in this context is that an attempt to exclude liability for negligence will require the use of clear, unambiguous language. It is therefore preferable for a clause excluding liability for negligence to refer expressly to negligence. However, a party may not wish to state that he is excluding for negligence (it may not go down too well with the other party). In this case, drafting an exclusion clause in softer, vaguer terms may fall foul of the *contra proferentem* rule.

In principle, the *contra proferentem* rule should not apply to standard form contracts drafted by representative bodies, such as the Joint Contracts Tribunal (JCT) or the Institution of Civil Engineers (ICE).

CHECKLIST

The key factors affecting the terms of a Project Manager's appointment that we have discussed in this section are as follows:

- What is the applicable limitation period? Is the appointment a simple contract or a deed?

- Does the appointment contain a cap or exclusion on 'consequential losses'?

- Does the Appointment contain a 'net contribution clause'?

---

10 In *Prenn v Simmonds* [1971] 1 WLR 1381.

- Are there any questions of construction?
  - parol evidence rule;
  - *contra proferentem.*

4 Collateral warranties

A collateral warranty or, more correctly, a collateral contract, is an agreement which exists alongside another contract and is related to that other contract. In the context of the construction industry, it is a method of creating contractual relations between the construction team involved in a project and certain parties who have an interest in that project (e g tenants, purchasers and funders) but would otherwise not have a contractual relationship with the construction team.

As was seen in Chapter 2, there are two means of obtaining redress if something goes wrong with a building project. First, if the injured party has a contract with the party who has caused him to suffer a loss, he can bring an action for damages in contract. Alternatively, the injured party could pursue a claim in tort where his claim would be founded upon the other party's action that has caused him damage. There are a number of factors might affect which of these options an injured party will choose to pursue, as discussed in more detail at Chapter 2.

The reason why collateral warranties are so important in the modern construction industry lies in a subtle distinction between losses that are recoverable in contract and those which are recoverable in tort.

Tort only allows for the recovery of financial compensation for certain types of damage. This covers personal injury and physical damage to other property, but, save in exceptional circumstances, damages in respect of 'pure economic loss' will not generally be recoverable in tort. That means that damages cannot be recovered in respect of damage caused to the item which caused the damage (i e 'the thing itself'). So, for example, if a building had been constructed negligently, any person injured could recover compensation, and any other damaged property, such as furniture, could be repaired or replaced. There could, however, be no recovery in tort for the repairs to the building itself, as this would be regarded as diminution in its value (i e 'pure economic loss'). Nor would there be recovery for renting another building, nor for loss of profit while those premises were uninhabitable: these would all be classified as economic loss (see the cases of *D & F Estates v*

Church Comrs for England[11] and *Murphy v Brentwood District Council*[12] discussed in detail in Chapter 2, above).

(a) Collateral warranties from the professional's viewpoint

In recent years, as a result of *D & F Estates v Church Comrs* and *Murphy*, we have seen the collateral warranty become an important document in the construction process. This is despite the fact that many clients (and construction professionals) regard collateral warranties as something of a nuisance. There can be delays while the terms of the contract and the warranty documentation are agreed with the construction team, and sometimes subsequently there can be further delay if amendments also need to be agreed with tenants, purchasers and funders.

For the construction professional such as the Project Manager, this means that his liability is extended to include numerous third parties (such as tenants, purchasers and funders) as well as the developer client with whom he originally contracted. However, in the main the ability to procure a collateral warranty is of such importance for a client that most Appointment documents have a clause providing that the Project Manager must provide 'x' number of warranties to certain third parties.

Although rarely a 'deal breaker', where there has been construction work at a property but no suitable collateral warranties are available parties will often seek alternative methods of protecting their position. For example, a purchaser might seek a reduction in the purchase price or a tenant may require the landlord to remain 'on the hook' in respect of those construction works. Neither of these is particularly palatable to the seller or landlord, as the case may be. Hence it is always better for a developer client to be able to call for a full suite of collateral warranties from his construction team.

(b) Parties requiring a collateral warranty

Before examining the content of a typical collateral warranty, it is perhaps instructive to examine the reasons why certain third parties will seek collateral warranties from each of the construction professionals and the main contractor ('the construction team') involved in a project.

11 [1988] 2 All ER 992.
12 [1991] 1 AC 398.

1 TENANT/PURCHASER

A tenant taking a leasehold interest in a property will require collateral warranties from members of the construction team, particularly if they are signing up to a full repairing and insuring lease. The tenant will want to protect his position in the event that repairs to the property are required for which he is liable under his lease.

A purchaser will require warranties from the construction team so that he has a course of action in contract against the construction team in the event that there is a defect in the building which reduces the value of his investment.

This warranty may or may not be transferred to any future purchasers or tenants of the building, depending on the restrictions contained therein.

2 FUNDER

As with a tenant or purchaser, a warranty will give the funder of a project (e g a bank or pension fund) means of recourse as regards any defects in the building which reduce the value of the investment. In addition, a funder may require warranties from the construction team to contain what are known as 'step-in rights'.

'Step-in' provisions enable the funder, in the event of a breakdown in the relationship between the developer client and the construction team (for example, if the developer goes into liquidation or otherwise disappears), to protect his investment by requiring the construction team to continue and complete the project.

A Project Manager should ensure that any 'step-in rights' are drafted on the basis that the party stepping in acquires responsibility for any outstanding fees as well as future fees due to the consultant. The step-in clause should also state that the Project Manager is entitled to rely upon any notice served on him stating that the funder is stepping in as being valid.

3 APPROVAL OF PROFESSIONAL INDEMNITY INSURER

The party receiving the collateral warranty (the beneficiary) will want it to cover every conceivable scenario, while the party providing the warranty (the warrantor) – or, more accurately, the warrantor's Professional Indemnity Insurer (who will ultimately be responsible for meeting any claim) – will want to limit the warrantor's liability as far as possible.

The existence of collateral warranties must, of course, be disclosed by a warrantor to his Professional Indemnity Insurer. Contracts of insurance are based on the principle of *uberrimae fidei* or 'utmost good faith'. Insurers require full disclosure of all material facts in connection with any risk for which they are being asked to provide cover. Clearly the existence of any collateral warranties is a material fact which would influence a prudent insurer's decision when considering whether to offer cover or not.

It is therefore necessary, and is common practice, for warrantors to submit any form of warranty they are being asked to provide to their insurer to consider and approve. Clearly this places a heavy administrative burden on both insurers and their insured. There are two means of avoiding this: using a standard form of warranty, or agreeing with the insurer a suitable policy amendment (by way of an endorsement) that sets out the circumstances in which insurers will extend cover for collateral warranties.

4 ENDORSEMENT TO INSURANCE POLICY

Typical wording for an endorsement will make it clear that liability under any collateral warranty shall be no greater and no longer lasting than the liability under the underlying Appointment. It will also usually set out those matters that are excluded from insurance cover under any collateral warranty.

5 STANDARD FORM WARRANTY

Negotiations between the British Property Federation (BPF), the RICS, the Royal Institute of British Architects and the Association of Consulting Engineers resulted in a standard form of collateral warranty being drawn up that is supposedly acceptable to developers, funders, purchasers, tenants and insurers alike. A model form for funders and another for purchasers or tenants is published by the BPF.

At the time of writing the BPF are updating their standard forms of warranty. The BPF hope the new versions will be available by the end of 2003[13]. Despite efforts to promote the use of a standard form warranty in the construction industry, bespoke collateral warranties prepared and favoured by developer clients in question still tend to proliferate in most construction projects. That said, most collateral warranties follow a similar pattern. The next section contains a detailed discussion of the provisions one would normally expect to find in a collateral warranty. Where we have made reference to one of the BPF collateral warranties (BPF CoWa/F) it is the version current at the time of publication of this book.

---

13 For this reason we have not reproduced a BBF standard form of collateral warranty in this book.

(c) Content of a typical collateral warranty

A collateral warranty, although an independent contract in its own right, is inextricably linked to the underlying contract of appointment and can only be read in conjunction with and by reference to the underlying appointment. In essence, the collateral warranty is a contractual promise by the warrantor, to the beneficiary, that the warrantor has complied with his contractual obligations under the appointment. The warranty will contain a duty of care clause in which the warrantor confirms that it has exercised reasonable skill and care when undertaking his duties under the appointment. This duty of care is often by reference to the standard to be expected of a competent Project Manager experienced in projects of a similar size, scope and complexity to the project in question.

From the warrantor's point of view, it is important to ensure that the obligations in the warranty should be no greater than the obligations contained in the appointment.

1 PROFESSIONAL INDEMNITY INSURANCE

It is also important to remember that collateral warranties are only of value when there is adequate insurance or other assets to back them up. As most Project Managers, and indeed constructional professionals, generally do not have the assets to meet large claims, most beneficiaries will look to a warrantor's professional indemnity insurance to meet any claim. It is therefore crucial to appreciate that, whatever the obligations undertaken, if the professional indemnity insurance policy supporting that warranty does not cover those obligations, there are unlikely to be sufficient funds to meet a claim.

Most warranties require the consultant to maintain a specified amount of professional indemnity insurance for the duration of the liability under the warranty. It may not always be possible to maintain such a policy, as the insurance market, and the cover available, changes over time. Consequently, insurance clauses should qualify the obligation to maintain professional indemnity cover with a proviso that it is generally available in the UK insurance market on reasonable rates and terms. An example of a professional indemnity insurance clause can be found at Clause 9 of the BPF Warranty.

It should also be noted that professional indemnity insurance works on the basis of the policy in force at the date of the claim, so if policies are not maintained at the required level there will be no cover.

2 NET CONTRIBUTION CLAUSE

Because of the notion of joint and several liability (discussed above), a consultant may find himself left to meet the whole of a claim even though the actual negligence rests with a number of parties. Increasingly, therefore, warrantors and insurers will require a warranty to contain a net contribution clause (the effect of which was discussed above in relation to the Project Manager's appointment).

Earlier in this chapter, when considering clauses you might find in an appointment document, we suggested some wording for a possible net contribution clause.

3   LIMITATION PERIOD

As with the appointment, where the warranty is executed as a deed the limitation period will be twelve years. If the warranty is a simple contract, it is only six years.

The BPF warranty contains a choice of attestation clauses (at the end of the warranty) giving the Consultant the option of executing the warranty as a simple contract or as a deed.

The BPF warranty also contains an express clause (Clause 13) enabling the warrantor to state precisely for how many years (from the date of practical completion of the development) the warrantor's liability under the warranty is to run for.

4   DELETERIOUS MATERIALS

Most appointments (and consequently most warranties) contain a 'deleterious materials clause' which requires the warrantor not to use or specify for use in the construction of the building certain materials which may be deleterious to the integrity or durability of the building. This is sometimes by reference to a prescribed list (as with Clause 2 of the BPF warranty) and/or by reference to materials generally known to be deleterious in the construction industry.

Of course, during the construction period legislation may re-classify certain materials, making them hazardous. Therefore, it will not always be possible to truthfully warrant that the completed building does not contain any deleterious materials. It is sensible to state a date at which such matters have been taken into account, such as completion of the design or, more commonly, date of specification.

5   ASSIGNMENT

An assignment of a warranty essentially transfers the benefit of the warranty from the beneficiary to a third party (e g a subsequent tenant/purchaser). If the warranty is silent on the question of assignment, the warranty will be freely assignable by the beneficiary to a third party. Most warranties contain a restriction on assignment.

Clause 11 of the BPF Warranty permits unlimited assignment of the warranty. This is because the CoWa/F is a warranty to a party providing finance and they will be able to insist on more preferable terms. By contrast, the BPF standard warranty to a purchaser/tenant contains an assignment clause which can be tailored to exclude assignments or limit the number of assignments that can be made. The recognised industry standard assignment clause will permit two assignments of the warranty without the warrantor's consent.

The reason for imposing a restriction on the number of assignments in warranties is driven by professional indemnity insurers. It is a method of imposing a further limitation on their potential exposure. In the usual course of things (especially in the case of a warranty executed as a deed with a twelve-year limitation period), the warranty will fall to be assigned on several occasions as the beneficiary divests itself of its interest in the property. Once the warranty has been assigned twice, it cannot be validly transferred again and, consequently, the warrantor's (and therefore the insurer's) liability falls away.

6   COPYRIGHT LICENCE

A warranty should contain a clause granting the beneficiary copyright licence to use and reproduce materials produced or prepared by or on behalf of the warrantor in connection with the project. This licence will often be limited to using those materials only in connection with the project. There will also be a proviso that the warrantor will not be liable for any misuse of such material by the beneficiary. An example of a copyright licence which addresses these issues can be found at Clause 8 of the BPF Warranty.

7   EXCLUSIONS/CAPS ON CONSEQUENTIAL LOSS

A difficulty with collateral warranties is that when the warrantor agrees to provide warranties in favour of, for example, purchasers and tenants (under the terms of his appointment), the identity of these parties is often not known. From the professional indemnity insurer's point of view, it is therefore hard to assess the exact risks and exposure it may have to claims for consequential loss.

One way the insurer is able combat this uncertainty is to restrict the categories of loss recoverable under the warranty, or to place a cap upon recovery. Capping or excluding liability for consequential loss was discussed in more detail previously in this chapter in connection with the appointment contract. Again, it is important to remember that the English courts, when considering clauses excluding liability for 'consequential and indirect loss', will still hold the excluding party liable for ordinary loss of profit, loss of revenue and such like which arise 'naturally' from the breach.

If a party wishes to exclude his liability for certain 'consequential' losses, he should always expressly refer to those losses that he wishes to exclude.

Insurers will not seek to do this in relation to all beneficiaries. Indeed, the BPF CoWa/F does not contain a clause excluding liability for consequential loss. Most funders will be in place at the outset of a project. Insurers will often therefore take the view that this risk is something they can manage. This is in contrast to the position under the BPF standard warranty to a purchaser/tenant, which does contain a clause excluding liability for consequential loss. This serves to illustrate the point that the contractual terms available to you depend upon the strength of your bargaining position. Generally speaking, funders have more clout than tenants and purchasers, hence the difference even in standard form warranties they will receive.

5 Alternatives to collateral warranties

(a) The Contracts (Rights of Third Parties) Act 1999

The Contracts (Rights of Third Parties) Act 1999 (C(RTP)A 1999) came into force on 11 May 2000. Prior to the introduction of C(RTP)A 1999, the doctrine of *privity of contract* meant that a contract made between A and B in which A purported to confer some benefit upon C was not directly enforceable in contract by C against A.

However, as an alternative to a contractual claim, liability can sometimes be established in tort, or a contracting party has been able to recover substantial damages on behalf of a third party, for example the original owner of a building has been able to recover damages from a building contractor on behalf of the current owner[14].

It is important for Project Managers to appreciate the effect of C(RTP)A 1999, as it can enable third parties to commence proceedings to enforce the contractual terms of a contract to which they are not a party.

In 1996 the Law Commission recommended changes to this area of law, which became law (with modifications) in the form of C(RTP)A 1999. The Law Commission identified two types of contract – construction contracts and insurance contracts – as prime illustrations of how the C(RTP)A could overcome the commercial difficulties of the rule of privity of contract.

14 *St Martins Property Corporation Ltd v Sir Robert McAlpine & Sons Ltd* [1994] 1 AC 85.

The Law Commission's Report[15] stated:

> The [privity of contract] rule means that only the parties within each contractual relationship can sue each other. The unfortunate result is that one cannot in the 'main' contracts simply extend the benefit of the architect's and engineer's duties of care and skill, and the contractor's ... to subsequent purchasers or tenants of the development, or to funding institutions who might suffer loss as a result of the defective execution of the works. This cannot be achieved ... without either joining the third party in question into the contract which contains these obligations, which in the case of a subsequent purchaser or tenant is impractical, since their identity may be unknown at the commencement of the works ... or executing a separate document – a 'collateral warranty' – extending the benefit of the duties in question.[16]

> Our proposed reforms would enable contracting parties to avoid the need for collateral warranties by simply laying down third party rights in the main contract. Moreover, our proposed reforms would enable the contracting parties to mirror the terms in existing collateral warranties[17].... So, in our view, our proposals would enable the contracting parties to replicate the advantages of collateral warranties without the inconvenience of actually drafting and entering into separate contracts.[18]

1 C(RTP)A 1999 – THE BASIC RULE

C(RTP)A 1999 applies to all contracts (save excepted contracts) made after C(RTP)A came into force. It also applies to contracts entered into during the six months prior to 11 May 2000 (i e after C(RTP)A was passed on 11 November 1999) where the parties expressly provided that the C(RTP)A applied.

Certain contracts are excluded[19] (e g bills of exchange or other negotiable instruments, contracts of employment).

It should be noted that the parties to a contract may exclude the effect of the C(RTP)A either in part or entirely[20]. Excluding the effect of the C(RTP)A is the approach which the majority of the construction industry, promulgated by professional indemnity insurers, has chosen to adopt. The reasons for this are discussed in more detail later in this chapter.

---

15 Law Commission Report LC242.
16 LC242, para 3.13.
17 LC242, para 3.17
18 LC242, para 3.18.
19 See C(RTP)A 1999, s 6 for full details.
20 C(RTP)A 1999, s 1(2).

Where the C(RTP)A 1999 applies, third parties will be able to enforce contracts in their own right (i e without involving the contracting party) if:

- the contract expressly provides they may do so; or

- the contract term confers a benefit on them, unless it is clear from the contract as a whole that the term was not intended to be directly enforceable by the third party[21].

The third party must be expressly identified in the contract, but it can be by name or by answering a particular description (e g funder, tenant, neighbouring landowner). The third party need not be in existence at the time the contract is created (e g a company not yet incorporated)[22].

C(RTP)A 1999 does *not* allow contracting parties to impose obligations upon a third party. They may only confer rights.

(i) Varying the contract

The party owing an obligation under the contract is referred to as 'the promisor'. The party entitled to performance of that obligation is 'the promisee'. Where a third party has a right to enforce a contract, there are limits on the power of the contracting parties to vary or cancel the contract without his consent[23]. They cannot do so if:

- the third party has communicated his assent to the relevant term (whether by words or conduct or in writing) to the promisor;

- the promisor is aware that the third party has relied on the term; or

- it is reasonably foreseeable that the third party will rely on the term and he has in fact done so.

However, in the contract itself the parties can expressly remove, limit or alter this right and there is power for the court to dispense with the third party's consent.

(ii) Enforcement

The remedies available to the third party are the same as if he had been a party to the contract[24]. Enforcement by the third party does not prevent the contracting party also enforcing the contract[25], although the promisor is protected from double liability[26].

21 C(RTP)A 1999, s 1(1).
22 C(RTP)A 1999, s 1(3).
23 C(RTP)A 1999, s 2.
24 C(RTP)A 1999, s 1(5).
25 C(RTP)A 1999, s 4.
26 C(RTP)A 1999, s 5.

The promisor has the same defences and rights to set-off available to him in an action brought by a third party as he would have available were the same proceedings brought by the promisee.

The promisor may also rely on any defences, set-offs and counterclaims that may have been available had the contract been between the promisor and the third party.

These provisions can be altered or excluded by contract[27].

Where the contract provides for disputes to be referred to arbitration, the third party will not be able to go to court to resolve disputes as between him and the contracting party, and is bound by that arbitration agreement[28].

2 C(RPT)A 1999 – a missed opportunity?

For the construction industry, C(RTP)A 1999 was hailed as the death knell for the existing method of conferring rights on third parties, the collateral warranty. As we have seen from our discussion of collateral warranties, above, clients and construction professionals share a mutual distaste for collateral warranties, the terms of which often require negotiation which can lead to increased costs and delay.

Two and a half years on, however, C(RTP)A 1999 has not made a significant impact on the construction industry. The collateral warranty is still very much alive and kicking. Indeed, many construction contracts expressly exclude the application of C(RTP)A. So why has the industry failed to embrace this legislation?

To answer this question it is necessary to consider the third parties on whom a client wishes to confer rights. These are the usual suspects we have already discussed – funders, purchasers and tenants. These parties currently receive contractual rights against construction professionals (including Project Managers) by means of a collateral warranty. Prima facie, there seems no obvious bar to conferring the same rights using C(RTP)A 1999. However, consultants, or, more accurately, their professional indemnity insurers, have balked at using the C(RTP)A. Why?

(i) Insurers' concerns

First, a fear exists amongst insurers that control of the liabilities a consultant has under an Appointment contract will be lost. Insurers are concerned that C(RTP)A 1999 may confer rights upon a larger group of beneficiaries than was intended – if you have to have a warranty before you can acquire contractual rights, it is easier

---

27 C(RTP)A 1999, s 3.
28 C(RTP)A 1999, s 8.

to keep track of how many people have a potential claim against any given consultant. Perhaps more importantly, insurers fear that the C(RTP)A will expose consultants (and therefore them) to liabilities over and above that contemplated when entering the contract.

(ii) A comfort zone?

A second reason for the failure of C(RTP)A 1999 to take off is that clients and construction professionals have become comfortable with the system of collateral warranties. In recent years, standard form warranties have been produced by organisations like the British Property Foundation (BPF) (see above) and the Joint Contracts Tribunal (JCT). These documents present what is seen by many as an acceptable compromise between the interests of clients (and potential beneficiaries) on the one hand, and construction professionals on the other. The use of standard form warranties, or at least the broad consensus on the clauses one would usually expect to see in a collateral warranty, should, in theory, make the process of negotiating warranties decidedly less painful.

A reluctance to use C(RTP)A 1999 can also be traced to the beneficiaries' desire to have their 'own document' setting out 'their rights'. If they use the C(RTP)A to assert their rights, they fear being confronted with a mass of documentation. This is a particularly baffling argument when one considers that in order to fully comprehend the rights conferred by a collateral warranty, it is necessary (for the reasons explored earlier in this chapter) to examine the content of the underlying appointment.

Although, by and large, collateral warranties achieve their objective, surely the real advantage of using C(RTP)A 1999, and setting out all the rights the parties intend to confer upon third parties in the Appointment, is the reduction in the mass of documentation. It would avoid the need for a plethora of warranties to be prepared, reviewed and executed by the various construction professionals (and their lawyers) involved in each project. The savings in time and cost are obvious.

3 C(RTP)A 1999 – Checklist

Creating effective third party rights (and avoiding the creation of unwanted ones) are eminently possible – it simply requires a bit of thought. Here is a simple checklist of issues to consider when using C(RTP)A 1999:

- Clearly identify the third parties who are to receive rights. This could be either particular named beneficiaries or a particular class of beneficiaries, providing the scope of the class can be determined with sufficient certainty, e g any first or second purchaser of the whole project or of any part.

- Set out precisely which terms of the appointment the third party may rely upon.

- Set out the limitations on the contracting parties' liability to any third party, for example a net contribution clause or an exclusion of certain specified consequential losses. This will be of particular importance to consultants with insurers keen to limit their exposure to as yet unknown third parties.

- Take care to state in a clearly worded clause that, save as where expressly provided, the appointment does not confer upon any party the right to enforce a term of the appointment pursuant to C(RTP)A 1999.

Although some pioneering souls have embraced C(RTP)A 1999, the feeling in the industry, particularly amongst the majority of lawyers and insurers, is that until C(RTP)A is tested before the courts, the collateral warranty will still hold sway as the preferred method of conferring rights on third parties.

(b) Latent defects insurance

Latent defects insurance (LDI) provides insurance cover, as the name would suggest, against any latent defects in the construction of a building which later manifest themselves, causing damage to the building and a loss to the insured. Sir Michael Latham in his report *Constructing the Team* recommended that legislation should provide for compulsory latent defects insurance for ten years from practical completion for all future new commercial developments. However, such insurance is still not compulsory.

An LDI policy will usually cover destruction, damage or the threat of imminent collapse to the building due to a latent defect in the structure, the external walls and the roof. Resultant damage to other elements of the insured building, including the cost of accessing the defects and reinstating such elements, are usually included within the indemnifiable repair costs. Further, where the building requires some remedial work or strengthening to relieve the continuing effects of latent defects, these costs may also be met by the policy.

In the past, insurers have placed so many restrictions upon LDI policies that they offered poor value for money and very limited cover. In recent years, however, premiums have become slightly more competitive and policies contain fewer limitations.

Traditionally, LDI insurance was previously only available in continental Europe (particularly in France) and very few owners/tenants of buildings in the UK managed to effect suitable and satisfactory cover.

When LDI first became available in the UK, it was necessary to bring the insurer in early on (usually before construction commenced) so that it could carry out a technical audit and monitor the construction process. This is still the case with many

LDI policies, although it is now possible (although it is the exception rather than the rule) to obtain cover for completed buildings and other major refurbishment contracts on existing properties. Tenants may also be able to obtain LDI insurance protection for only the part of a building that they occupy, although the condition of the whole building will obviously be considered by the underwriters.

Traditionally, LDI was only available to cover a period of ten years from practical completion. However, cover is now available for a twelve-year period from the date of practical completion (in line with the traditional limitation period for collateral warranties).

The cost of LDI cover will vary from project to project, but as a rule of thumb it will be between 1% and 3% of the total construction cost. However, there is often a substantial excess and the insurance is usually non-cancellable over the policy period, or a one-off premium is payable at the start of the policy period (which amounts to the same thing).

There are also usually limitations attached to the policy. Examples of typical limitations that may be carved out of an LDI policy include:

1   what types of consequential losses are capped/excluded;

2   defects in non-structural works and equipment;

3   defects due to lack of maintenance or misuse;

4   defects due to structural alterations after inception;

5   normal fire perils, war and kindred risks;

6   defects known prior to inception;

7   deficient weatherproofing/waterproofing;

That said, an LDI policy does have the following advantages.

1   there is usually no need to prove fault or liability on the part of third parties before insurers will respond to any claims;

2   a policy will usually be assignable to future owners and tenants of buildings;

3   cover for mechanical and electrical services should be available over and above that provided by current engineering policies and a degree of 'fitness for purpose' cover should also be available;

4   the physical characteristics of buildings or components may be guaranteed, e g capacity of lifts, floor loading etc; and

5   separate policies for business interruption insurance may also be available.

Therefore, although latent defects insurance is yet to be made compulsory, more and more policies are becoming available which are more attractive to building owners and their financiers. It is fair to say that any increase in the use of such LDI in the construction industry in the coming years will very much be driven by price and a cost benefit analysis, which at present is not particularly attractive for most projects.

Bibliography

Emden's Construction Law (looseleaf), LexisNexis UK.

Duncan Wallace I N *Hudson's Building and Engineering Contracts* (11th edn, 1995) Sweet and Maxwell.

Cornes D L and Winward R *Collateral Warranties – A Practical Guide for the Construction Industry* (1990) Blackwell Scientific Publications.

Furst S and Ramsey V (eds) *Keating on Building Contracts* (7th edn, 2001) Sweet and Maxwell.

CHAPTER 4

Project managers' appointments

By Sally Marsden, Frances Fowler and Keith Andrews

Summary

In this chapter we look at the form and content of the Project Manager's appointment. The chapter provides a useful commentary on four of the standard forms containing terms of engagement for Project Managers. It also looks at the general principles applicable when entering into an appointment.

This chapter covers:

*   The meaning and effect of certain standard words used in the Project Manager's appointment:
    *   advise
    *   recommend
    *   monitor
    *   supervise
    *   establish
    *   in conjunction with
    *   check
    *   ensure.

*   Review of the RICS Project Management Memorandum of Agreement and Conditions of Engagement:
    *   focus on key clauses in the Memorandum of Agreement
    *   guidance on key points to note in respect of those clauses.

*   Detailed commentary on the 16 services listed in the Guidance Note. The commentary covers what those services mean in practice, followed by some key points to watch out for when performing those services:
    *   1   Site selection
    *   2   Analysis

3   Agency, valuation, funding and relocation
4   Legal services
5   Consultant appointments
6   Brief, design and quality control
7   Reporting and meetings
8   Programming
9   Capital budgeting
10   Construction economics and financial management
11   Cash flow
12   Statutory and compliance
13   Contract procedures
14   Contract management
15   Building management, commissioning and maintenance
16   Tenancies and fitting out.

- Introduction to the Association for Project Management – Standard Terms of Appointment of a Project Manager – and a useful comparison of the differences between the APM form and the RICS Agreement.

- Introduction to the Professional Services Contract accompanying the New Engineering Contract, with some key points to note on that contract.

- Introduction to the RIBA Form of Appointment of Project Managers (1999) together with a short commentary and comparison between this agreement and the RICS and APM Agreements.

- Review of some areas of project management which form current good practice but do not necessarily form part of the Project Manager's terms and conditions:
  - management of risk
  - business case preparation
  - value engineering
  - electronic information management systems.

- Guidance on how to approach writing a contract or reviewing a contract document.

- Practical guidance on employing a sub-consultant.

1 Introduction

As can be seen from Chapter 1, the role of Project Manager has evolved over the last 20–25 years. In that time there has been a substantial amount of change in the way projects are run, and project management is now recognised as a distinct profession. With the development of new technology, projects are much more complex to run than they were 20 years ago. The services which a Project Manager provides are becoming increasingly standardised but, as has been seen, the term 'Project Manager' still means different things to different people and is used not just in the construction industry but in other industries such as information technology, oil, automotive and the health sector, to name but a few. If you tell someone you are a quantity surveyor or an architect, most people will have a fairly good idea of the types of work you are undertaking. Say you are a Project Manager, however, and they will not necessarily associate it with the construction industry. It is for this reason that careful attention must be paid to those documents which evidence a Project Manager's appointment.

Chapter 2 gave a very useful refresher of the basic legal principles in relation to forming a contract. However, the editors recommend that, when taking on the role of Project Manager, it should always be ensured that there is a detailed appointment document in place.

The Chartered Institute of Building has produced a Code of Practice for Project Management for Construction and Development (3rd edn, 2002). The objective of this Code is:

> ... to define the responsibilities of all the participants involved in order to achieve the completion of the project on time, to the specifications defined by the project brief and within the budget.

The Code lists five standard forms containing terms of engagement for Project Managers. To keep this chapter brief, we do not intend to deal with one of these – the NHS Estates Agreement for the Appointment of Project Managers for Commissions for Construction Projects in the NHS – as this is a specialised document for use in the health sector. The remaining four are:

- RICS Project Management Agreement and Conditions of Engagement (3rd edn, 1999) (the RICS Agreement);

- Association for Project Management Terms of Appointment for a Project Manager (1998) (the APM Agreement);

- NEC Professional Services Contract (1998);

- RIBA Form of Appointment for Project Managers (1999) (the RIBA Agreement).

We consider the RICS Agreement in some detail below and then look briefly at the other three by way of comparison. These four standard form contracts may be more relevant to large or complex projects, and if you are involved in small or simple projects you may not need such a comprehensive document. Some of the standard headings may also be inappropriate if, for example, you are acting for a tenant rather than for a developer. We concentrate on these contracts, however, to assist your understanding of the standard clauses available and aspects to be aware of. You can therefore draw on this knowledge when drafting or amending your own terms and conditions.

Some employers prefer to prepare their own bespoke contracts, and we will also discuss the importance of carefully scrutinising such contracts to ensure that they accurately reflect the services you are to provide and that you are aware of what the client expects of you.

(a) Common words used in standard form contracts

Before we look in detail at the standard form contracts that are available for use by Project Managers, it is worth considering the dictionary definitions and reviewing some of the standard words used to describe the type of services Project Managers are to provide, and how that wording can impact on a Project Manager's liability:

1 LIAISE

'Liaise' means to establish and maintain mutual understanding and co-operation or to act as a link. The duty to liaise means that the Project Manager should act in a co-ordinating facility in relation to many aspects of the project. However, if this is the extent of your duty you should beware of doing more than that – you are not required to give the advice that third parties may be required to give. The duty to liaise appears in the RICS Agreement Schedule of Services. If the Project Manager is involved from the outset of the project, he is required to liaise with the funding institution, the ground landlord, agents and the client. Later on in the project, the duty to liaise relates to the client or agents in relation to maintenance and commissioning.

2 CO-ORDINATE

'Co-ordinate' means to ensure harmony or effective operation, to work or act together effectively. The Memorandum to the RICS Agreement provides that the Project Manager's role is to be responsible for the 'administration, management and communication co-ordination' of the project. The Schedule of Services requires the Project Manager to co-ordinate, in particular with the consultants in relation to the preparation of the design brief and the preparation of contract documents. The co-ordination of the contract documentation goes so far as to make it the Project Manager's responsibility to arrange signatures of parties to the contract. This can be a significant responsibility if a dispute arises. The client's position could be seriously compromised if it transpired that the appropriate contracts were not in place or signed. If the fault for that was yours, the client could look to you to recover its losses.

3 ADVISE

'Advise' means to recommend, inform or notify. Two of the key obligations of the Project Manager under the Memorandum to the RICS Agreement are that the Project Manager shall:

> ... advise the client with regard to the general application of the Construction (Design and Management) Regulations (clause 3(f)).

and

> ... advise client with regard to the obligations under Housing Grants, Construction and Regeneration Act 1996, regarding payment and rights to an arbitrator (clause 3(g)).

The editors believe this reference to 'arbitrator' is an error in the RICS Agreement. The Housing Grants, Construction and Regeneration Act 1996 ('the Construction Act') is concerned with adjudication, and we assume that the reference should correctly be to an 'adjudicator'. You obviously need to be familiar with these statutes. The Construction (Design and Management) Regulations 1994 (CDM Regulations 1994)[1] are looked at in more detail in Chapter 7 and the Construction Act is examined in Chapter 6.

The duty to advise is a pro-active one. It can therefore be onerous, in that clients will often require advice from you in relation to many important aspects of the project. The RICS Agreement Schedule of Services requires the Project Manager to advise on the need for other consultants, the terms of their appointment and fee structures and their professional indemnity insurance, amongst other things. If you are contractually required to advise on certain areas you should do so, but confine your advice to practical guidance on issues which you have knowledge of. The case of *Pozzolanic Lytag Ltd v Bryan Robson Associates*[2] (discussed in Chapter 9) was a case in which the Project Manager's obligations included ensuring that suitable insurance arrangements were put in place by contractors. In this case, the Project Manager obtained evidence as to the proposed insurance arrangements and passed this on to the client to consider. The judge held that it was not sufficient for the Project Manager to act merely as a 'post-box'. If the Project Manager did not have the necessary expertise to assess the adequacy of the proposed insurance arrangements, he should have either obtained expert evidence from somebody who had or advised the client to seek expert advice themselves.

However, you should beware of giving advice on matters of which you have no knowledge or expertise. This problem arose in the case of *St Albans City and District Council v International Computers Ltd*[3] (discussed in Chapter 9). In this case, the Project

1   SI 1994/3140.
2   [1999] BLR 267.
3   [1996] 4 All ER 481.

Manager was found to have acted negligently in giving an assurance which he did not have the technical knowledge to give. If you are required to advise on areas in which you do not have sufficient knowledge, the safest course of action is to recommend that the client take the appropriate specialist advice.

Your responsibility to advise on contract terms will require you to ensure that all necessary blanks and appendices are completed in the relevant form of contract and that these documents are formalised and executed by the parties. In any case, if you are not sure about the legal effect of the terms of the contract or any bespoke amendments, you should take legal advice or advise your client to do so. You should consider recommending that the contract should be executed by way of deed to ensure the longer twelve-year limitation period.

4 RECOMMEND

'Recommend' means to suggest as fit for purpose or use or advise as a course of action. Clause 5 of the RICS Agreement Schedule of Services requires the Project Manager to make recommendations for the appointments of other consultations by the clients. The case of *Pratt v George Hill Associates*[4] (discussed in Chapter 9) concerned an architect, but the principle applies to Project Managers. In this case the defendant's Architects recommended a builder as being 'very reliable'. When the builder turned out to be very *un*reliable, the Architects were held liable for their negligence and misrepresentation. Recommending a contractor or consultant without making suitable enquiries in relation to, or having actual knowledge of, their solvency and capability could be hazardous. However, subject to the Project Manager's obligation to act with reasonable skill, care and diligence, clause 6.2 of the Memorandum to the RICS Agreement explicitly states that no liability shall attach to the Project Manager (either in contract, tort or otherwise) for loss, injury or damage as a result of any defect, act, omission or insolvency of any person other than the Project Manager. It is not clear whether this is intended to exempt the Project Manager from a duty of care in relation to the recommendation of contractors or consultants. However, it should not be relied upon and the safe course of action is to carry out appropriate enquiries in the first place.

5 MONITOR

'Monitor' means to check or warn about a situation. Clauses 3(b), (c), (d) and (e) of the Memorandum to the RICS Agreement all require the Project Manager to monitor the progress of design work/progress/consultants, advisers, contractors and suppliers/

---

4   (1987) 38 BLR 25, CA.

costs of the project. In the case of *Chesham Properties Ltd v Bucknall Austin Project Management Services Ltd*[5] (discussed in Chapter 9) Judge Hicks QC concluded that 'monitoring' could not sensibly be confined to passive observation but should include reporting on the performance being monitored by reference to the standards which should be achieved.

6 SUPERVISE

'Supervise' means to oversee the execution of a task or the actions or work of a person. Supervision of the contractor is usually the responsibility of the architect or engineer. It is thought that this obligation is a more pro-active and therefore onerous one than to 'monitor'. If you are only required to 'monitor' you should therefore ensure that you do not actually try to 'supervise', or you may open yourself up to unnecessary additional liability for which you may not be covered under your insurance policy. Neither the RICS Agreement Schedule of Services nor the APM Agreement Model C Schedule of Services include an obligation to supervise, save for a requirement within the RICS Agreement that the Project Manager checks that consultants are providing adequate supervision in accordance with their terms of appointment.

This obligation can be an onerous one, as it turned out to be in the case of *Chesham Properties Ltd v Bucknall Austin Project Management Services Ltd*[6] (discussed in Chapter 9). In this case, the court found that the Project Manager was under a duty to report to the client on the failings of the other professionals and that he was negligent in failing to do so. To make sure you are not in danger of being held liable for a failure which is not even your responsibility, ensure that there are meetings and reports at regular intervals and particularly at key points in the project. Use these meetings as checks on the performance of individuals or groups to ensure that progress is in accordance with the programme and costs are within the project budget. Ensure that all meetings are accurately minuted and minutes promptly circulated so that action points can be followed up and problems identified.

7 ESTABLISH

'Establish' means to set up or consolidate on a permanent basis or to find out or to ascertain. This obligation is referred to a number of times in the RICS Agreement Schedule of Services, where the Project Manager is required to establish the responsibility of consultants, contractors and sub-contractors; establish appropriate channels of communication between members of the project team, and establish regular meetings.

5   (1996) 82 BLR 92.
6   (1996) 82 BLR 92.

8 IN CONJUNCTION WITH

The dictionary definition of 'in conjunction with' is 'together with'. This is a similar obligation to 'liaise' and requires the Project Manager to consult with other consultants in the preparation of, for instance, guarantees, cost plans, payments and cash flow forecasts and statements for monitoring project expenditure. You could be exposing yourself to potential liability if you fail to consult with a relevant party and consequently do not benefit from or take account of their contribution.

9 CHECK

'Check' means to examine the accuracy, quality or condition of. This is a positive obligation which arises numerous times within the RICS Agreement Schedule of Services – for instance to check that consultants' responsibilities are clearly stated, to check and recommend consultants' applications for payment, to check that variations and instructions are being issued, and to check with other consultants that statutory approvals are required and applications for approval submitted. This is a similar obligation to 'monitor'.

10 ENSURE

Whilst there is no requirement to 'ensure' within the RICS Agreement or the APM Agreement, the editors note with interest that this word was recently removed from the standard form project management appointment documents in South Africa. The dictionary definition of 'ensure' is 'to make something certain to happen'. It is easy to see therefore why you would not want an obligation to 'ensure' some event within your contract – this could be construed as being tantamount to giving a warranty. You should check that this word does not appear in any amendments to a standard form contract or in any bespoke contract.

Failure to act in accordance with any of the above definitions will not necessarily imply negligence. However, it may provide some evidence of a failure to act with reasonable skill, care and diligence.

(b) Some key points about using bespoke or standard form contracts

1   Make sure that you are contracting with the correct party. It has been known for consultants to be appointed by one company within a group and the contractor to be appointed by a different company.

2   Make sure that the party who signs the contract has authority to do so. This applies to both the client's signatory and the Project Manager's signatory.

3   Whilst it is not uncommon for a Project Manager to have dual roles on a project, such as acting as both Project Manager and as architect/engineer/quantity surveyor, you should consider carefully whether you can maintain your independence as a Project Manager in the light of your other duties.

4   The Project Manager should bear in mind that in the light of the decision in *Merrett v Babb,*[7] they may have personal liability.

CASE LAW

Liability for professional negligence

Diana Eileen Merrett v John R H Babb[8]

This case concerned a valuation report prepared and signed by Mr Babb, a professionally qualified surveyor and valuer, in relation to a mortgage advance. At the time of preparing and signing the report, Mr Babb was employed by a firm of surveyors and valuers. Mr Babb's valuation report was later found to be negligent. The principal of the firm Mr Babb worked for was adjudged bankrupt and the firm's professional indemnity insurance cancelled. An action was brought against Mr Babb personally by the purchasers of the property who relied upon his negligent report. Mr Babb contended that he owed no duty of care to the purchasers.

Held that a professional person who carried out an inspection of a property and prepared a valuation was a person on whom a purchaser relied to exercise proper skill and care. Consequently, Mr Babb did owe a duty of care to the purchasers. By signing the report in his personal capacity, Mr Babb had assumed responsibility for it and knew that the purchasers would rely upon his report.

---

2 RICS Project Management Memorandum of Agreement and Conditions of Engagement

(a) Introduction

The RICS Agreement was first published in 1989 for use as a model set of terms and conditions for use between client and Project Manager. It has twice been updated

---

7   [2001] EWCA Civ 124, [2001] QB 1174, [2001] BLR 483.
8   [2001] EWCA Civ 124, [2001] QB 1174, [2001] BLR 483.

by a drafting committee to reflect changes in the industry. The latest edition is the third edition, published in 2001.

The RICS Agreement is in three parts:

- the Memorandum of Agreement;

- the Conditions of Engagement;

- Appendices A to F.

The Memorandum of Agreement sets out the principal responsibilities and objectives of the parties and clarifies the definitions used within the documents. The Conditions of Engagement set out the main conditions of the contract. The Appendices are left blank to enable the client and Project Manager to incorporate appropriate services and other information pertinent to the project in question.

There is also an accompanying Guidance Note to give advice on completion of the documents and on the procedures which, in the opinion of the RICS, would comply with the standard expected of the RICS. The Guidance Note also provides a commentary on suitable terms for insertion in the Memorandum of Agreement and the Appendices.

(b) Memorandum of Agreement, Conditions of Engagement and Appendices A–F

The main body of the RICS Agreement comprises the Memorandum of Agreement and Conditions of Engagement. The Memorandum of Agreement contains the principal areas of agreement between the parties, whereas the Conditions of Engagement set out in more detail the terms of the contract between the parties. The key clause of the Memorandum of Agreement is that the client agrees to engage the Project Manager subject to and in accordance with the Conditions of Engagement, and the Project Manager agrees to provide the services set out in Appendix A subject to and in accordance with the Conditions of Engagement. Accordingly, both parties need to be aware of and familiar with the Conditions and to have discussed and agreed the content of the Appendices.

The Memorandum of Agreement itself contains blanks to be completed by the parties. The key provisions of the Memorandum are as follows:

- **Clause 2** states that the Project Manager acts as agent of the client and is responsible for the administration, management and communication co-ordination of the project.

- **Clause 3** sets out the key obligations on the Project Manager. These are to communicate to the consultants the requirements of the client's brief; to monitor the progress of design work/progress/consultants, advisers, contractors and suppliers/costs of the project; and to advise the client in relation to their obligations under the Construction Act and the CDM Regulations. These will be supplemented by those services set out in Appendix A.

- **Clause 4** states that the Project Manager's authority to instruct is limited to the extent that he cannot, without the prior written consent of the client, give any instruction which would materially vary the project or increase the cost of, or time taken to complete, the project. The Project Manager is also obliged to inform the client promptly in writing of anything likely to materially affect either the cost or duration of the contract. This clause does not actually work in practice, because it gives a Project Manager little scope to manoeuvre. Delegation of authority is much more workable if the Project Manager is given a cost limit to work within, i e his authority is limited to instructions up to a certain level.

- **Clause 5** limits the Project Manager's liability in that he shall not be responsible for any forecasts of financial viability unless prepared by him, or for the consultant's designs and technical co-ordination thereof, or for the advice or recommendations that may be provided by any consultant or adviser appointed by the client. A limit on your liability in relation to financial forecasts could be a very useful one (see the case of *Copthorne Hotel (Newcastle) Ltd v Arup Associates*[9], discussed in detail in Chapter 9).

- **Clause 6** states that the Project Manager shall perform his services with reasonable skill, care and diligence. The level of skill, care and diligence will be measured against that of an ordinarily competent Project Manager in the circumstances. Clause 6.1 gives various options for the restriction of the liability of the Project Manager. (Limitation of liability is discussed in more detail in Chapter 3.)

- **Clause 10** sets out the fee arrangement between the parties and cross-refers to Appendices A and C in relation to the level of the fee and the payment structure. The blanks in this clause and Appendices A and C should be completed to express the agreement between the parties. Project Managers often agree a fixed fee for their services. If you agree a fixed fee, make sure there is a comprehensive list of the items included in the fixed fee. You may want to exclude specific services from the arrangement, such as assisting the client with litigation. You should specify hourly rates for those matters excluded from the fixed fee arrangement to avoid disputes over fees at a later stage. Clause 10(c) requires you to insert a date for completion of the project beyond which the fixed fee shall be adjusted. This is an important caveat to a fixed fee agreement to limit the fee to a point in time beyond which further fees should be negotiated. In practice, the date inserted is often one or two months after the project completion date to allow for a certain degree of slippage to the programme.

---

9 (1996) 12 Const LJ 402.

- **Clause 11** provides for the naming of a principal person who will undertake the direction and control of the duties on behalf of the project management company. The Conditions of Engagement provide that this person can be replaced at the client's request and that any replacement should be approved by the client in writing.

- **Clause 12** obliges the Project Manager to enter into a collateral warranty upon written request by the client and specifies that such a warranty should be in the form published by the British Property Federation (see Chapter 3 on collateral warranties). The clause also requires the insertion of the level of professional indemnity insurance required. Check that the amount is sufficient to cover your liability on the project. This is particularly important if you trade as a partnership (see Chapter 8 on insurance).

- **Clause 15** expressly provides the right to refer a dispute to adjudication and gives space for the naming of an adjudicator if required (see Chapter 10 on dispute resolution for more information).

The Memorandum of Agreement ends with the signatory section. The document can be signed 'underhand' or as a deed. If signed 'underhand' the applicable limitation period is six years. If signed as a deed, it must be signed in the presence of a witness who should then also sign and complete the details as required on page 6 of the Memorandum. By signing as a deed, the parties' liability under the document is extended to twelve years.

Make sure you understand the effect of signing as a deed and that your PI insurance continues to run for the duration of your liability (see Chapter 8).

The Memorandum of Agreement asterisks each clause which should be completed and emphasises that parties should be sure to complete every clause that has an asterisk.

It may seem an obvious point, but it is important to check that the blanks are completed. It is very common to find sections that should have been completed left blank.

It should be noted that the RICS Agreement was published prior to the implementation of the Contracts (Rights of Third Parties) Act 1999 (C(RTP)A 1999). The effect of C(RTP)A has not therefore been considered within the Agreement. See Chapter 3 for an explanation of C(RTP)A.

(c) Guidance Note to the RICS Agreement

The Guidance Note considers the Memorandum of Agreement and provides a commentary on how to complete each section. It states that, while members are not obliged to follow the advice and recommendations contained in the Note, they should be aware that the court is likely to take into account the content of any relevant guidance notes published by the RICS when deciding whether or not its members have acted with reasonable competence. The RICS rightly goes on to point out that, in the event of litigation, the court may require members to explain why they decided not to adopt recommended practice. The Memorandum of Agreement is compliant with the Construction Act 1996 and expressly includes a right to refer a dispute to adjudication in accordance with the Scheme for Construction Contracts (England and Wales) Regulations 1998.[10] The Construction Act and the Scheme are discussed in more detail in Chapter 6 and the adjudication procedure is explained in Chapter 10.

The Guidance Note refers to the fact that RICS Insurance Services Ltd have made a distinction between what they call 'project management' and 'project co-ordination'. It is deemed to be project co-ordination where the client appoints other consultants, whereas project management is where the Project Manager appoints the other consultants. It is not clear to the editors why this distinction has been made by the RICS, but no such distinction has been made in this chapter.

The key section in the Guidance Note is the explanation of Appendices A–F. In particular, the Guidance Note goes into some detail about the kinds of services which should be specified in Appendix A, the Schedule of Services. The Guidance Note provides a list of 16 services which should be considered, but emphasises that not all of these services will apply to every project, and, indeed, some other services may be appropriate, depending on the requirements of the particular project.

• Remember that if the Project Manager is appointed from the very outset of a project, the extent of the services required may not yet be clear. In these instances, the Schedule of Services should be completed to the best of the ability of the client and Project Manager, and any subsequent changes formally recorded between the parties.

• Make sure the services included are relevant to the particular project being worked on.

• It is important to avoid duplication of responsibilities by the professional team. If other consultants have been appointed before the Project Manager he should check their appointments carefully for duplication.

It is the editors' view that the Schedule of Services would benefit as a whole from a glossary. Terms used should be standardised and used consistently throughout all the contract documentation. There is inconsistency or lack of clarity in relation to a number of key phrases, such as:

10 SI 1998/649.

- **'Client brief' and 'design brief'.** The client brief should define the client's business needs and objectives and set limits on time, cost and quality. The design brief is prepared by the design consultants and should comply with the client brief. These phrases refer to distinct documents and should not be used interchangeably.

- **Project budget/master cost plan.** It should be clear whether the reference is meant to be to the project brief or to the master cost plan. Usually the cost plan is the breakdown of the construction cost controlled by the quantity surveyor. The project budget is usually the overall budget to be monitored by the Project Manager. The editors believe that the reference to 'master cost plan' in section 9.2 of the Schedule of Services should in fact be to the 'project budget'.

A good starting place for a glossary is contained within the CIOB Code of Practice. It is important, however, to add to the glossary as appropriate.

The services suggested by the Guidance Note to be incorporated into the contract are set out below. In considering these, we have begun by summarising in italics the requirements of each clause. Keith Andrews, a practising Project Manager and Partner of EC Harris, has then set out the practical issues to consider within a box, which is followed by bullet points of key items to note and legal comment.

I SITE SELECTION

Liaising with the consultants in advising the client on the arrangement of market appraisals, surveys, investigations, valuations and models.

As the client's principal consultant, the Project Manager co-ordinates the other project consultants and develops the client's brief. The brief will need to identify the client's business need for the project, and this specific need will determine the main aspects of site selection.

One primary purpose (objective) of the brief is to clarify the **function** of the product building the client wishes to develop. The Project Manager is likely, but not guaranteed, to be given this information at his appointment. It may be part of the Project Manager's role to co-ordinate the work of the client's marketing, business development and property consultants in identifying the particular function of the building required.

Property agents usually advise on the **location** of the new building. They will provide a list of alternative sites with their recommendation for the client's consideration. The Project Manager plays a large role in facilitating the effective assignment of alternative sites, especially for soil investigations, structural and

---

other surveys. Often the Project Manager will appoint structural engineers on behalf of the client, soil investigation engineers and geologists to oversee these undertakings.

Even at this early stage, a client is faced with concurrent working by a multi-disciplinary team of consultants who require co-ordination, supervision and steering. The Project Manager acts as the client's closest adviser in so far as being responsible for ensuring timely and satisfactory completion of work to agreed parameters (cost is not always necessarily the primary driver, as programmes can sometimes be). The Project Manager uses his expertise in eliciting from the other consultants the characteristics of the proposed sites. Any special site logistics that might impact on the building will affect whether the building can be brought to the marketplace within the requirements of the development appraisal.

- It is important to remember that the requirement is to 'liaise'. If you do more than that you could be liable if things go wrong and, worse, you may not be insured.

2 ANALYSIS

Co-ordinating initial viability studies and advising on the need for research and feasibility studies.

Viability studies determine whether the project is feasible or not and can realistically proceed without committing financially to full design. The Project Manager co-ordinates the output of other consultants' work for collation into the study. Off-the-shelf development appraisal software is now generally available and, more frequently than not, the Project Manager is now being requested to fulfil this task. Viability is usually an iterative process whereby numerous alternatives need to be considered before a viable scheme is achieved. The financial objective at this stage is to maximise profitability for the client.

This is a critical stage that commits the client to minimum liability before choosing and agreeing to develop the design for a single preferred scheme.

If you are not appointed from the outset of a project and therefore not involved in the feasibility studies, it is recommended that, upon appointment, you carry out a 'project audit' to establish where the project is and to deal with any problems. The client should pay for this additional exercise. This should enable the Project Manager to then take 'ownership' of the project.

3 AGENCY, VALUATION, FUNDING AND RELOCATION

Liaising with the client, agents, landlords and funders.

Advice on the specific agency, valuation and funding is performed by the client's specialist development Consultants, Property Agents and Solicitor. However, the need for co-ordination and monitoring of workload within agreed time, cost and scope of work parameters is essential. While some clients deal with their property agents direct, other clients will expect the Project Manager to co-ordinate the work of the valuation of land and site. The Project Manager seeks to bring about a regulated flow of tasks using their experience and expertise to see that activities are carried out concurrently wherever possible and within the master programme (i e a project specific strategic delivery programme which is prepared and agreed by the client and meets with the parameters defined under the brief). Seeking pre-lets, usually by letting agents, need to be co-ordinated alongside the work of the team and this is another role for the Project Manager to co-ordinate. Funding organisations may deal direct with the client, although the Project Manager may be required to provide specific project information for agreement between the funder and the client.

- At this stage it is all about co-ordinating all these individual professional consultants to meet the business needs of the client.

4 LEGAL SERVICES

Co-ordinating the activities of legal agents on legal matters and obtaining a full understanding of all contracts and directing consultants accordingly.

While it is usually the client's Solicitor who deals with the legal issues and the contract documents concerning the project, the Project Manager increasingly sets the brief for the client's solicitor to avoid the client incurring

---

abortive costs. The Project Manager is often expected to co-ordinate the activities of the client's Solicitor and other legal consultants. Making sure this happens within the master programme is the Project Manager's task.

The Project Manager is the practising construction expert, and key information on actual roles and responsibilities etc is needed to prepare the brief for the Solicitor. It is the role of the client's legal adviser to set out the roles and responsibilities as obligations under the contract or consultants' appointments, ensuring that all contracts/appointments are consistent and coherent.

Usually the client appoints both a property and construction solicitor, although this is very much dependent on the size and complexity of the scheme.

- Obtaining a full understanding of all the contracts is a very onerous task. On large projects the contract documents can stand several feet off the floor! Unfortunately for the Project Manager, he does have to read it all. In accordance with the wording of the Guidance Note, the Project Manager is required to direct the consultant in accordance with the contracts and therefore he needs to know what each consultant's role is and ensure they comply with their contracts.

- It is important to note that the Project Manager does not draft the contract documents. Therefore, he must take care not inadvertently to get involved in agreeing changes to contract documents. The editors have seen cases where Project Managers have agreed to change the wording of, for example, a collateral warranty, notwithstanding the fact that there was an agreed wording for the warranty. Project Managers are likely to be held liable for any loss suffered if they revise contract documents without their client's authority. Always recommend that the client's legal advisers check and sign off on the final contract documents.

- If the project is a complex one with a large number of contracts, it is advisable to ensure that it is being dealt with by a Project Manager with sufficient knowledge and experience of the contract documents to be able to make sure all provisions are complied with.

5 CONSULTANT APPOINTMENTS

Advising the client on the need for, and making recommendations for the appointment of, other consultants; advising on the terms of consultants' appointments and fee structures; advising on the need for warranties; advising the client to check professional indemnity insurances; determining the limit of the architect's authority to issue instructions; advising on the need for a clerk of works and other supervisory staff; monitoring the performance of consultants, clerk of works and contractors.

The Project Manager has a vital role to play in co-ordinating and leading the consultants' design team. It is only logical that the Project Manager is therefore centrally involved in advising on the detailed services, responsibilities and duties of each consultant. It is eminently sensible for the client to consider the Project Manager being brought in at the earliest stage of the project when selecting and appointing the consultant team. Indeed, some clients make a point of drawing up the list of prospective consultants in conjunction with the Project Manager and delegating to the Project Manager the task of conducting interviews with prospective consultants.

It is rare that the standard terms and conditions of a consultant's appointment are used without significant amendments being made to suit either the client's requirements, the needs of the particular project or the consultant himself. The professional institutions often do not provide standard terms of appointment for all the services to suit the client's requirements, as the standard terms and conditions are provided merely to serve as a datum from which to develop the final terms. The Project Manager is ideally placed to advise the client on amendments and specific duties to be included in the consultants' appointments. These amendments have to be considered in the light of the type of project, procurement method and client management ethos.

- The Project Manager is required to 'recommend' other consultants (see Chapter 9 and the case of *Pratt v George Hill and Associates*[11]). Project Managers can be held liable for negligent misrepresentation in relation to the recommendation of other consultants/contractors. However, as it is quite common to recommend other consultants/contractors in the course of a Project Manager's work, so long as reasonable skill and care is exercised in making the recommendation (i e recommending a firm of which you have actual knowledge or experience), it is unlikely that you could be found to have acted negligently.

- The Project Manager should advise on the necessity of the consultants providing duty of care warranties for the design of the scheme.

- In terms of professional indemnity insurance cover, the Project Manager should advise the client on the need for the relevant professional indemnity insurance cover for all consultants and the level of cover that needs to be provided, which will be dependent on the size and complexity of the scheme.

---

11 (1987) 38 BLR 25.

6 BRIEF, DESIGN AND QUALITY CONTROL

Co-ordinating with consultants regarding the preparation of a design brief and amplification during design development, including obtaining authorisation from client; establishing responsibilities of consultants, contractors and sub-contractors; reporting to the client and co-ordinating submission of final proposals to the client for approval; checking that the consultants review the buildability and technical design of the proposals, and that these conform to the project brief; advising on the need for quality assurance schemes, defects insurance and product guarantees.

The Project Manager is generally involved in assisting the client to develop their Business Case, which will provide requirements for the strategic development brief, procurement route, budget, delivery programme and risk analysis for the project. This will be alongside the client's overview of the definition of need, re-investment and option selection process for the alternative routes for developing the site.

The client's brief is an important document. The client has to communicate to the design team the functional needs of the development, whilst at the same time providing all-important limits or constraints. These are usually expressed in terms of time, cost, quality and functional need. The Project Manager can input an extra dimension to make the client's brief more effective, as a tool for clear communication.

How the designers go about developing the designs through the outline and detailed design stages, and at the same time gaining client's feedback, comment and approval, is driven by the Project Manager. Changes to the project are controlled by the Project Manager through a change control system, which is managed by the Project Manager. Keeping progress, cost and quality of the design within the client's brief but also within master programme deadlines is a vital project management role. The Project Manager's experience and skill comes to the fore in steering these activities while maintaining the focus on the key design, cost and programme issues. A project execution plan will be produced by the Project Manager in conjunction with the client and other consultants in order to set out the chosen processes, framework of relationship of roles and specific procedures selected for the project. It sets a vision as to what the project is to achieve. The project handbook then sets out *how* the project will be achieved, in terms of practice and procedure.

- Many of the obligations under this heading are to check, co-ordinate or report, that is, to ensure that others are carrying out their roles properly rather than advising personally. However, see Chapter 9 and the case of *Pride Valley Foods*

Ltd v Hall & Partners and Hall & Partners (Contract Management) Ltd[12], where Hall, the Project Managers, were found to be negligent in failing to warn about unsuitable materials. It is important to have procedures in place for checking suitability of materials and ensuring all relevant factors are taken into account.

- It is important to co-ordinate all consultants' Schedules of Services to ensure there are no overlap or gaps.

- In relation to the client's brief, there is no point waiting for a client to draft a brief if they are unable or unwilling to do so. Often a Project Manager needs to take the lead and prepare a draft brief for the client's comment and approval.

7   REPORTING AND MEETINGS

Establishing appropriate channels of communication; establishing a meeting structure; monitoring communications and distribution of information; checking that appropriate information is provided to the client and that they are notified of decisions required from them; agreeing reporting and recording procedures with consultants; and convening and chairing all principal project meetings.

The Project Manager is the main organiser when it comes to meetings and reports. The Project Manager is at the interface between project and business operation by the client and therefore requires judgment to inform upwards and to manage and instruct in relation to the project. A skilful mix of perseverance and eye for both detail and the big picture, together with enthusiasm, are the usual prerequisites. Clients require clear feedback on the key issues with recommendations in order to make their decisions in accordance with the programme. The Project Manager keeps the team members fully engaged at meetings, where the atmosphere is kept constructive and progressive with concise conclusions recorded. As face-to-face conversations beat correspondence or even e-mails, the Project Manager is not slow to call a meeting to resolve an issue, at the same time being cautious not to overload people with too many meetings.

Initiating and maintaining momentum is one of the Project Manager's watchwords. At the same time, the Project Manager is there to protect the client's interest, and that often means keeping full and detailed records of decisions, advice and recommendations by the other consultants on whom the client is relying. Obtaining signature from the client for sign-off of approvals at gateways/milestones and decisions is usually organised and controlled by the Project Manager.

12 [2001] EWCA Civ 1001, 76 Con LR 1.

- This obligation should be a straightforward one and, if a practical procedure is in place, should run itself. The extent, form and frequency of communications with the client should be agreed. This sort of information could form the 'project handbook'. However, it is important to ensure that all meetings actually take place and are attended by the requisite personnel. Minutes should be turned around and circulated in a short, defined period of time, for example 48 hours.

- The editors cannot stress highly enough the importance of ensuring that there are accurate written records of what has been agreed upon. Practically, the emphasis should be on recording action notes (including who is to follow up on the action, and the timescale) and confirmation of decisions. From a legal perspective, it can also be important to minute the reasons for changes. It is important that these records are properly circulated in order that parties can review the action points, and, if clarification is necessary, it can be obtained prior to the work being carried out.

8 PROGRAMMING

In conjunction with other consultants, preparing and maintaining a master programme for the life span of the project, recording principal activities and identifying critical dates; verifying and incorporating consultants' programmes for production of detailed design information; monitoring progress; checking that applications for consents, grants etc are submitted in accordance with the programme; advising the client of changes and obtaining authorisation; checking the contractor's programme and incorporating it into the master programme.

The master programme is a key project document. It will set out the 'market window' in which the client wishes to have delivered its project. The Project Manager will draft detailed programmes within the overall parameters of the master programme for the client's consideration and discussion with the other consultants. The skill is to allow people sufficient time in which to perform their tasks diligently and effectively whilst at the same time performing within the master programme constraints. It is crucial that all the important events and milestones are identified and incorporated into the master programme and in the short-term programmes.

The design programme is another key project document. The Project Manager obtains and agrees a design programme with each of the designers. Individual design programmes are incorporated into a single document, often called an integrated design programme, which displays the tasks, timing and relationship between production of all design on the project.

The procurement programme picks up where the integrated design programme finishes. It shows the various steps through the procurement process to award of contract, manufacture, delivery and start on site. Modern project processes rely on the skills of specialist contractors within the supply chain. Individual work package programmes are produced to show the stages of design, appointment, manufacture and installation for each of the specialist contractors.

The construction programme is of prime consideration. What is designed and procured must equally be carefully implemented with close control to ensure timely completion on site. In today's market a project requires more detailed programming than ever before. With the availability of proven off-the-shelf software, it is now the norm that programmes are produced showing critical path and dependency between tasks using reliable methods. The Project Manager is experienced in all these methods and is able to converse in detail on all aspects of the programmes and to brief the client in depth.

Protecting the client's interests also includes maintaining detailed records of actual events so that, where a consultant or contractor is entitled to additional time, the amount of additional time can be calculated with some precision and transparency. In addition, the client's rights to levy any damages are protected. The project activities, duration and links between activities all need to be considered in the context of project risk so that programmes are efficient and yet reliable.

9 CAPITAL BUDGETING

Monitoring the consultants in the preparation of budget costs and presenting feasibility studies to the client for approval; in conjunction with the consultants, preparing and maintaining a master cost plan; advising the client of any alterations and obtaining authorisation.

The Project Manager will organise and co-ordinate the production of a budget estimate, which will be included within the client's business case. The Project Manager will liaise with the consultant in refining the anticipated construction costs. As cost is one of the three fundamental aspects of a project, identifying an approved construction cost plan is a key requirement for any Project Manager. The cost plan is produced by the cost consultant with the active involvement of the other consultants under the guidance of the Project Manager. The format of the cost plan is worked out between the consultants and the client with the Project Manager facilitating this process. Once the business case budget is approved and fixed, this must be translated into the brief being fully developed and delivered. Therefore, in developing cost plan certainty, the Project Manager must facilitate and co-ordinate the team to constantly develop, review and test costs to maintain the approved budget. Where this cannot be achieved, the Project Manager should facilitate by holding value management/value engineering workshops to review functionality, scope and cost parameters that may need to be changed and present revised solutions (shopping lists) to the client in order to maintain the budget. Cost analysis is encouraged by the Project Manager so that expenditure of the client's financial resources is steered towards his priority, design and construction issues.

- Ensure that you advise the client immediately, clearly and in writing of any changes to the project budget. Ensure that there are adequate contingencies in the project budget and the construction cost plan for each main head in the cost plan, and clearly identify those costs which are simply budget figures.

10 CONSTRUCTION ECONOMICS AND FINANCIAL MANAGEMENT

Advising on costs of alternative designs and materials, energy budgeting, financial procedures; advising on procedures for dealing with insurance claims; checking that consultants are providing adequate and timely information for the preparation of tender documentation; obtaining client's authorisation for costs of variations and checking costs agreed; reporting to client regularly on all aspects of costs and implications on the programme and final costs forecasts; checking that consultants prepare regular valuations and that works are valued and payment certificates issued in accordance with the contract; checking and recommending payment of clients' copies of certificates; checking that consultants prepare and agree final accounts; checking and recommending consultants' applications for payments and all other invoices related to the development.

The principal aim of the Project Manager in the field of construction economics and financial management is, having set the project budget, to lay down a framework for the overall financial management of the project.

It is usual for the Project Manager to be responsible for the overall project budget and reporting thereof, and he may devolve the management of the construction element of the project budget to the quantity surveyor. Once again, division and clarity of responsibilities is essential, such that the quantity surveyor is clear on the part of the overall project budget which is his responsibility to control, the remainder – largely consultant fees, third party costs etc – being the responsibility of the Project Manager.

The Project Manager progresses the work of the team within the cost limits of the capital budgeting and advances the work to a more detailed stage where elements and trades can be compared with benchmark costs and key performance indicators. The Project Manager will be keen to initiate value-engineering exercises from as early as the design stage. He will co-ordinate these exercises, possibly using a specialist facilitator, in a workshop setting. The Project Manager will also carry out risk analysis exercises and produce a risk register and risk management plan. Once again, this is increasingly initiated via a specialist risk management workshop.

The client's business case will dictate the attitude adopted towards use of life cycle costing. The Project Manager will steer the cost consultant and other consultants to meet the client's financial objectives: e g a building which is to be retained as an investment will dictate construction materials, with a longer-term view on life-cycle costs.

A change control system will have been established once the cost plan is approved, and the scope of works fully defined and frozen on the project pre-contract. The Project Manager will supervise the operation of the change control system post-contract, in particular checking that prospective changes are raised in good time for discussion, and decision before any commitment is made or delay caused.

Variations are an inevitable fact of life, particularly where a client wishes a building to incorporate all the latest market specifications or tenant's requirements. The Project Manager will seek to deal with all variations in a proactive manner, wherever possible agreeing prices in advance or at least obtaining estimates for notification to the employer. Variations will be part of the change control system, although the Project Manager will be particularly concerned to check that the budget and project completion date are not compromised without the employer being specifically informed and giving his approval.

The Project Manager will oversee a system of regular interim certificates in keeping with the precise requirements of the contract. This will include a system of proactive inspections by the designers to identify any work that is not carried out in accordance with the contract – the Project Manager will be alert to see that the quantity surveyor does not inadvertently include such works within the interim payment.

Limits of financial authority to issue instructions that have financial consequences will need to be agreed for the Project Manager (by the client) and for the architect (by the client and the Project Manager). Management of contingencies in terms of both cost and time will be one of the Project Manager's key considerations so that the project is kept within the client's overall objectives. Maintaining a rolling final account is a desirable objective so that the employer is kept advised of a realistic anticipated out-turn cost for the project.

As the project nears practical completion, the Project Manager will co-ordinate the team in highlighting any outstanding works or defects which are required to be completed to achieve practical completion. The Project Manager will seek to protect the employer's interests so that any building handed over is truly ready for the purpose intended by the employer.

After practical completion, the Project Manager will co-ordinate the notifying of any defects that arise during the defects liability period so that the contractor is kept advised of its obligations to remedy defects within a reasonable period – and at the latest by the end of the defects liability period. The Project Manager will supervise the issue of the Certificate of Making Good Defects and oversee progress in the agreement and settlement of the final account.

At the appropriate time, the Project Manager will advise the employer as to the issue of a final certificate subject to completion of all works and defects and correct financial settlement with the contractor.

- Preserving the employer's right to deduct liquidated and ascertained damages in the event of any delay is one of the Project Manager's key tasks. This will involve assessing interim extension of time submissions and forming an opinion as to any entitlement to extension of time. It is important therefore to fully understand this duty.

- Make sure you understand your role as Project Manager in the certification and issuing process. Often a Project Manager's role is simply to check that another consultant is performing his obligations. Do not undertake that role yourself if it is not part of your brief. Make sure you understand the effect of each type of certificate.

11 CASH FLOW

In conjunction with consultants, arranging for the preparation and maintenance of cash flow forecasts and statements for monitoring the project expenditure; monitoring all payments made, and checking that expenditure is in line with the cash flow forecast and that payments are made within the stipulated time.

Cash flow is always an important issue for clients. The Project Manager will co-ordinate advice on cash flow to assist the client with meeting their payment obligations under the contract. The first cash flow is likely to be prepared after approval of the project brief when liability for significant payments of consultants' fees will commence. The Project Manager will usually authorise interim payments of consultants' fees, planning application fees and the like, as the Project Manager is in the best position to provide an overview of the client's cash flow requirements.

As the project enters a construction phase, the quantity surveyor will provide detailed cash flows for construction costs, reflecting the procurement method and the projected construction programme.

After the contract is awarded, the Project Manager will co-ordinate the submission by the contractor of his proposed cash flows and will see that an appropriate cash flow is agreed between the quantity surveyor and the contractor and updated throughout the project. The Project Manager's aim throughout will be to warn the client of any unexpected change or additional funding requirements brought about by events on the project.

- Your duty to monitor all payments made and to check that the client makes payment within the stipulated time is tied into the client's obligations under the Construction Act. Your client could hold you liable if the requisite withholding notices are not issued within the required timescales in relation to applications for payment which are not being paid in full (see Chapter 6 for more details).

12 STATUTORY COMPLIANCE

Co-ordinating with planning authorities; checking planning applications with the architect; checking with the consultants which other statutory approvals are required; checking that consultants obtain clearance from fire officers; advising the client on their obligations under the CDM Regulations and monitoring compliance.

The Project Manager will oversee the setting up of meetings with statutory authorities, in particular with local planners, building control officers and fire officers. Usually the Project Manager will attend some of the early meetings and intermittently see that progress is in accordance with the master programme. Whilst the designers will deal with the detailed tasks, the Project

Manager will be keen to oversee the progress that is being made so that early warning of problems can be identified and notified to the client.

The health and safety plan and health and safety file are areas where the Project Manager will also have an involvement, primarily to satisfy himself that close co-operation is taking place between the planning supervisor and the designers, and that health and safety is being managed satisfactorily.

The Project Manager will liaise with the planning supervisor so that timely issue of statutory notices are submitted to all relevant authorities and that the client is assured that the regulations are being fully complied with in good time.

- Health and safety compliance is of vital importance (see Chapter 7). Ensure that you know and understand the CDM Regulations and the various responsibilities under the Regulations.

13 CONTRACT PROCEDURES

Deciding with consultants the selection and method of appointment of preferred/nominated sub-contractors; advising the client accordingly; deciding with consultants the procurement procedure for the selection of contractors, and the form of contract; monitoring the consultants in the preparation and assembly of tender documents; together with the consultants, preparing a list of tenderers and conducting selection procedures and obtaining approval; arranging tender analysis with consultants; arranging interviews of tenderers; preparing tender award recommendation and obtaining instructions; co-ordinating the preparation of contract documentation and warranties, including arranging signature of parties to the contract; arranging for the contractor's insurance certificate and checking renewal of insurance at renewal dates.

As the client's adviser, the Project Manager will advise on the procurement procedure in conjunction with co-ordinating advice from the designers and discussing alternative options with the client. The project brief and the client's objectives and risk profile will be key considerations in the choice of procurement route and which form of contract is selected.

The selection of specialist contractors (i e preferred sub-contractors, work package contractors etc) is increasingly a critical issue for any project. Enabling full involvement of specialist contractors at the earliest stage and obtaining their continued responsibility for design and construction will often dictate the choice of procurement route and selection of building contract.

The Project Manager will co-ordinate the drawing up of a long list of prospective tenderers from which the tender list of suitable main contractors and/or specialist contractors is produced.

These days it is increasingly common that the client wishes to have a much closer relationship with the specialist contractors than before. The Project Manager will advise on and organise these arrangements.

Tender adjudication involves input from the entire team. The Project Manager will facilitate this process by seeking a clear selection criteria for award of the main contract and specialist work packages. The Project Manager will organise proposed evaluation criteria, selection process and tender analysis procedures for agreement with the client and the team.

Just as it is important that the right tenderers be selected to submit tender prices on complete tender documents, so it is vital that a thorough tender evaluation be then carried out to select the most appropriate tenderer to be recommended to the client. The Project Manager will organise the process of preparing contract documents for signature and copying to the client, contractor and the project team.

Before any commitment is undertaken, and in particular before a contractor enters the site, the Project Manager will seek to conclude all signing and issue of contract documents, together with confirming that contractors' insurances are valid and in place.

- Beware that if you select the wrong form of procurement method, you may not be acting with reasonable skill and care.
- It is interesting to note how the Guidance Note refers to the appointment of sub-contractors before the appointment of the contractor. However, the appointment of the main contractor is obviously the more important of the two stages.

14 CONTRACT MANAGEMENT

Advising the client of any works to be carried out under separate direct contract; co-ordinating the consultants to ensure information is being provided to contractors within an appropriate timescale; checking that consultants are providing adequate supervision and undertaking regular site inspections; checking that variations and instructions are being issued and correctly circulated; checking that consultants are fulfilling their contractual obligations in assessing and dealing with extensions of time and issuing the appropriate certificates; checking that consultants' obligations are being met in relation to confirming completion; issuing appropriate certificates of making good defects and completion.

The Project Manager will identify components on long delivery and arrange for orders to be placed. Any direct contracts between the client and third parties outside of the main contract will be identified by the Project Manager and organised on the client's behalf.

An information release schedule is a critical document which the Project Manager will co-ordinate and see is prepared using the input of the designers and the reasonable requirements of the contractors. During the construction works, the Project Manager will have identified key areas and critical periods where site supervision and inspection should be made by the contractors and designers respectively. The Project Manager will seek to protect the client's interests by seeing that the consultants team carry out their duties fully and on time throughout the construction phase.

Instruction of variations will require a follow-up in checking to see that the instruction has been correctly circulated and is being properly acted upon. The Project Manager will check that this is happening properly as the works proceed.

As extension of time claims often relate to design change, further information etc, the Project Manager will seek to obtain the considered opinion and assessment by the other consultants of the submissions made by the contractor. Before considering whether to issue sectional completion or practical completion certificates, the Project Manager will organise inspections by the designers for the purpose of identifying outstanding work and defects to be remedied before completion can be accepted. The same process will take place at appropriate times during the defects liability period and before the Project Manager considers which items should be included on the schedules attached to the certificate of Making Good Defects.

- The case of *Chesham Properties Ltd v Bucknall Austin Project Management Services Ltd*[13] concerned the breach of the kind of duties covered by this clause. It concerned a finding on a preliminary issue that the Project Manager was under a duty to report to the employer on the failings of the other professionals and was negligent in failing to do so. This case is discussed in more detail in Chapter 9.

13 (1996) 82 BLR 92.

- If, in accordance with your contract, you do not have the responsibility for issuing certificates, do not start issuing them. If you do, you are accepting a potential liability if the work is subsequently found to be defective.

- Clause 14.3 requires you to 'co-ordinate the consultants using *reasonable endeavours* to secure the provision of information to contractors in an appropriate timescale'. What constitutes 'reasonable endeavours' can be difficult. If faced with difficulties, you should produce Information Required Schedules and monitor the consultants' performance against the schedule. Ultimately, if you are concerned that a consultant is not performing, you should report this to the client.

15 BUILDING MANAGEMENT, COMMISSIONING AND MAINTENANCE

Liaising with client/agents on practical management, maintenance and services pending occupation; with consultants and contractors arranging hand-over and full commissioning of services; with client/agents/consultants on commissioning and equipping programmes; checking that all follow-up material, such as the Health and Safety file, test certificates, guarantees and maintenance information, is provided to the client as appropriate.

Part of the contract works will be for appropriate contractors to provide maintenance programmes of the completed building for use by the user in occupation. The Project Manager will organise the review, approval and delivery of these maintenance programmes in good time.

Commissioning of new facilities is becoming recognised as a vital component of the works, which sometimes need to be managed by a separate commissioning engineer/consultant. The Project Manager will liaise and organise the work of the commissioning engineer and oversee the carrying out of commissioning work before practical completion.

As with all work on the project, the client will look to the Project Manager to see that works are fully operational and properly commissioned before hand-over occurs. The Project Manager will co-ordinate the liaison and interchange between commissioning personnel and client representatives so that that the client is fully conversant with operating the completed facility after hand-over. The Project Manager will see that the contractors provide all documentation at hand-over in the required format and detail before practical completion is agreed.

With out-sourced facility management contracts being used by many clients, it is becoming more important that hand-over documents are meticulously organised and provided in full to the client on hand-over. These documents will include maintenance manuals, test certificates, guarantees, operating instructions and 'as-built' drawings and specifications.

- It is important that hand-over documents are provided in full, as they may well form part of the client's contract documents if he is selling or letting the building.

16 TENANCIES AND FITTING OUT

Preparing and implementing a marketing or promotional campaign with the client and consultants; liaising with the client/agents/solicitor to agree the terms of the agreements for the lease; procuring documentation required for marketing or contracts; providing tenants with information to enable them to prepare fitting out proposals and arranging for client approvals; preparing any necessary regulations required for the client to control the undertaking of the tenant's fitting out; monitoring the fitting out and checking that the completed works comply with client regulations and approvals; obtaining appropriate certificates relating to the tenant's fitting out.

Increasingly, the Project Manager is involved from the drafting of a business case through all the stages of the project including marketing, letting and occupation by the end user. It is also becoming more commonplace that the Project Manager will be involved to some extent with the co-ordination of a marketing or promotion campaign, of commercial prospects for letting and/ or sale on completion. The Project Manager is well positioned to advise on current drawings, specifications and other documents to be used in marketing.

Often the Project Manager will meet prospective tenants when arranging site visits, explaining the specification and progress of the works and co-ordinating answers to technical questions from the prospective tenants' design team. The Project Manager is ideally situated to undertake management of the tenants' fitting out works. It is more common for an incoming tenant to instruct the landlord's Project Manager also to carry out project management of the fitting out works, i e effectively a 'turn key package', or where speed is of the essence for the tenant.

- Whilst not an expert in terms of agreements for lease, the Project Manager will often be asked to contribute with ideas on the drafting or attachments to the lease and to be aware of the provisions of the lease.

The remainder of the Appendices deal with the balance of the Project Manager's appointment.

- **Appendix B** relates to clause 6 of the Conditions of Engagement, which sets out the obligations of the client, including specifying the authority given to the Project Manager to act on behalf of the client in the performance of his duties. This is subject to a requirement for the Project Manager to obtain the client's written consent for the items listed in Appendix B before proceeding. Appendix B should specify matters of importance to the scope and/or cost of the project, such as any variation of design, amendment of contract or confirmation to the architect for issue of a contract instruction over a certain value or agreement to delay the completion date of the project.

- **Appendix C** sets out the fees to be paid by the client to the Project Manager for the performance of the services. This should include dates for payment in accordance with the Construction Act 1996 (see Chapter 6 for more details).

- **Appendix D** relates to clause 7.9 of the Conditions of Engagement, which states that the fee agreed between the parties is calculated assuming completion of the project by the date stated in clause 10(c) of the Memorandum of Agreement. If the project is extended beyond this date, the fee shall be adjusted in accordance with the provisions of Appendix D. Appendix D should therefore state the basis on which any adjustments of fee should be calculated.

- **Appendix E** also relates to the Project Manager's fee and should be completed to expressly specify any site office accommodation or special project offices costs which are not included in the fee and are an additional cost for the client. Similarly, Appendix F should specify any items which will be invoiced in addition to the Project Manager's fee, such as taxi fares, printing costs and hotel accommodation costs.

3 The Association for Project Management – Standard Terms for the Appointment of a Project Manager

(a) Introduction

The APM Agreement was first published in 1998. It was drafted in response to increasing pressure from practising Project Managers for standard terms which would be applicable to different sectors of industry.

The APM Agreement is in two parts: first, the Standard Terms for Appointment, which consist of a set of core terms and conditions designed to be used by Project Managers in all industries and for any project; secondly, the Schedule of Services which supplements the Standard Terms and is appropriate to the particular industry.

There are alternative Schedules of Services available for IT projects, manufacturing, construction and smaller projects. The Schedule of Services relevant to construction is Model C.

(b) Standard Terms for the Appointment of a Project Manager

The format of the Standard Terms is similar to the RICS Agreement and is broken up into five sections:

Part 1 – Form of Agreement

Part 2 – General Terms

Part 3 – Schedule of Particulars

Part 4 – Fee Schedule

Part 5 – Scope of Services.

The Form of Agreement is comparable to the Memorandum of Agreement in the RICS Agreement and sets out the details of the parties and the purpose of the contract. Whereas the Project Manager's duties, authority to instruct and liability are set out in the Memorandum to the RICS Agreement, the APM Agreement simply states that the Project Manager agrees to provide the Services (as set out in Part 5 of the Agreement) and the client and Project Manager agree to perform the obligations imposed on them subject to and in accordance with the Agreement. The Form of Agreement can be executed underhand or as a deed, as discussed above in relation to the RICS Agreement.

The General Terms state that they have been drafted 'to be fair to the Client, the Project Manager and third parties, and to be consistent with all the alternative model Schedules of Services', the intention being that they should be used without addition or alteration. The Project Manager's obligations as set out in the General Terms of the APM Agreement can be compared to those set out in the Memorandum of Agreement and General Conditions of the RICS Agreement. The notable similarities and differences are as follows:

1   The RICS Agreement states that the Project Manager shall be responsible for the 'administration, management and communication co-ordination of the project' (clause 2). Most of his specific obligations under clause 3 are to communicate or monitor the design/progress/consultants/contractors/cost, by reference to the client's brief which the client shall provide to the Project Manager (clause 6.1). In practice, few clients actually have a written or complete brief in a form which

could act as a brief for the purposes of the design team. The client will usually rely on the Project Manager in this regard.

The APM Agreement requires input from the Project Manager at an early stage. Clause 7.2 of the General Terms states that:

- 'Within 14 days of the date of this Agreement, the Client shall issue to the Project Manager or request that within a further 14 days the Project Manager prepares and issues to the Client a draft written statement of the Client's goals and objectives in relation to the project. Following issue of such draft statement the parties will endeavour in good faith to agree the same within a further 14 days. The Client and the Project Manager shall initial a copy of the agreed statement which shall thereafter constitute the Project Brief.'
- Although the Project Manager is provided with copies of all existing programmes, cost plans, etc under the APM Agreement, thereafter he is required to prepare and agree with the client and continually monitor and update a programme, a cost plan and Project Procedures Manual (clauses 2.4–2.6).

2   Under the RICS Agreement the Project Manager's authority to instruct is limited, in that he cannot give instructions which would either vary the project or the cost or time taken to complete the project. If anything occurs that would be likely to affect any of these, the Project Manager should 'promptly' inform the client in writing of the likely effects (clauses 4.1–4.2).

Under the APM Agreement, the Project Manager has full authority save that, without the approval of the client, he cannot appoint or determine the appointment of a consultant or contractor; waive the client's rights; execute a document on behalf of the client; 'knowingly' do anything which would delay the project or (except in an emergency), 'knowingly' do anything which would increase the cost of the project in the cost plan (clause 5). Both of these clauses emphasise that you must, at all times, know the limits of your authority and act within them.

3   Both agreements place the Project Manager under a similar duty of care, that is, to use reasonable skill, care and diligence in the performance of his duties (clause 6.1 of the RICS Agreement and clause 2.1 of the APM Agreement). Clause 6.1 of the RICS Agreement then goes on to set out a number of options for limiting the Project Manager's liability for his own acts or omissions. These options include the insertion of a net contribution clause (see Chapter 3 on liability), a cap on the level of liability, and a time limit on when claims can be brought. The APM Agreement includes an optional clause (clause 6.4) providing for a cap to be placed on the Project Manager's liability (to be specified in the Schedule of Particulars) and an express provision that the client indemnifies the Project Manager for any liability in excess of this sum.

4   The Project Manager's liability is expressly limited to his own acts or omissions in the RICS Agreement, that is, he cannot be held liable for the acts or omissions

of any other persons involved in the project (clause 6.2). There is no similar provision in the APM Agreement. This is something you should consider when selecting which contract to use.

5   Clause 6 of the APM Agreement covers professional indemnity insurance/liability. It provides for PI cover to be maintained to the limit and for the period specified in the Schedule of Particulars. The availability and cost of insurance cover is no longer a straightforward matter (see Chapter 8 on insurance).

   The RICS Agreement (clause 17) allows for some flexibility in that it only requires PI insurance to be effected and maintained 'so long as it remains available at reasonable rates in the market'. However, it raises the question as to what the Project Manager should do if it is no longer available at reasonable rates in the market. Any Project Manager would be foolhardy to proceed with no PI cover at all.

   Clause 6.2 of the APM Agreement is slightly more helpful when it states that: 'The Project Manager shall inform the Client if the Project Manager believes that insurance could not be maintained at the level required ... in order that the Client and the Project Manager can discuss means of best protecting their respective interests in such circumstances.'

6   The RICS Agreement requires the Project Manager to execute a collateral warranty, upon written request of the client, in favour of each and any third party who takes an interest in the project. The warranty should be in the form published by the British Property Federation (see Chapter 3). There is no such requirement in the APM Agreement.

7   Under the APM Agreement, the client is required to take out and maintain appropriate insurances in respect of the project in the joint names (amongst others) of the Client and the Project Manager (clause 8.1). There is no similar obligation on the client in the RICS Agreement. See Chapter 8 on insurance.

8   The provisions as to payment under the RICS and the APM Agreement are very similar. Both provide for payment of an agreed fee and payment is made upon application by the Project Manager. The RICS includes an agreed Schedule of Payments as Appendix C and the APM Agreement includes a Fee Schedule at Part 4. Both agreements are compliant with the Construction Act 1996 (see Chapter 6 for more details), although the payment periods are not the same. There is also provision for payment by the client of additional fees for additional services and reimbursable expenses. Both agreements provide for interest to be paid on late payments at a rate to be specified. The payment provisions of both agreements are dependent on the accurate completion of the blank spaces and the appendices.

9   Both agreements contain comparable clauses as to copyright.

10 The APM Agreement allows for the sub-contracting of services only with the approval of the client, which shall not be unreasonably withheld or delayed (clause 11.1). There is also a restriction on either the client or Project Manager assigning or otherwise transferring their rights or obligations under the APM Agreement without the prior approval of the other (clause 11.2). There are no such restrictions within the RICS Agreement.

11 While, for most construction contracts, the right to adjudication is a statutory right in any event, the APM Agreement and the RICS Agreement contain clauses obliging the parties to refer any dispute or difference that cannot be resolved amicably between the parties to adjudication in the first instance (clause 14 of the APM Agreement and clause 14 of the RICS Agreement).

Under the APM Agreement, the adjudication procedure is that under the Construction Act. Under the RICS Agreement, the adjudication shall be conducted in accordance with the Construction Industry Council Model Adjudication Procedures current at the time the notice of dispute is given.

The APM Agreement has provision for the naming of an adjudicator within the Schedule of Particulars. The RICS Agreement also allows for the identity of the adjudicator to be agreed between the parties within two days of the notice being given. Failing agreement, the RICS Agreement is inconsistent on which appointing body should be used. Clause 15 of the Memorandum of Agreement states that the default appointing body is the RICS. However, clause 14.1 of the Conditions of Engagement states that the default appointing body is the Chartered Institute of Arbitrators. This inconsistency within the documents could potentially have a significant impact on the validity of an adjudication. The editors suggest that the best way to deal with such an inconsistency is by seeking to agree between the parties an adjudicator to be named in the contract. Alternatively, although the editors would discourage amending standard forms, it may be that one of the references to the default appointing body should be deleted prior to signature of the contract.

Both Agreements expressly prohibit either party from raising any right of set-off, counterclaim or abatement in connection with any enforcement proceedings. The APM Agreement also states that, in any enforcement proceedings, the court shall not be entitled to open up the adjudicator's decision for inspection or review other than to determine whether the decision has been reached in accordance with the adjudication procedure (see Chapter 10 for more details on adjudication proceedings).

12 If either party is unsatisfied with the adjudicator's decision, the APM Agreement provides that the dispute shall be heard through the English courts. The RICS Agreement provides that any dispute should be referred to arbitration in accordance with clause 15 of the Agreement. See Chapter 10 for a detailed discussion of the merits of each dispute resolution procedure.

The remainder of the APM Agreement is made up of:

- **Part 3 – Schedule of Particulars.** This part is for the insertion of specific information relating to the project. The introduction to the APM Agreement states that all of the Schedule of Particulars except sections D (Project Manager's personnel) and M (Project Manager's address) should be completed by the client before inviting offers from prospective Project Managers to undertake the services required. The project management companies tendering for the works will therefore be aware of the pertinent information relating to the project and the key clauses to be included in the agreement.

- **Part 4 – Fee Schedule.** The introduction to the APM Agreement suggests that the payment terms proposed by the client should be indicated when inviting offers from prospective Project Managers. These obviously may be open to negotiation.

- **Part 5 – Scope of Services.** For a construction project, by inserting the appropriate model and date of publication, the 'Basic Services' comprise all those services set out in the Model C Schedule of Services. There is provision within the Scope of Services to then exclude certain services and to add further services to form part of the 'Basic Services'. There is also space for the clarification of 'Additional Services'.

MODEL C SCHEDULE OF SERVICES

As discussed above, Model C relates to construction projects and sets out a suggested range of services which should be provided by the Project Manager. All of these services should be carried out unless excluded within the Scope of Services – and remember, it is possible to add to these services by including a further list within section 2 of the Scope of Services.

The services set out in the APM Model C Schedule of Services are broadly comparable to those suggested in the Guidance Note to the RICS Agreement. Some of the variances are due to the differences between the agreements as discussed above. For example, the APM Agreement specifically refers to the active involvement of the Project Manager from an early stage in the project and, accordingly, includes a section entitled 'Project Concept Stage'. The RICS Agreement Schedule of Services does not have such a preliminary stage but one could be added.

An interesting term within the APM Schedule of Services is the one at 7.9 which is to: 'Endeavour to engender a culture of confidence, trust, safe working and mutual respect between all members of the Project Team'. The spirit of this term is fundamental to the whole basis of project management – that is, team working. This does not come out elsewhere in the APM Agreement and is not mentioned anywhere in the RICS Agreement.

Another term to be aware of is the one at 11.3, which is to 'Assist the Client regarding the settlement of contractual disputes'. This obligation is notable, as it could potentially involve the Project Manager's involvement for many months, and possibly years, while a dispute is taken through the courts or arbitrated. It could be an onerous obligation without appropriate provision for further payment.

Another interesting service at 11.6, which is not included within the RICS Agreement, is the requirement to hold a 'Project completion review' before the project team is dispersed to effectively review the project's successes and failures and determine what lessons can be learnt. It is suggested that this sort of term, along with a term requiring a culture of confidence, trust and mutual respect, is current good practice and should be standard terms in all project management agreements.

Like the RICS Agreement, whilst the APM Agreement expressly takes into account the Construction Act, it was drafted prior to the implementation of the C(RTP)A and therefore does not take into account the effect of this Act (see Chapter 6 for more detail).

APM and RICS Agreements: key differences

- Involvement from early stage and more involvement with and therefore responsibility for the client's brief.

- No arbitration clause.

- Restriction on sub-contracting and assignment.

- No requirement for collateral warranties.

- Requirement to engender a culture of confidence, trust, safe working and mutual respect.

---

4 New engineering contract – the professional services contract

Introduction

The New Engineering Contract ('NEC') is a series of documents which are civil engineering based rather than construction based. The NEC suite of contracts is based on three fundamental characteristics:

- They aim to stimulate good management between the parties to the contract.
- They are flexible and can be used in a wide variety of commercial situations.

- They are drafted in clear and simple language which can be easily used and understood.

The NEC is arranged so that the key documents are:

- the core clauses;
- the optional clauses;
- the schedule of cost components;
- the contract data.

The responsibilities and the role of the engineer as Project Manager are set out in the NEC Professional Services Contract (PSC). This contract is in a form which can be used by the employer for the engagement of a Project Manager, or, indeed, for the engagement of a designer or supervisor, and can also be used jointly by the employer and the contractor for the engagement of an adjudicator.

As with the APM Agreement and to a lesser extent the RICS Agreement, the PSC envisages the involvement of the Project Manager from the feasibility stages of the project, and the Project Manager is involved in advising the client right from the outset. In the PSC, the Project Manager is the 'contract administrator'.

The Guidance Notes to the PSC state that the Project Manager is constrained from acting unreasonably in his role by statements in the contract governing *how* his decision should be made, but not *what* decision should be made. The PSC gives the Project Manager extensive authority to carry out his role and to take decisions. The Guidance Notes state that the Project Manager may 'change the work, alter or impose constraints on how the Contractor is to carry out the work, and generally apply his managerial and engineering judgment to the conduct and outcome of the work'.

As with the APM Contract, the PSC's general clauses include an obligation for the employer and consultant to act in a spirit of mutual trust and co-operation.

The PSC is updated by way of addenda and, accordingly, takes into account the Construction Act and the C(RTP)A.

NEC PSC – key points

- Contract drafted to be clear and simple to understand and use.
- Envisages involvement of Project Manager from an early stage.

> • Project Manager given extensive authority to carry out role and take decisions.
>
> • Obligation to act in a spirit of mutual trust and co-operation.

5 RIBA form of appointment for Project Managers (1999)

The RIBA Agreement is drafted for the architect as Project Manager. It is made up of:

• the Articles;

• the Conditions;

• the Appendix;

• the Schedules.

The Articles of Agreement are comparable to the Memorandum of Agreement in the RICS Agreement and the Form of Agreement in the APM Agreement.

The client appoints the Project Manager to perform the services as set out in Schedule 2 to the agreement and undertakes to pay the Project Manager the fees and disbursements specified in Schedule 3. The client also agrees to appoint the consultants, and others, listed in Schedule 4. Guidance on how to complete the RIBA Agreement, and in particular the Schedules, is set out in the accompanying notes.

Schedule 2 states that the Project Manager shall:

1   Perform the Services necessary for completion of the Work Stages indicated below
    and in accordance with the Services Supplement.*
2   Make visits to the Works in accordance with clause 2.8.
3   Perform any other Services identified below.

* Delete as appropriate.

The Project Manager can therefore undertake responsibility for all or some of the Work Stages as identified within Schedule 2.

The Work Stages are the standard stages used by the RIBA in their standard form contracts, covering feasibility, pre-construction and construction stages. They are defined in the definitions section of the conditions. Performance of the services is in accordance with the Services Supplement which set out a list of standard services, which can then be supplemented by 'other management services' that do not form

125

part of the normal services of the Project Manager but may be used if the Project Manager is also acting as design leader, lead consultant or contract administrator/employer's agent.

The standard list of services includes:

- receiving the client's requirements;

- implementation of any feasibility studies;

- development and maintenance of a project management strategy;

- advising on the selection and appointment of professional skills;

- development and maintenance of a management structure and communications environment;

- management of development of the strategic brief and its development as the project brief.

The key clauses are similar to those contained within the RICS and APM Agreements, that is:

- development, implementation and maintenance of project procedures;

- preparation and maintenance of a master programme and co-ordination with any programmes prepared by consultants or contractors;

- preparation and maintenance of a master cost plan;

- co-ordination with any cost estimates and cashflow projections;

- monitoring, regulating and reporting to the client on performance and activity, cost planning and control, and programme and progress.

Schedule 2 then goes on to specify that the Project Manager shall make visits to the Works in accordance with clause 2.8 of the conditions, which requires the Project Manager to make such visits to the Works 'as the Project Manager at the date of the appointment reasonably expected to be necessary'. There is also scope for specifying any other services the Project Manager shall be required to undertake at the end of Schedule 2.

The Conditions of Engagement can be compared to the General Conditions of the RICS Agreement and the General Terms of the APM Agreement as follows:

1   As with the RICS and the APM Agreements, the RIBA Agreement requires the Project Manager to exercise reasonable skill and care in conforming to the normal standards of the Project Manager's profession (clause 2.1). The Project Manager's authority is governed by clauses 2.2–2.3 where the Project Manager shall obtain and confirm in writing the authority of the client before proceeding with the services or initiating a work stage.

2   The Project Manager is expressly required by clause 2.4 to advise the client on the appointment of consultants or to provide specialist advice if required. As we have previously discussed in relation to the RICS Agreement and the case of *Pratt v George Hill Associates*[14], you should beware of making recommendations without ensuring that you are acting with reasonable skill and care. However, this obligation within the RIBA Agreement is limited by clause 7 in relation to liability, which states that the Project Manager does not warrant the performance, work or products of others or the solvency of any other body appointed by the client, *whether or not such appointment was made on the advice of the Project Manager*. The Project Manager's liability is expressly limited to his own acts or omissions in the RICS Agreement; but it seems to the editors that the RIBA clause goes further to clarify that the Project Manager is expressly not responsible for the acts/omissions of a third party, even where the appointment of the other party was made on the advice of the Project Manager. The RIBA clause 7 seeks to provide a contractual defence to the situation which arose in the *Pratt v George Hill* case.

The second part of clause 2.4 requires the Project Manager to provide specialist advice if required in connection with the project. See our earlier discussions on what is meant by 'advise' and the cases of *Pozzolanic Lytag Ltd v Bryan Robson Associates*[15] and *St Albans City and District Council v International Computers Ltd*[16]. If you are required to give advice on an area outside of your knowledge, make sure you either take specialist advice yourself or advise your client to do so.

3   It is the editors' view that the RIBA Agreement is drafted in the Project Manager's favour. For instance, clause 7 (which relates to liabilities and insurance) goes slightly further than the limitation of liability clauses in the RICS or APM Agreements. It limits the warranties given by the Project Manager, provides for a limit to be set on the extent of liability of the Project Manager (to a sum as expressed in the appendix), and has the option of a net contribution clause.

4   As with the APM Agreement, the Project Manager or client cannot assign the whole or any part of the agreement without the consent of the other in writing, and the Project Manager shall not appoint any sub-consultants without the consent of the client (which shall not be unreasonably withheld) (clause 4).

5   The payment provisions of the RIBA Agreement are compliant with the Construction Act. The methods of calculation of the fees are set out in Schedule 3 and can be either a percentage of the project cost, a lump sum, on a time charge basis, or worked out by any other agreed method. The specific clauses for working out the fees payable are set out in clause 5. There is also a provision for the payment of additional fees for additional services if the Project Manager is involved in extra

---

14   (1987) 38 BLR 25, CA.
15   [1999] BLR 267.
16   [1996] 4 All ER 481.

work 'for reasons beyond his control'. These will be calculated on a time basis unless otherwise agreed.

A key payment provision which is drafted in the Project Manager's favour is clause 5.11. This states that the Client may not withhold payment of any part of an account for a sum or sums due 'unless the amount to be withheld has been agreed by the Project Manager as due to the Client, or has been awarded in adjudication, arbitration or litigation in favour of the Client'. The Client's rights of set-off at common law or in equity which they would otherwise be entitled to exercise are expressly excluded. This contractual provision is a strong one in favour of the Project Manager and will mean that, in the event of a dispute, the Project Manager should be paid the disputed sum. It will be up to the client to obtain an award in adjudication, arbitration or litigation in order to recover such money. The Project Manager is also expressly entitled to interest on late payments at a rate of 8% over Bank of England base rate pursuant to clause 5.13.

6   The RIBA Agreement contains comparable clauses as to copyright with the RICS and APM Agreements.

7   The RIBA Agreement obliges the Project Manager to maintain professional indemnity insurance in the amount stated in the Appendix for any one occurrence or series of occurrences arising out of any one event. As with the RICS Agreement, such insurance is required provided it is available at commercially reasonable rates and generally available in the insurance market to the Project Manager. The RIBA Agreement also goes further, in line with the APM Agreement, in that the Project Manager shall inform the client if such insurance ceases to be available at commercially reasonable rates, so that the Project Manager and client can discuss the best means of protecting their respective positions in the absence of such insurance.

8   As with the RICS Agreement, the RIBA Agreement requires the Project Manager to enter into an agreement with a third party or third parties (i e a collateral warranty) on request (clause 7.5).

9   Unlike both the RICS and APM Agreements, the RIBA Agreement gives the parties the choice as to whether any dispute should be referred to arbitration or legal proceedings (without prejudice to any right to adjudication) (Article 5). Clause 9 provides that, in the event of a dispute, the parties *may* attempt to settle by negotiation or in accordance with the RIBA Conciliation Procedure. If unsuccessful, parties are then free (but not obliged) to refer the dispute to adjudication.

As in the RICS Agreement, the adjudication procedure is to be governed by the Construction Industry Council Model Adjudication Procedures current at the date of the reference, and the adjudicator can be named in the Appendix or be appointed by a nominating body. Interestingly, clause 9.2 states that clause 28 of the Model Adjudication Procedures (which states that parties shall bear their own costs in an adjudication) shall be deleted and replaced with:

> The Adjudicator may in his discretion direct the payment of legal costs and expenses of one party by another as part of his decision. The Adjudicator may determine the amount of costs to be paid or may delegate the task to an independent costs draftsman.

10 This provision avoids the usual position on the costs of an adjudication and expressly gives the adjudicator the power to order either party their costs of the adjudication.

Whether a dispute subsequently goes to arbitration or to the courts depends on how the parties complete Article 5. If it is to be referred to arbitration, it is accordance with clause 9.5 of the RIBA Agreement. Clause 9.6 states that the client shall indemnify the Project Manager in respect of any legal and other costs in any action or proceedings, together with a reasonable sum in respect of his time spent, if the Project Manager obtains a court judgment/arbitrator's award in his favour for the recovery of fees and/or expenses under the agreement, or the client fails to obtain a court judgment/arbitrator's award in its favour in respect of any claim against the Project Manager.

The Appendix to the Conditions provides the basis for completion of information to supplement the Conditions, such as the limit of liability, the amount of professional indemnity insurance and the name of the adjudicator or arbitrator.

The RIBA Agreement is compliant with the Construction Act and drafted to take into account the C(RTP)A. It specifically excludes the application of the C(RTP)A.

RIBA Agreement – key issues

- Choice of court/arbitration.

- Project Manager expressly does not warrant performance, work, products or solvency of others.

- Restriction on sub-letting and assignment.

- Requirement for collateral warranties upon request.

---

6 Additional terms for consideration when completing an appointment document

Having reviewed these four standard terms of appointment for a Project Manager, it is apparent that there are a number of areas which form current good practice but do not come out in the standard forms. These are areas which should be considered and, where appropriate, inserted into any standard terms or bespoke agreement you enter into.

(a) Management of risk

It is usual and advisable for Project Managers to implement a risk management regime to manage the risk in the project on behalf of the client. This could be resourced in a number of ways, including commissioning a specialist risk management expert. While aspects of this may fall under some of the general services, it is a significant enough area to be addressed in isolation. Risk management could be added as an additional service at present, although the editors suspect it will one day be added to the core services. Monitoring of project risk should form part of your monthly report to the client.

(b) Business case preparation

This can be especially important if acting for tenants or corporate owner/occupier clients. The client's business case will underpin and justify the whole project and dictate priorities in relation to life-cycle cost, financial objectives, function and programmes etc.

(c) Value engineering

The Project Manager should, where appropriate, initiate value engineering exercises from an early stage, in conjunction with the project team. Few of the agreements reviewed above deal adequately with the Project Manager's role and duties in connection with value engineering and value management. Specific duties should be written into agreements until standard clauses are available from the relevant Institutions.

(d) Electronic information management systems

Nearly all projects utilise some sort of electronic information management system. This can vary between the uncontrolled use of email through to the use of sophisticated web-based information management systems such as ProjectNet. Which system is to be used and the management of their use, particularly on big projects, is an area which should be controlled by the Project Manager and addressed within the project management appointment document.

7 How to approach writing a contract or reviewing a contract document

You should ensure that all fee quotations are sent out with a set of your terms and conditions attached. This is the best way of ensuring that you contract on *your* terms and conditions rather than the client's. If you are contracting on the client's terms and conditions and are presented with one of the standard forms mentioned above, the document may be familiar to you and you should be able to identify clauses you are not happy with. However, if you are presented with a bespoke contract you need to read through the terms and conditions carefully to ensure that it accurately reflects the agreement you have reached with your client and the level of experience you and your team have.

Most bespoke documents will have a section similar to the Memorandum of Agreement in the RICS Agreement. You should ensure that all items are correctly completed and that it reflects what you have agreed and does not invalidate your professional indemnity insurance in any way. What is likely to be more difficult is the list of services you are expected to provide. At the beginning of this chapter we stressed the importance of looking closely at the wording used – e g 'supervising' has much more onerous responsibilities and therefore potential liabilities than simply 'monitoring'. Remember that if you are meant to be 'co-ordinating' the work of others, you should not take on the actual responsibility of doing that work, because the liability will rest with you if things go wrong. The CIOB Code of Practice mentioned at the beginning of this chapter, while a self-confessed 'client-orientated document', is 'the only authoritative code for project management'. The Code sets out the Project Manager's duties at each stage of the contract. This, together with the RICS Guidance Note, forms very useful checklists for considering what services should be included in a bespoke contract. You should give careful thought to the wording of each service you are to provide, and if you are in any doubt over the meaning of the contract, you should always seek clarification and/or advice prior to signature.

8 Employing sub-consultants

From time to time Project Managers employ sub-consultants to assist them with their tasks. Before sub-contracting work out, the Project Manager should ensure that his agreement with his client does not contain any prohibition against appointing a sub-consultant. If it does, it will be necessary to obtain the client's consent prior to entering into any agreement. Below are some key points when acting as or employing a sub-consultant:

- Ensure the terms and conditions upon which you contract with the sub-consultant are back-to-back with the terms under which you are employed.

- Insurance: the sub-consultant should maintain sufficient professional indemnity insurance cover to meet his responsibilities under the agreement. If possible this insurance should be at least equal to the level of cover the Project Manager is required to maintain under the project management appointment. When employing a sub-consultant, the Project Manager should request evidence of such cover in the form of either a broker's letter or copies of the insurance certificate. It is also important to ensure that the insurance cover remains in place for the entire period that the Project Manager is liable to the client, and not just the duration of the sub-consultancy agreement. Insurance is dealt with in more detail in Chapter 8.

- Chapter 3 discusses collateral warranties. It is important to check any collateral warranties to ensure that any responsibilities the Project Manager has under those collateral warranties are mirrored in his agreement with the sub-consultant. Usually where there are collateral warranties there will be an obligation on the Project Manager to execute a deed of warranty on behalf of the sub-consultant if the sub-consultant fails to execute a warranty itself when requested to do so within a specified time limit.

- Both the Project Manager and the sub-consultant need to consider the question of copyright. Usually the copyrighted materials produced by the sub-consultant will remain vested in the sub-consultant. However, that sub-consultant will be obliged to provide an irrevocable non-exclusive royalty-free licence to use or reproduce such materials.

- If you are undertaking a sub-consultancy and you are part of a partnership, each partner will individually and jointly be responsible for the activities of the partnership, and sub-consultants should bear that in mind when entering into a sub-consultancy agreement.

At the time of going to print, the RICS is shortly to produce a sub-consultancy agreement for project management services to be used in conjunction the RICS Agreement.

The standard forms referred to above can be obtained from the following sources:

RICS Agreement: RICS Books, Surveyor Court, Westwood Business Park, Coventry CV4 8JE (www.ricsbooks.com).

APM Agreement: The APM Group Ltd, 85 Oxford Road, High Wycombe, Bucks HP11 2DX (www.apm.org.uk).

NEC PSC: NEC Users Group, Thomas Telford Ltd, 1 Heron Quay, London E14 4JD (www.newengineeringcontract.com).

RIBA Agreement: RIBA, 66 Portland Place, London W1B 1AD (www.riba.org).

CIOB Code of Practice: Englemere, Kings Ride, Ascot, Berkshire SL5 7TB (www.ciob.org.uk).

CHAPTER 5

Duties and obligations of the Project Manager arising under the terms of the construction contract

By Adrian Smith

Summary

This chapter follows on from Chapter 4. A Project Manager's obligations may arise not just under his appointment contract but also under the main building contract.

The chapter covers:

- Introduction to the most usual standard forms of construction contracts with which a Project Manager will be involved.

- Review of those contracts which make no specific provision for a Project Manager but impose obligations often undertaken by a Project Manager:
  - JCT family of contracts
  - ICE Standard Form of Contract for Civil Engineering Works.

- Review of those forms of contract which specifically refer to Project Managers, with a detailed analysis of the Project Manager's role under:
  - GC/Works Suite
  - New Engineering Contract Engineering and Construction Contract Suite
  - Institution of Chemical Engineers Model Forms of Contract: for Lump Sum Contracts (the 'Red Book') and for Reimbursable Contracts (the 'Green Book').

- Review of those forms of contract which incorporate an individual carrying out some typical project management functions but using an alternative designation. In this section the following are reviewed:
  - JCT Standard Form of Building Contract with Contractor's Design 1998 edition
  - ACE Standard Form of Contract for Project Partnering (PPC 2000)
  - FIDIC Conditions of Contract for EPC/Turnkey Projects (the 'Silver Book')
  - FIDIC Short Form of Contract (the 'Green Book').

- Some key pointers on reviewing standard forms of contract and bespoke contracts to ensure that the Project Manager is aware of his obligations under the main construction contract and that those obligations are covered in the Project Manager's appointment document.

I Introduction

This chapter addresses the Project Manager's possible obligations, duties and responsibilities which might arise directly from the use of standard form contracts for construction work. The majority of this chapter is therefore concerned with obligations arising out of standard forms of contract, but significant additional problems may arise either where the standard forms are amended in an attempt to provide the Project Manager with some degree of contractual legitimacy, or where bespoke contracts are used. The chapter therefore concludes with some general remarks regarding these options.

2 Standard forms of construction contract

Many of the standard forms of contract most commonly used in the United Kingdom do not specifically mention the Project Manager. However, some forms do allocate specific duties and responsibilities to the Project Manager, while others allocate duties and responsibilities to individuals carrying out some or all of the functions normally carried out by the Project Manager, but using a different terminology.

Arguably the most popular standard forms used for building in the United Kingdom are those published by the Joint Contracts Tribunal (JCT). Most of the forms in the JCT family assume that the Employer's principal representative will be either 'the Architect' or, in cases where the representative is not entitled to use the term 'Architect'[1], 'the Contract Administrator'. It is perfectly possible for the Project Manager to be named as the Contract Administrator, indeed in many cases it may be impossible for the Project Manager to carry out the duties specified in his contract of appointment if this is not the case. The JCT Standard Form of Building Contract (JCT 98), the Intermediate Form of Contract (IFC 98), and the Standard Form of Management Contract (MC 98) all fall into this category. The JCT Standard Form of Contract with Contractor's Design (CD 98) uses a rather different approach and incorporates an Employer's Agent.

A general review of the duties and obligations of the Contract Administrator under the JCT forms is given later.

---

1   Architects Act 1997.

Similarly, in civil engineering many of the standard forms in common use, including those published by the Institution of Civil Engineers (ICE) and some of those published by the Fédération Internationale des Ingénieurs-Conseils (FIDIC), assume that the employer's principal representative will be the Engineer.

There are, however, a number of standard form contracts which do specifically require the Project Manager to be named in the contract documentation, require him to undertake contractual duties, and impose upon him particular contractual obligations. The following standard forms of contract are selected as some of the most popular examples of contracts of this form.

- The GC/Works suite published by the UK government through the Stationery Office and widely used for public sector work.

- The Institution of Civil Engineers' New Engineering Contract Engineering and Construction Contract (NEC ECC) suite published by Thomas Telford.

- The Institution of Chemical Engineers' Forms of Contract for Lump Sum Contracts (the Red Book), and for Reimbursable Contracts (the Green Book).

Each of these forms is supported by a set of terms and conditions for the appointment of the Project Manager, the use of which should ensure that the Project Manager's roles and responsibilities are consistent with the requirements of that particular standard form of contract. The Project Manager's duties and obligations under each of these forms are reviewed in some detail in the following sections.

In addition, there are other standard forms which allocate contractual duties and responsibilities to an individual fulfilling some typical project management functions, although not under that specific title. The principal examples considered here are:

- The JCT Standard Form of Building Contract with Contractor's Design 1998 edition (JCT CD 98), which refers to the 'Employer's Agent'.

- The Association of Consultant Architects' Standard Form of Contract for Project Partnering (PPC 2000), published by Trowers and Hamlin, which refers to the 'Client Representative'.

- The FIDIC Conditions of Contract for EPC/Turnkey Projects (the Silver Book) first published in 1999, which permits the Employer to appoint an 'Employer's Representative'.

- The FIDIC Short Form of Contract (the Green Book) first published in 1999, which:
  - requires the Employer to appoint an 'Authorised Person' to act for him under the contract;
  - permits the Employer also to appoint a firm or individual (the 'Employer's Representative') to carry out particular and specific duties.

Failure by the Employer's Representative correctly to fulfil the duties and obligations set out in the construction contract may have extremely serious consequences, and may be potentially damaging to the client's position in the event of a dispute. Such a failure by the Project Manager would expose him to the risk of the Employer's taking action for breach of the Project Manager's terms and conditions of appointment. It could also potentially give rise to obligations to others, which might in turn lead to actions for negligent misstatement by other parties affected by the Project Manager's failure to carry out his duties properly.

Project Managers should also note that, if they are appointed to act as Project Manager under one of the standard form contracts in which the Project Manager is expressly mentioned (or indeed where the Project Manager represents the Employer in some other capacity, for example as Contract Administrator, Employer's Agent or Client Representative), then the Contractor will have legitimate reason to believe that they will have the authority to act in the way required by the contract, unless they are specifically informed to the contrary by the Employer. It is therefore most important that the Project Manager's conditions of engagement provide him with the necessary authority and autonomy to carry out his contractual obligations, bearing in mind that the employer will be bound by his actions.

Note also that, wherever the Project Manager acts in this way, he may well also be responsible for explaining the terms of the contract to the Employer (*William Tompkinson and Sons Ltd v Parochial Church Council of St Michael in the Hamlet*[2]).

CASE LAW

Responsibility of the Contract Administrator

William Tomkinson and Sons Ltd v Parochial Church Council of St Michael in the Hamlet[3]

The case concerned a project for alterations to a church carried out under the JCT Minor Works form. Insurance of the building was required to be carried by the Employer.

The Architect failed to inform the Employer that this was the case. The Contractor failed to waterproof a hole in the roof adequately, and rain caused damage far in excess of the contract value. There was no insurance protection.

The Architect was held liable in negligence for the Employer's losses.

(See also *Pozzolanic Lytag Ltd v Bryan Hobson Associates*, Chapter 9[4]).

---

2 (1990) 6 Const LJ 814.
3 (1990) 6 Const LJ 814.
4 [1999] BLR 267.

The principal duties and obligations undertaken by the Project Manager/Employer's Agent/Employer's Representative under each of the above standard forms of contract are summarised below.

3 Forms of contract which make no specific provision for a project manager

The major British standard forms in common use which fall into this category are:

- for building: the majority of the JCT family of contracts;
- for civil engineering: the ICE Standard Form of Contract for Civil Engineering Works.

In the international arena the most popular standard forms falling into this category are probably:

- the FIDIC Conditions of Contract for Construction (the Red Book);
- the Conditions of Contract for Plant and Design-Build (the Yellow Book).

Note that while the FIDIC forms were originally developed from the ICE Standard Form of Contract for Civil Engineering Works, they are now increasingly used in the international arena, in a wide range of translations, for both building and civil engineering work. FIDIC regards the English language edition of the contract to be the definitive version, but this may of course be overruled by foreign jurisdictions and by the specific documentation used for particular projects.

(a) ICE Standard Form of Contract for Civil Engineering Work and FIDIC Conditions of Contract for Construction (the Red Book)

These forms both assume that the design of the works will be carried out by the Employer's Engineer using a traditional procurement methodology, and the Contractor's primary obligation is therefore to construct the works as designed under the Engineer's supervision. The client's main representative in respect of the construction contract is the Engineer, who also acts as the Contract Administrator. The role of the Engineer under these contracts is very traditional, and it is not intended here to review his duties and obligations in detail.

The role does, however, include all of the traditional contract administration functions including:

- providing all the necessary information for the construction of the works;
- issuing instructions as required by the contract;
- valuation of variations;

- dealing with extensions of time and claims for additional loss and expense;
- ensuring that the work is carried out in accordance with the contract, identifying defects and ensuring that they are rectified;
- dealing with interim payments due to the Contractor;
- certifying completion of the works;
- agreeing the final cost of the works with the Contractor.

As noted above, the Contractor will have reasonable grounds for assuming that the Contract Administrator has the necessary authority to act as agent for the Employer in so far as it is necessary for the proper execution of the contract.

As regards the FIDIC contracts, these were initially developed from the ICE Standard Form of Contract for Civil Engineering Work, and therefore adopt the principles set out above. They probably now constitute the most popular standard forms in use in the international arena for both building and civil engineering work, and for the construction of process plant installations such as petro-chemical plants.

The FIDIC contracts may, however, impose significant additional responsibilities on the Project Manager, particularly in terms of language. All the major contracts in the FIDIC suite are now available in a wide variety of languages, and as a general rule FIDIC regards the English language version to be the definitive version. This may, however, be amended by foreign jurisdictions and by the Particular Conditions of Contract for specific schemes. Clause 1.4 of the contract establishes that it will be governed by the law of the country or jurisdiction stated in the Particular Conditions, and that:

> ... if there are versions of any part of the Contract which are written in more than one language, the version which is in the ruling language stated in the Particular Conditions shall prevail.

There is also provision for a separate 'language of communications' to be stated in the Particular Conditions (clause 1.4), and this need not necessarily be the same as the language of the contract itself. Where no language of communication is specified, then it is assumed to be the language in which the contract (or, if it is written in multiple languages, most of it) is written.

The appointment of a separate Project Manager for projects using these forms is therefore problematic unless:

1   the Project Manager also holds a concurrent appointment as Engineer, either under the terms of his consultancy agreement or as a separate parallel appointment. Note that since the Engineer is responsible for designing the works and for quality control during construction, if this alternative is used then the

Project Manager must be either appropriately qualified to undertake this work or given the authority to delegate parts of the work to a properly qualified Engineer under an appropriate sub-consultancy agreement. Note also that the power to sublet elements of the work must be carefully agreed with the Employer. Failure to do so, and to agree an appropriate division of responsibility and accountability, may lead to the Project Manager's being held wholly responsible to the Employer for the work carried out by his sub-consultants. This issue is dealt with in some detail in Chapter 2;

2   the Project Manager's terms and conditions of appointment are so worded as to place him in a purely strategic role as the Employer's agent, perhaps with responsibility for selection of the procurement approach and the appointment of the Engineer, but with no direct responsibility or involvement in the administration of the construction contract itself.

This second alternative has been successfully used by a number of large, usually multi-headed organisations for both building and civil engineering works. Here the management of the various interested parties within the client's organisation (sometimes called management of the demand chain) is separated from the management of the construction work itself (sometimes called management of the supply chain). In these cases the Employer's principal representative (the manager of the demand chain) is typically called the 'Project Sponsor' or 'Project Director', and also has overall responsibility for delivery of the whole project. The title of Project Manager is typically given to the supply chain manager, who is generally responsible to the Project Sponsor/Director for management of the construction process. The relationship is shown diagrammatically in Figure 1.

Note that if this approach is used, then the relationship between the Project Sponsor/Director and the construction Project Manager must be both properly documented and appropriately reinforced.

Figure 1 – Separation of demand chain and supply chain management

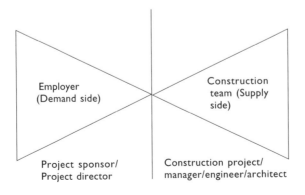

JCT family of contracts (excluding Standard Form of Building Contract with Contractor's Design)

The major forms in this group in which Project Managers are likely to be involved are:

- Standard Form of Building Contract (JCT 98).

- Standard Form of Management Contract (JCTMC 98).

- Standard Form of Prime Cost Contract (JCTPC 98).

- Intermediate Form of Building Contract for Works of Simple Content (JCTIFC 98).

All these forms adopt a common approach to contract administration, and they may therefore be dealt with together. All provide for the contract administration to be carried out either by an Architect or by a Contract Administrator. The alternative designation was initially included to provide for forms to be used by the public sector where the work might be supervised by an official who was not entitled to use the title 'Architect' under, and in accordance with, the Architects Act 1997. It is, however, now also used for the same purpose within the private sector where the Contract Administrator is either the Project Manager or an employee of the Employer's organisation. Note that separate public sector and private sector editions of the Standard Form of Building Contract (JCT 98) are still published. The private edition of the form provides only for the term 'Architect', whereas the Public Sector Edition uses the term 'Contract Administrator'. All the other forms are published in a single combined edition, and alternative clauses permitting the use of the term 'Architect' or 'Contract Administrator' are given in the Articles of Agreement.

It should, however, be particularly noted that all these forms assume that the design of the works will be carried out by the Employer or his agent, and the basic assumption is therefore that the Employer (through his agent, the Architect) is therefore responsible for the technical and functional adequacy of the design. It is also part of the Architect/Contract Administrator's function to ensure that the works are properly constructed in accordance with the contract requirements. It is therefore plainly necessary, as in the case of the civil engineering forms discussed above, for the Employer to employ a competent designer, and it is largely for this reason that the Architect is named in the contract. If the individual named in the contract as Contract Administrator is not competent to carry out these functions, then appropriate arrangements must be made outside the construction contract for the necessary skills to be provided. This could be accomplished through a separate consultancy appointment for an architect to act as client adviser, but in cases where a Project Manager is employed it would probably be preferable for the architectural consultancy to take the form of a sub-consultancy agreement with the Project Manager.

As with the civil engineering forms previously discussed, it is not intended here to review in detail the duties of the Contract Administrator under these forms. Note, however, that although the specific responsibilities do differ in detail from one form to another, they all none the less include the usual contract administration functions, including:

- providing the necessary information for the construction of the works;

- issuing instructions as required by the contract;

- dealing with extensions of time and claims for additional loss and expense;

- ensuring that the work carried out is in accordance with the contract;

- dealing with interim payments due to the Contractor, possibly in conjunction with the Quantity Surveyor;

- certifying practical completion of the works;

- certifying non-completion of the works where the Contractor fails to complete within the contract period;

- in conjunction with the Quantity Surveyor, agreeing the final cost of the works with the Contractor and issuing the final certificate.

As noted above, the Contractor will have reasonable grounds for assuming that the Contract Administrator has the necessary authority to act as agent for the Employer in so far as it is necessary for the proper execution of the contract. The Contract Administrator may also be held responsible for ensuring that the Employer fully understands the terms of his contract and the duties and obligations imposed upon him.

The appointment of a separate Project Manager for projects using these forms can therefore be accomplished in a number of different ways:

(i) the Project Manager, if appropriately qualified to do so, holds a concurrent appointment as Architect; or

(ii) the Project Manager is named in the contract as the Contract Administrator, with assistance from a qualified architect either directly employed by the Employer or employed by the Project Manager under some form of sub-consultancy agreement; or

(iii) the Project Manager's terms and conditions of appointment are so worded as to place him in a purely strategic role as the Employer's agent, perhaps with responsibility for selection of the procurement approach and the appropriate consultants (Architect, Quantity Surveyor etc), but with no direct responsibility or involvement in the administration of the actual construction contract. In this case it will probably be necessary to split the management of the demand chain and the supply chain as previously described and shown in Figure 1 above.

As set out earlier, whether or not the Project Manager is also the Contract Administrator, it is important to ensure that the duties set out in the Project Manager's terms and conditions of appointment are consistent with those of the Contract Administrator under the construction contract.

Particular difficulties may arise in this respect under contracts where the main Contractor undertakes part of what might otherwise be considered to be the Project Manager's responsibilities. Under the JCT Standard Form of Management Contract, for example, the services required of the Management Contractor include, inter alia, things like:

- preparing the contract programme;

- preparing material and component flows;

- advising on the layout of site facilities and services;

- advising the professional team (defined as the Architect/Contract Administrator, the Quantity Surveyor, and any others included in Article 5 of the Conditions of Agreement) on the division of the contract into work packages;

- preparing lists of potential works contractors, investigating as appropriate and making recommendations to the professional team;

- instituting a system of documentation and records for recording the performance of the works contractors;

- enforcing the terms of the works contracts through adjudication, arbitration or legal proceedings as necessary.

All these activities include aspects which appear to conflict with and/or duplicate activities that might normally be considered to be well within the role of the Project Manager and are listed as typical project management services in the Chartered Institute of Building's Typical Terms of Engagement for Project Managers.

4 Forms of contract which specifically refer to the Project Manager

(a) The GC/Works suite

The GC/Works suite of contracts is widely used by the UK government for a large part of its construction workload, and it is therefore one of the most widely used forms in the UK. The suite is used for both building and civil engineering projects, and there are separate versions to cover major and minor works, and building services contracts.

The current edition of this suite of contracts places the Project Manager firmly at the centre of the contractual process, and he is completely responsible for all contract administration duties. The contracts and the associated Conditions of Appointment also carefully document the relationship between the Project Manager and other consultants, and spell out clearly the limits of his authority and responsibility.

This form is treated here in some depth, in view of the popularity of the suite for government work, and in the light of the fact that this suite is such a good example of how the Project Manager's terms and conditions of appointment should be integrated with the contract conditions.

The following forms include specific contract administration duties to be carried out by the Project Manager:

- GC/Works/1 Contract for Building and Civil Engineering Major Works;

- GC/Works/2 Contract for Building and Civil Engineering Minor Works;

- GC/Works/3 Contract for mechanical and Electrical Engineering Works;

- GC/Works/4 Contract for Building, Civil Engineering, Mechanical and Electrical Small Works.

The duties and obligations required under each of the separate forms of contract are co-ordinated with the terms of the Project Manager's appointment through the fifth element of the suite, the General Conditions of Appointment for Consultants (GC/Works/5).

1 GENERAL CONDITIONS OF APPOINTMENT FOR CONSULTANTS (GC/WORKS/5)

The appointment of consultants, including Project Managers, under GC/Works contracts is governed by GC/Works/5 General Conditions for the Appointment of Consultants: Framework Agreement (1999) (the Conditions).

In addition, the Project Manager's role as manager and co-ordinator of the consultant team, and as overall financial controller of the project, is set out in clause 1.5 of the Conditions, which states that:

> ... the ... [Project Manager] ... shall act on behalf of the Employer in issuing instructions to [other] Consultants and for receiving reports, requests or statements or in dealing with any other matter concerning the [other] Consultant's Appointments. [The Project Manager] will assume responsibility for the day to day financial control of the project ...

The obligations are set out in more detail in clause 1.9A, which states that the Project Manager is required to:

... undertake the co-ordination and integration of the work of other consultants in all communications with the employer, and shall similarly be responsible for communicating to those consultants all instructions emanating from the Employer.

The Project Manager also carries additional responsibilities in respect of the design and programming of the works:

> The Project Manager ... shall in conjunction with the other appointed consultants prepare an achievable design and information programme which allows completion of the Project by the date agreed by the Employer. [The] Project Manager ... shall monitor the production information and shall report any deficiencies to the Employer and, at the same time, ... shall inform the Employer of the action it proposes to take to overcome such deficiency (Conditions clause 1.9A (2)).

On the other hand, the Project Manager does not enjoy full and unlimited powers of agency. Clause 1.28 of the Conditions limits the Project Manager's authority as follows:

> The [Project Manager] shall ensure that either in correspondence or by any other means [he] shall not commit the Employer to any cost or to any action while dealing with others on behalf of the Employer unless the Employer's written approval has been obtained.

Specific duties required for particular projects will be set out in the Order to Undertake Services, but the possible breadth of the range of services which may be required is illustrated in Tables 1 to 5, which are extracted from Annex 1 of the Conditions.

TABLE 1 — STAGE 1: PROJECT INCEPTION

- Receive an initial brief from the Employer and assist in identifying possible options and expenditure limits.

- Develop and submit to the Employer for approval a Project Procurement Strategy and, following approval by the Employer, carry out the Services and obligations necessary to achieve the satisfactory completion of the Project at or below the approved cost limit which Services and obligations shall include, but shall not be limited to, the Services and obligations set out in this Annex.

- Assist the Employer to select and procure the site and assess the implications of any constraints attaching to it and report thereon to the Employer.

- Make recommendations to the Employer on the need for any site investigations or tests to be undertaken including any tests to ascertain the presence of contaminated ground and implement any decision taken by the Employer.

- Make recommendations to the Employer on the need to appoint Consultants to the Project Team and on the scope of their Services. Subsequently assist the Employer in all matters leading to their appointment and prepare detailed briefs covering the scope of the Services for which they will be responsible.

- Establish contact with Consultants following their appointment and establish formal communication procedures and hierarchy of responsibility between them and introduce procedures to ensure that they work closely as a team.

- Following consultation with the Employer, arrange for any necessary surveys to be undertaken.

- Arrange for the Consultants to undertake preliminary feasibility studies based on the Employer's brief and, if these studies highlight the need to amend that brief, discuss with the Employer and obtain instructions.

- Co-ordinate the views of the Consultants in order to submit a detailed report to the Employer on the recommended scope of the Works together with a recommended programme and anticipated costs, the report to include reviewing alternative design and construction solutions together with estimates of cost of those options and provide assistance to the Employer in selecting the preferred option and in formulating the brief.

- Confirm the final brief with the Employer which shall include a detailed programme for completion of the Project and an agreed cost limit.

- Communicate the details of the agreed brief to all Consultants and ensure that the Consultants confirm in writing their commitment to that brief. If this highlights the possibility of difficulty in implementing the brief, take the necessary action to resolve such difficulties and, if this proves to be impossible, report to the Employer making recommendations.

- Where there is duplication between the Services provided under the terms of this Appointment and the Services of another consultant commissioned in connection with this Project, resolve the duplicated Services by agreement with the Consultant concerned, confirm the matters agreed in writing and copy to the Employer.

- Assess the need to take action to protect the interests of the Employer in respect of neighbouring properties and accordingly make recommendations to the Employer
- Undertake risk assessments
- Undertake value management exercises.
- Obtain the Employer's approval to proceed to Stage 2.

TABLE 2 — STAGE 2: SCHEME DESIGN AND TENDER DOCUMENTATION

- Ensure that a cost plan is prepared for the project based on the approved cost limit and ensure that copies of the cost plan are given to all Consultants and that they confirm their agreement to the content applying to their own discipline.
- In co-operation with the other members of the Project Team prepare a detailed programme for the production of design information leading up to obtaining tenders for the Works and obtain the Consultants commitment to that programme in writing.
- Establish rigorous cost control procedures and ensure that designs are strictly monitored against the agreed cost plan and that any difficulties are rectified and the approved cost limit is maintained.
- Establish rigorous management procedures to monitor the production of design information produced by the members of the Project Team in order that any shortcomings are immediately highlighted and rectified and continue to implement the monitoring procedure until completion of the Project. Where difficulties are encountered which cannot be satisfactorily resolved, inform the Employer of those difficulties and make recommendations.
- Establish and chair regular meetings with the other members of the Project Team and others in order to monitor progress and to highlight any shortfall in design information and take any action necessary to correct any deficiencies. Circulate minutes of the meetings to the Employer and to the members of the Project Team. The minutes shall record the action taken to rectify any deficiencies and shall indicate who is to be responsible for taking that action.

- In conjunction with the other members of the Project Team, make recommendations to the Employer on the need for specialist contractors to design and execute any sections of the Works or for specialist suppliers to provide any materials or equipment and obtain the Employer's approval and take any action necessary to implement the Employer's decision.

- Co-ordinate the production of all design work, ensure that the designs are fully integrated and are tested throughout the design phase against cost targets and that the designs fully comply with all Statutory requirements or Regulations including, but not confined to, requirements concerning Health and Safety, Planning, Fire, Building Control etc, and take any action necessary to rectify deficiencies.

- At monthly intervals, submit a written report to the Employer showing the progress made against the agreed design programme and the present estimated cost of the Project relative to the approved cost limit and, if required by the Employer, arrange to meet the Employer in order to discuss the content of the report and to receive instructions.

- Agree materials and construction specifications with the Consultants and keep the Employer fully informed.

- Ensure that statutory approvals for the Project are obtained and that all utilities and other necessary services are in place both for the construction phase and for permanent operation following completion of the Project and, where action by the Employer is necessary, assist the Employer to take that action.

- Give the Employer sufficient notice of all approvals, decisions or other matters which require action by the Employer and, where appropriate, assist the Employer by providing information and by making recommendations.

- Where difficulties are highlighted during the design phase which may not be capable of being resolved and may result in a failure to meet the Employer's brief, submit a report to the Employer giving recommendations and options.

- Receive and certify all applications from the members of the Project Team for the payment of fees and pass to the Employer for payment.

- Ensure that all notices required under EC regulations are given at the proper time and that all procedures comply with EC legislation.

- Ensure that life cycle costings and environmental assessment techniques are applied to the development of Consultants' designs and adopt solutions giving the best overall value for money and, where this may result in the cost limit for the project being exceeded, make recommendations to the Employer and obtain instructions.

- Make recommendations to the Employer on the preferred method of procuring the construction and completion of the Works and obtain the Employer's instructions.

- Arrange for any required submissions of designs, drawings, models, calculations or other material to regulatory bodies and expedite any necessary approvals.

- Act as witness at any hearing or planning enquiry and the like or, alternatively, act on the Employer's behalf to arrange for other appointed Consultants to do so and manage their activities.

- Ensure that all drawings, specifications, schedules, bills of quantities or other documents necessary for the obtaining of tenders are completed and are fully co-ordinated, are in accordance with the brief approved by the Employer and are available on the programmed date.

- Discuss with the Employer the general arrangements for obtaining tenders and implement the action approved.

- In co-operation with the other members of the Project Team submit to the Employer the names of firms who are considered to be suitable to be invited to tender for the Works and specialist Works and obtain the Employer's instructions.

- Ensure that a pre-tender estimate is prepared based on the tender documentation and check against the cost target for the Project approved by the Employer and report to the Employer accordingly.

- Undertake risk assessments.

- Undertake value management exercises.

- Obtain the Employer's approval to proceed to Stage 3.

TABLE 3 — STAGE 3: TENDER

- Ensure that tenders are invited on the programmed date and in accordance with the Employer's instructions and arrange for tenders to be returned direct to the Employer in accordance with the Employer's procedure.

- Accompany tendering contractors or sub-contractors or the representative of the Employer or occupying Department to the site of any works being undertaken in connection with this Appointment.

- Ensure that all enquiries from contractors during the tendering period are answered satisfactorily and ensure that any clarification on the content of the documentation given to a tenderer is copied to other firms tendering.

- Copy to the Employer all correspondence concerning the obtaining of tenders.

- Where full-time site inspection staff are to be appointed, ensure that arrangements are made in good time to implement that instruction.

- Co-ordinate tender appraisals from the other members of the Project Team and submit a report to the Employer with recommendations. If the lowest tender obtained is higher than the approved cost for the Works, obtain whatever advice is necessary from other consultants in order to make recommendations to the Employer and arrange to implement the Employer's instructions.

- Arrange for any tender under consideration for acceptance to receive an arithmetical and technical check and ensure that any errors are resolved in accordance with the Employer's procedure.

- Obtain the Employer's decision regarding the acceptance of a tender or tenders and implement the Employer's instructions.

- Co-ordinate the collection of documents from the other members of the Project in the event of any difficulty, keeping the Employer fully informed.

- Undertake risk assessments.

- Undertake value management exercises.

- Before Stage 4 is implemented, ensure that the Employer has accepted the selected Contractor's tender and that the Employer approves that the matters referred to in Stage 4 can proceed.

TABLE 4 — STAGE 4: CONSTRUCTION

- Administer the terms of the construction contract while the Project is under construction, undertaking the full range of duties imposed on the Project Manager by the Works contract in accordance with the time scales therein.

- Agree a detailed programme for the Works with the Contractor which specifies completion by the agreed date.

- Agree a date with the Contractor and the Employer for the commencement of work on site.

- Establish and chair regular meetings with the Contractor and Consultants as necessary in order to monitor the progress of the Works and the production of design information to the Contractor and circulate minutes of the meeting to the Employer and to others.

- The minutes shall record the action to be taken to rectify any deficiencies and shall indicate who is to be responsible for taking that action. Inform the Employer if any delay in the production of design information cannot be resolved in time to prevent a delay to the Works.

- Ensure that rigorous quality management procedures are in place throughout the construction phase.

- Arrange for any special inspections or tests necessary to ensure that proper and adequate standards of construction are maintained and that all Works are constructed in accordance with the contract documents.

- Throughout the construction phase and until all construction accounts are settled, inform the Employer of any contractual claims which have been received or are likely to arise. Make recommendations to the Employer and implement the Employer's instructions.

- Continue to monitor the construction phase and take any necessary action in order to ensure that the Project will be completed within the cost approved by the Employer and by the programmed completion date. When matters arise which affect the contract completion date or the approved cost, keep the Employer fully informed.

- Ensure that adequate records are maintained and photographs of the Works are taken throughout the construction phase recording progress of the Works and, particularly, highlighting any delays including those resulting from interaction between Contractors or Sub-Contractors working on the site.

- Keep accurate records of all payments and other matters relating to the service provided under this Appointment and retain all vouchers and invoices and, if requested, make these available to the Employer.

- Ensure that Consultants observe the provisions of their Appointment regarding cost control procedures and the procedures for obtaining the Employer's approval to introduce variations. On behalf of the Employer, receive the Consultants' financial statements and submissions in accordance with this Condition and submit to the Employer with recommendations.

- Ensure that Certificates are issued in accordance with the terms of the contract.

- Co-ordinate site visits of Consultants and ensure that the frequency of those visits is satisfactory.

- Arrange for any necessary spare equipment, 'as built' record drawings, maintenance manuals and general guidance on the operation of the Building and Services to be made available in good time in order that they can be provided to the Employer on completion of the Project.

- Inform the Employer four weeks prior to the anticipated date of completion of the Works.

- Co-ordinate the preparation and issue of Certificates relating to the completion of the Works.

- Ensure that lists of defects are issued at the appropriate time under the Works contract.

TABLE 5 — STAGE 5: COMPLETION

- Advise the Employer on the resources and skills required to operate and maintain the completed Works and make recommendations on the timing of their appointment or on the need for any maintenance agreements.

- Ensure that all defects are rectified.

- Ensure that the Works are cleaned, tested and commissioned prior to handover to the Employer.

- Ensure that all statutory Certificates and Approvals are given to the Employer.

- Ensure that an appropriate Certificate is issued to the Contractor when all defects have been made good.

- Make recommendations to the Employer regarding any outstanding claims, counterclaims, liquidated damages or other contractual issues and receive and implement the Employer's instructions.

- Co-ordinate the production of Final Accounts and the issue of Final Certificates and, accordingly, make recommendations to the Employer.

- Prepare a completion report to the Employer showing:

  - a comparison between the out-turn cost and the approved budget cost;

  - the actual expenditure against sums includes in the contract for specialist works and provisionally measured work;

  - the costs included against any Variation of Price Condition;

  - the expenditure against approved variations and additional Works authorised by the Employer;

  - a comparison of programme dates against actual dates achieved;

  - any lessons obtained form the scheme which could be applied to future Projects;

  - the performance of Project participants.

- Assist the Employer in dealing with any outstanding insurance claims.

- In the event of any arbitration or litigation resulting from the Project, prepare any necessary documentation and reports and, if required by the Employer, attend any hearings acting if necessary, as a witness (and subject to the payment of an additional fee in accordance with Condition 1.46 (Payment for changed Services and variations).

2 CONTRACT ADMINISTRATION UNDER THE GC/WORKS SUITE

In addition to the general project management duties set out above, under the GC/Works suite of contracts the Project Manager is required by the Standard Form of Contract to undertake the contract administration duties more normally carried out by the Architect or the Engineer.

The most comprehensive set of duties and obligations are included in GC/Works/1 and summarised in Table 6 below. The provisions included in GC/Works/2, 3, and 4 are similar, but are modified to reflect the specific purpose of each form.

A Schedule of Time Limits, listing the various time limits within which actions (including those of the Project Manager) must be taken, is included the form of contract.

TABLE 6 - LIST OF DUTIES AND OBLIGATIONS OF THE PROJECT MANAGER UNDER GC/WORKS/1 CONTRACT FOR BUILDING AND CIVIL ENGINEERING MAJOR WORKS

- Approve unforeseen ground conditions (clause 7(3) and (4))
- Provide setting out information (clause 9(1))
- Approve the Contractor's design (clause 10(1))
- Confirm that the Contractor's Health and Safety Plan is 'of an appropriate standard' (clause 11(5))
- Receive from the Contractor's Agent a daily list of people employed on the works (clause 15)
- Approve the foundations (clauses 16 and 17))
- Instruct the Contractor in respect of access to the site by unauthorised persons (clause 26) and issue any necessary passes (clause 27)
- Give (or withhold) consent for the Contractor to take photographs (clause 28)
- Instruct the Contractor in respect of the disposal of surplus or rejected materials (clause 30(4))
- Inspect and approve the works (clause 31)
- Instruct the Contractor in the event of archaeological finds (clause 32(3))
- Agree and/or amend the Contractor's programme (clause 35(2))

- Convene progress meetings, and subsequently report to the Contractor on:
  - the extent to which he believes the works are proceeding in accordance with the programme and budget
  - any steps which he has agreed with the Contractor to limit the effect of delays or extra costs
  - consideration and award of extension of time (clause 36)
- Early completion of parts of the work (clause 37)
- Consider and act as necessary upon any Contractor's proposals to enhance the works or reduce the cost (clause 38(4)–(7))
- Certify completion (clause 39) and the completion of making good defects clause 49(5))
- Issue instructions as necessary (clause 40)
- Undertake various duties in respect of lump sum quotations for varied work (clause 42)
- Certify payments (clause 50)
- Instruct the Contractor in respect of any emergency work required (clause 54)
- Approve (or withhold approval) for the Contractor to sub-contract parts of the work (clause 62(1))
- Instruct the Contractor in respect of Provisional and PC Sums (clause 64)

(b) New Engineering Contract Engineering and Construction Contract suite (NEC ECC)

This suite of contracts also represents a modern attempt to integrate the Project Manager's role into the contract. The suite consists of a set of Core Clauses applicable to all contracts, which may be supplemented by a range of major and minor options to accommodate the specific needs of a wide variety of contractual approaches, including:

- lump sum contracts;
- management contracts;
- prime cost contracts;

- target cost contracts;
- design and build contracts.

The Project Manager's role is central to the operation of the Core Clauses, and is described in the accompanying contract Guidance Notes[5] as '... to manage the contract for the Employer with the intention of achieving the Employer's objectives for the completed project'. The Project Manager carries out the majority of the routine contract administration duties.

The notes state that the Employer will normally appoint the Project Manager at the feasibility stage and that, in addition to administering the construction contract, his duties may include:

> ... acting on behalf of the Employer and advising him on the procurement of design, on estimates of costs and time, on the merits of alternative schemes, and on choosing the most appropriate contract strategy.

It is clear that the ECC places considerable emphasis on the Project Manager's contribution to the project. It assumes as a starting point that he has full authority to act for the Employer in all respects, and to make all decisions which are required of him. The contract information stresses that if the Project Manager's authority is constrained in any way by his terms of engagement, it is his responsibility to ensure that he is able to obtain the necessary sanction from his client in good time to be able to meet his obligations under the contract.

Note that the ECC makes a distinction between the 'Project Manager' and the 'Supervisor'. The role of the Supervisor is defined as checking:

> ... that the works are constructed in accordance with the contract. It is similar to that of a resident engineer or architect who may be assisted by an inspector or clerk of works.

Finally, it is important to note that the ECC[6] requires all members of the project team to work together in a spirit of mutual trust and co-operation in order to achieve the project objectives.

---

5   *The Engineering and Construction* Contract (2nd edn, 1995) Guidance Notes.
6   ECC Core Clauses Clause 10.1.

(c) Institution of Chemical Engineers Model Forms of Contract Lump Sum contract (Red Book) and for Reimbursable Contracts (Green Book)

These forms were both revised in 2001. The Red Book is currently in its fourth edition and the Green Book in its third edition. In addition to their use for chemical and petrochemical process plant installations, these forms are also widely used for civil engineering work, particularly in the sewage disposal and water treatment industries.

The Project Manager's role under both forms is to manage the construction contract on behalf of the Employer, and his position as Employer's agent is clearly defined in clause 11:

> The Project Manager has full authority to act on behalf of the Purchaser in connection with the Contract' and 'any obligation stated under the contract to be an obligation of the Project Manager shall be deemed to be an obligation of the Purchaser.

His power is limited by only one condition: although the Employer may, under the provisions of clause 36.6, unilaterally take possession of the works before completion, the Project Manager is not permitted to do this on the Employer's behalf.

The main contract administration duties assigned to the Project Manager are as follows. Note that the Project Manager's duties and responsibilities are similar under both forms, although there are minor differences in the clause numbers. Clause numbers used here relate to the Red Book unless otherwise stated:

- To provide setting out information to the Contractor (clause 3.3).

- To review, and, if appropriate, to approve as variations, suggestions for improvements made by the Contractor (clause 3.5).

- To pass on to the Contractor all project documentation required to be supplied to the contractor by the Employer (clause 4.1).

- Valuation of variations to the contract works, assessment of Contractor's claims and agreement with the Contractor (clauses 6, 18 and 19).

- To nominate Sub-contractors (clause 10).

- To nominate a Project Manager's Representative to act on his behalf as an inspector of the works and in respect of day-to-day construction issues (clause 11.4).

- To notify the Contractor of any members of the Contractor's supervisory staff (clause 12.5) or workmen (clause 28.4) that he considers to be incompetent and to require their removal from the site.

- To receive and approve the Contractor's programme, to monitor progress and to inform the Contractor if he believes that the rate of progress is insufficient to ensure completion on time (clause 13).

- To determine the extent of any extensions of time to be awarded to the Contractor (clause 14).

- To issue the necessary documentation in respect of any variations required to the works (clauses 16 and 17).

- To receive and approve key drawings and other relevant documentation provided by the Contractor (clause 21).

- In conjunction with the Contractor, to carry out any tests required (clause 22).

- To convene progress meetings at regular intervals, including taking and distributing the minutes (clause 29).

- To inspect the completed works (including any specified performance tests), to carry out the necessary maintenance inspections at the end of the defects liability period, to certify practical completion and final acceptance of the plant, and to issue the Final Certificate (clauses 32–38).

- To review the Contractor's payment applications, to issue instructions in respect of the expenditure of prime cost and provisional sums, to certify payments to the Employer, to agree the Final Account with the Contractor (clauses 39 and 40), and to reach a final settlement with the Contractor in the event of suspension or termination of the works (clauses 42 and 43).

- To review and determine disputes (clause 45.3).

In addition to the above duties, the Project Manager also has the right to vary the works as required, or to suspend performance of the works (clause 41). While broad-ranging provisions such as these are typically granted to the Contract Administrator under many of the standard forms of contract, it should be noted that, where they are specifically given to the Project Manager, they may impose significant additional obligations and liabilities on top of those which the Project Manager would normally assume under typical terms of engagement.

The Green Book also imposes on the Project Manager an additional duty of checking and auditing as necessary the Contractor's costing system (Green Book, clause 19), and this again may impose significant additional obligations on the Project Manager.

5 Forms of Contract in which an individual carries out some typical Project Management functions but using an alternative designation

(a) JCT Standard Form of Building Contract with Contractor's Design (1998 edition)

The philosophy of this contract is that the Contractor is responsible for the design of the entire works. There is therefore no need for the Employer to commission his own architect, although it is common for the Employer to retain an architect/design consultant to provide ad hoc advice at least during the early stages of the project. The form does, however, require the Employer to be represented by an Employer's Agent, who effectively acts as the Employer's Project Manager. The Employer's Agent is only referred to directly in clauses 5.4 (availability of drawings) and 11 (access to the site), but Article 3 of the Conditions of Contract makes it plain that the role of the Employer's Agent is far more wide-ranging:

> The Employer's Agent is responsible for] the receiving or issuing of such applications, consents, instructions, notices, requests or statements or for otherwise acting for the Employer under any other of the Conditions.

A full discussion of the role of the Employer's Agent is provided by Chappell and Powell-Smith[7], and only a brief overview is included here.

The Employer's Agent may be responsible for carrying out, on behalf of the Employer, any or all of the duties which are required of the employer under the contract, including:

- Issuing instructions as necessary (clause 4).
- Custody of the contract documents (clause 5).
- Quality assurance (clause 8).
- Valuation of variations (clause 12).
- Issue of a certificate of practical completion (clause 16) and/or non-completion (clause 24).
- Assessing applications for extensions of time (clause 25).
- Ascertaining additional loss and expense (clause 26).
- Checking and approving interim and final payments (clause 30).

7 D Chappell and V Powell-Smith (1993) The JCT Design and Build Contract.

(b) ACA Standard Form of Contract for Project Partnering (PPC 2000)

This multi-party contract is intended for the use of partnering teams, and all members of the team become parties to the contract. Under more conventional construction contracts only the Employer and the Contractor are parties to the contract and third party rights provisions are typically excluded. Under this contract, however, each member of the partnering team becomes a signatory to the contract, and assumes rights and obligations in respect of every other member of the team. The document is therefore more akin to a partnership agreement than a conventional construction contract. The contract also places the parties' agreed partnering obligations into a formal legal framework. The Client is required to be represented in the PPC 2000 contract by a Client's Representative.

Much of the detail of these mutual obligations is project- and team-specific, and will be the subject of discussion during the early stages of the contract. The precise duties of the Client's Representative may therefore be modified at this time, and the results of these discussions are recorded in the Project Partnering Agreement which forms an integral part of the contract documentation.

Under this contract the Client's Representative undertakes many, mainly administrative, duties on behalf of the Client. His role is set out in detail in clause 5 of the Conditions of Contract, and clause 5.2 provides a reasonable summary:

> The Client Representative shall be authorised to represent the Client in all matters relating to the Project ... subject to such restrictions as are stated in the Project Partnering Agreement and in accordance with such procedures as are stated in the Partnering Documentation.

In summary, the major aspects of the Client's Representative's role are to:

- Administer meetings of the Partnering Core Group.
- Organise any necessary value and risk management workshops.
- Organise partnering workshops as required.
- Monitor the implementation of the project both on and off site.
- Issue any necessary instruction on behalf of the client, including varying the works, accelerating, postponing or rescheduling the works, and inspecting and making good defects.
- Receive the Contractor's programme.
- Liaise with the partnering adviser in the preparation of any necessary joining, pre-possession or commencement agreements.

- Jointly with the Client, consider any changes proposed by the Constructor or any other partnering team members, and either accept or reject them.
- Issue extensions of time.
- Issue interim valuations as required and agree the final account.
- Test and accept the works on behalf of the Client, issue notice of any defects and/or certify practical completion as appropriate.
- Review key performance indicators.
- Convene a post-project review meeting.

(c) Incorporation of a Project Manager into JCT CD 98 and PPC 2000

The simplest way to incorporate an Employer's Project Manager into the above contracts would appear to be to appoint the Project Manager as Employer's Agent/ Client's Representative, either as a part of the Project Manager's terms and conditions of appointment or as a separate and concurrent appointment. In either case there is plainly the need to ensure that the Project Manager is either appropriately qualified, or empowered to delegate the Employer's Agent/Client Representative function to another through an appropriate sub-consultancy agreement.

Again, it will be vitally important to ensure that the terms and conditions of the project management appointment support the role and duties required of the Employer's Agent/Client Representative under the construction contract.

(d) FIDIC Conditions of Contract for EPC/Turnkey Projects (the Silver Book)

This form of contract is specifically written for turnkey projects or other projects in which the Contractor is required to engineer, procure and construct (EPC) the complete scheme, and where:

1   either a higher degree of certainty of final price and time is required than might be available with the Conditions of Contract for Plant and Design–Build (the Yellow Book), and/or

2   the Contractor takes total responsibility for the design and execution of the project with little or no involvement of the Employer.

As explained earlier, the FIDIC contracts are available in an increasingly wide range of different languages but, as with the other contracts in the family, FIDIC regards the English language version to be the definitive version. This may, however, be overruled in foreign jurisdictions and by the Particular Conditions of contract for specific schemes. Clause 1.4 of the contract establishes that it will be governed by the law of the country or jurisdiction stated in the Particular Conditions, and that:

> ... if there are versions of any part of the Contract which are written in more than one language, the version which is in the ruling language stated in the Particular Conditions shall prevail.

There is also provision for the 'language of communications' to be stated in the Particular Conditions (clause 1.4), and this need not necessarily be the same as the language of the contract itself. Where no language of communication is specified, then it is assumed to be the language in which the contract (or most of it) is written.

Since the philosophy of this contract is that responsibility for the entire design and procurement of the works lies with the Contractor, there is no provision within the contract for the Employer to appoint his own Engineer, although it is common for the Employer to commission independent engineering advice as a way of validating the Contractor's proposals.

The Employer may, however, should he so wish, appoint an Employer's Representative to act on his behalf under the contract (clause 3.1). It is established in the contract that the Employer's Representative 'shall be deemed to have the full authority of the Employer under the contract', the only exception to this general rule being in respect of termination of the contract (clause 15), where only the Employer himself may exercise the powers given.

The contract also provides for either the Employer or the Employer's Representative to employ and delegate authority to assistants (clause 3.2), and examples given in the contract include resident engineers and inspectors such as clerks of works. Such appointments are of no effect until the Contractor has been informed of their details. There is also a contractual requirement (clause 3.2) that such assistants must be:

> ... competent to carry out these duties and exercise this authority, and [be] fluent in the language for communications defined [in the contract].

The scope for delegation of powers to assistants foreseen in the contract is very broad, and may include inspection, approval, certification, and the issue of instructions, notices and similar acts (clause 3.3).

The more important powers and duties given in the contract to the Employer (or to his Representative and authorised assistants) may be summarised as:

- Provision to the Contractor of all available relevant information on subsurface and hydrological conditions including environmental aspects (clause 4.10).

- Provision of a statement of Employer's Requirements upon which the design and procurement of the work will be based. Note that the Employer is required to take responsibility for 'the design of the Works and for the accuracy of such Employer's Requirements (including design criteria and calculations)' with the exception of the areas listed below (clause 5.1). Further, the Employer:

    ... shall not be responsible for any error, inaccuracy or omission of any kind in the Employer's Requirements as originally included in the Contract and shall not be deemed to have given any representation of accuracy or completeness of any data or information [with the exception of items listed below].

    The exclusions from this provision comprise:
    - Data stated as being immutable or the responsibility of the Employer.
    - Definitions of the intended purpose of the works.
    - Criteria for testing and performance.
    - Data which cannot be verified by the Contractor.

- Issue of instructions as necessary during the course of the work.

- Nomination of any nominated sub-contractors.

- Review of any Contractor's documents which the contract requires the Employer to review within the stated periods.

- Carrying out any tests required in accordance with the contract conditions, including providing the Contractor with reasons for failure.

- Giving the Contractor seven days' notice of the contract commencement date when not stated in the Contract Agreement. The commencement date must be within 42 days of the date in which the contract comes into full force.

- If the contract is delayed by events other than those for which the Contractor would be entitled to an extension of time, the Employer has the right to instruct the Contractor to provide an amended programme describing the methods he proposes to use to complete the project on time. Unless the employer notifies otherwise, the Contractor shall implement the revised programme at his own cost, and must reimburse the Employer for any additional loss and expense suffered in addition to any delay damages due.

- Suspension of the works at will.

- Taking possession of the works once the completion tests have been satisfied.

- Varying the works either at his own request or in response to a proposal from the Contractor.

- Checking the contractor's interim valuation claims and making appropriate payments.

- Terminating the contract either at will (clause 15.5) or in the event of severe failure by the Contractor (clause 15.2).

- Indemnifying the Contractor and his personnel against negligence of the Employer.

- Taking the risks set out in clause 17.3.

- Responding to the Contractor's claims within a reasonable time.

Even a cursory study of the above duties and responsibilities must lead to the conclusion that this form of contract is in many respects a Project Manager's dream. Virtually the whole project risk is carried by the Contractor, and the duties of the Employer or his Representative are far less onerous than in most of the other forms considered here.

(e) FIDIC Short Form of Contract (Green Book)

This form, first published in 1999, is intended for engineering and construction works of relatively small capital value, of short duration, and without the need for specialist sub-contracts.

The form both *requires* the Employer to appoint an Authorised Person to act for him under the contract, and also *permits* the Employer, should he so wish, to appoint a firm or individual (the Employer's Representative) to carry out particular and specific duties, these to be notified in advance to the Contractor.

The positions of the Authorised Person and Employer's Representative are summarised in the accompanying Notes for Guidance as follows:

> There is no Engineer or Employer's Representative in the formal sense used in some other FIDIC Conditions. The Employer takes all necessary actions. However, the Employer must nominate his authorised spokesman and, if he wishes to engage a consultant to administer the contract, may appoint a representative with specific delegated duties and authority.

The Notes for Guidance go on to explain that plainly the Contractor needs to know who speaks for the Employer in connection with the contract, and that this will be the Employer's Authorised Person. In the absence of a separate Employer's Representative, the Authorised Person will also act as Contract Administrator. Where, however, the Employer wishes to appoint a professional consultant to undertake all or part of the Employer's duties, then he may appoint an Employer's Representative. Where this is done, the Employer's Representative acts for and in the interests of the Employer; and there is no duty to be impartial as there would be for an Architect or Engineer acting under a more conventional appointment.

If it is the Employer's wish to use his Employer's Representative to act as a conventional architect or engineer, it is suggested by the Notes for Guidance that the contract wording be amended to make it clear that the Employer's Representative is required to '… exercise in a fair and impartial manner the powers of the employer …'. Where the Employer does employ an Employer's Representative there is plainly the need to ensure that there is no conflict between the duties assigned to the Employer's Representative and those exercised by the Employer himself through the Authorised Person.

Clearly the role of Employer's Representative could easily be incorporated as part of a wider project management function, and the contract is sufficiently flexible to allow the duties of the nominated person to be as broad or as narrow as the Employer requires. There should therefore be little difficulty in marrying the duties of the Employer's Representative to the terms and conditions of the Project Manager's appointment, if necessary through the Particular Conditions.

In essence, the contract is a very simple one. The Employer's duties are basically limited to providing the site and appropriate access, and paying for the work in accordance with the contract conditions. The Employer (through either his Authorised Person or his Employer's Representative, depending upon the particular appointments made and the duties set out in the particular Conditions) has some limited right to vary the works and must agree the value of any variations with the Contractor. Disputes are referred to independent adjudication and arbitration. The decision as to when the works are sufficiently complete rests solely with the Employer, and there is no right of termination save in the event of default by the Contractor.

6 Modified standard forms of contract and bespoke contracts

This chapter has reviewed some of the potential liabilities faced by Project Managers under some of the more important standard forms of construction contract in common use. Having completed the review, it becomes plain that, for project management to be successful, it is essential that Project Managers must be aware of, and competent to perform, the duties and obligations placed upon them by the chosen Conditions of Contract. In addition, the Project Manager's own terms and conditions of appointment must be:

- consistent with the duties and obligations placed upon the Project Manager by the Conditions of Contract;

- consistent with the terms and conditions of other consultants' appointments, in order both to give the chosen form of contract business efficacy and to ensure that the Client receives a combination of professional services which is appropriate to the project in hand.

Particular problems of legal drafting frequently arise when Employers and their consultants attempt to amend standard forms of contract, either to incorporate a project management role into a standard form which does not specifically provide for it, or to amend in some way the duties and obligations of the Project Manager as set out in the standard forms. Project Managers and their fellow consultants need to be aware that many of the standard form contracts in common use, especially perhaps those produced by the Joint Contracts Tribunal, have evolved into their present form largely through a process of addition and amendment of earlier versions. They are now so complex in structure, with so many cross-references, that careless amendment may easily give rise to unforeseen and unwelcome consequences.

Successful amendment of standard form contracts is thus an extremely skilled process, which should only be undertaken by an experienced construction lawyer.

Bespoke contracts have in the past been commonly used for large infrastructure projects such as build/own/operate schemes or other projects where particular and special conditions apply. Contracts of this type should not pose too many problems provided that the role and function of the Project Manager, and the terminology to be used, are sufficiently well defined and agreed before the contract is drafted. If this is so, then the duties and obligations imposed on the Project Manager under his terms and conditions of appointment can usually be successfully integrated into the contractual framework.

Problems may, however, arise when the contract is drafted prior to the Project Manager's appointment. When this is the case, then special care must be taken to ensure that the integrity of the complete contractual package is not compromised as a result of discussions and negotiations with the Project Manager over his precise terms and conditions of appointment during the pre-contract stage.

Bibliography

Chappell D and Powell-Smith V *The JCT Design and Build Contract* (1993) Blackwell Scientific Publications.

The Engineering and Construction Contract Guidance Notes (2nd edn, 1995) Thomas Telford.

CHAPTER 6

Review of legislation which affects Project Managers

By Sam Townend

Summary

As there is a huge volume of legislation which potentially affects Project Managers, this chapter focuses on some key legislation. However, Project Managers should be aware that there are many other statutes that may impact upon their liability.

The chapter covers:

- Review of the important environmental statutory provisions that the Project Manager may have to deal with, including:
  - control of noise
  - considerations that Project Managers should give to waste on land.

- Introduction to building control, the Building Act 1984 and the Regulations issued under it, with an explanation of 'how' local authorities enforce them.

- Explanation of what a building notice contains and a review of some of the other notices under the Building Regulations.

- Review of some of the European procurement legislation which the Project Manager should be aware of at tender stage.

- Review of the Housing Grants, Construction and Regeneration Act 1996 and the key terms which Project Managers should be aware of, in particular:
  - payment terms
  - notices to be issued in accordance with the Act
  - withholding notices
  - prohibition on 'pay when paid' clauses
  - introduction of statutory adjudication.

- Introduction to the Contracts (Rights of Third Parties) Act 1999 and how this can affect the Project Manager.

- Reminder of the provisions of Limitation Act 1980.

1 Introduction

The various parties engaged on a construction project – Employer/owner, Contractor, Consultants and those who intercede between or represent them, specifically Project Managers – are in a minefield of statutory regulation and required procedures. This chapter aims to introduce those areas of statutorily imposed regulation and procedures which are of most relevance to Project Managers and are not dealt with in other chapters of this book.

The extent to which a Project Manager himself has to ensure compliance with the procedures will depend upon the scope of his appointment, to which careful reference should always be made. However, even if direct responsibility is severely limited – for example, when merely acting as the Employer's Representative on a design and build contract – the Project Manager should have an overview of the regulatory framework and ongoing efforts at compliance, and should warn his Employer of potential pitfalls and hold-ups to progress of the works.

Project Managers should not worry about mastering every last aspect of this chapter, as ongoing guidance and assistance (at least as to regulatory procedures) is often given by local authorities, who are usually called upon to enforce the regulations.

2 Environmental safeguards

The following paragraphs introduce the most important environmental statutory provisions that a Project Manager may have to deal with. In recent years governments have been more inclined to interfere in construction operations in a desire to protect neighbours and the general environment, as well as employees. The primary duty of many Project Managers will be to ensure that work progresses regularly in accordance with the programme. In doing this they must make sure that the works at no time fall foul of sanctions, resulting from breaches of the environmental protections, that will often impede the progress of the project, even a suspension of construction activities.

(a) Control of noise

Control of noise is of considerable importance to project management, particularly of urban developments. If it is not monitored by the Project Manager and a strict control kept, the owner of the property under development (whom the Project Manager will usually be representing) or the Contractor may find they are at the wrong end of a court action.

First, and obviously, the Project Manager must ensure that the works carried out keep within the express conditions of planning permission or any Party Wall Award[1]. For example, it is typical for there to be a condition that noisy works, such as the use of plant, be restricted to business working hours only.

Secondly, the Project Manager should also bear in mind the requirement of common law that no undue inconvenience ought to be caused to neighbours. The law recognises that when a property is undergoing building works more noise (and, indeed, dust etc.) will arise than when a property is in ordinary occupation, and that this is reasonable and is permitted. However, the maker of the noise should use reasonable skill and care to avoid annoyance to his neighbours and passers-by in carrying out the works[2]. If the maker of the noise (for whom the Owner/Developer will almost always be held responsible in law) acts unreasonably, the Owner/Developer may become the subject of an action in nuisance, potentially resulting in damages and/or an injunction prohibiting the nuisance. This may have a serious effect on the ability of the involved parties to progress the works.

Thirdly, and more complicatedly, there are statutory interventions directly targeting noise pollution which require the active participation of those involved in the construction works. These are dealt with in some detail below.

Common law nuisance has been supplemented by the Control of Pollution Act 1974 (CPA 1974) and more recently the Environmental Protection Act 1990 (EPA 1990). EPA 1990 provides (as did CPA 1974) that a person who is an occupier of premises and has been aggrieved by noise amounting to a nuisance may apply to the magistrates' court for an order either requiring the owner/occupier to abate the nuisance or prohibiting the recurrence of the nuisance[3]. If the Project Manager is the owner's or occupier's representative on site, it will fall to him to ensure the implementation of the court order.

The Acts go further than simply being an enactment of the common law. CPA 1974 also provides, by s 60, that a local authority may impose conditions on the work being carried out (which the Project Manager will have to ensure are adhered to) by way of a written notice. For example, the local authority may serve a notice imposing requirements as to the way in which the works are to be carried out[4]. The notice may also require the execution of specified works and the taking of certain steps for the purpose of the notice, and specifying the time within which such works

---

1   A party wall is a wall adjoining property belonging to different owners. A Party Wall Award under the Party Wall etc Act 1996 may determine, inter alia: (a) the right to execute any work; (b) the time and manner of executing any work; and (c) any other matter arising out of or incidental to the dispute.
2   *Clerk and Lindsell on Torts* (18th edn, 2000) para 19–15.
3   EPA 1990, s 82.
4   CPA 1974, s 60(2).

are to be carried out[5]. There is no need for the local authority to show that a common law nuisance has been caused. The ambit of the conditions that may be imposed on the works by way of the notice is wide. CPA 1974, s 60(3) provides that:

> (3) The notice may in particular—
> (a) specify the plant or machinery which is, or is not, to be used;
> (b) specify the hours during which the works may be carried out;
> (c) specify the level of noise which may be emitted from the premises in question or at any specified point on those premises or which may be so emitted during specified hours; and
> (d) provide for any change of circumstances.

CPA, s 60(5) prescribes on whom a notice can be served. It can be any person 'who appears to the Local Authority to be carrying out or going to carry out the works and on such other persons appearing to the Local Authority to be responsible for or to have control over the carrying out of the works'. Certainly it will often fall to the Project Manager to ensure compliance with the notice, but further, in the light of CPA, s 60(5) it is perfectly possible for the Project Manager to be held personally liable[6]. Where there is any doubt about the person responsible, the local authority has power to serve notice requiring information (for instance, to obtain relevant documents to ascertain who is in control for the purpose of the notice)[7].

The recipient may appeal the issue of a notice to a magistrates' court within 21 days of receipt; otherwise it becomes an offence to contravene any requirement of the notice without 'reasonable excuse'[8]. It is the duty of the local authority to include in the 'CPA 1974, s 60' notice a statement notifying the recipient that there is an appeal procedure and specifying the time within which such an appeal must be brought[9]. Failure to include such statement renders the notice void and the restrictions imposed by the notice will not be enforceable by the local authority[10].

There is a provision of assistance to Project Managers for obtaining the prior consent of the local authority to work that is to be carried out[11]. This is a useful device for the Project Manager or Contractor to ascertain the limits of what the Contractor may do without risking the service of a notice, and should be utilised. Compliance with the prior consent of the local authority is a good defence to a subsequent relevant prosecution.

---

5 CPA 1974, s 60(6).
6 *City of London v Bovis* (1988) 49 BLR 1. It was held that a construction manager, Bovis, came within CPA 1974, s 60(5) and was properly to be held accountable for breaches of the notice. It was sufficient that Bovis under their contract were given control of the building operations.
7 CPA 1974, s 93.
8 CPA 1974, s 60(7), (8).
9 CPA 1974, s 87(4).
10 *Rayner v Stepney Corpn* [1911] 2 Ch 312.
11 CPA 1974, s 61.

Where contravention of a notice occurs without reasonable excuse, the local authority may prosecute the person or body responsible, who, in the event of conviction, will be liable to a fine[12]. These fines have not kept up with inflation, and for major construction works this penalty by itself may not be regarded as sufficient to require any restriction on the works. More importantly, however, where the offences are serious or repeated, and where the local authority considers it expedient for the promotion or protection of the interests of the inhabitants of their area, it may apply for an injunction to prevent a breach or to restrain (further) contravention of the notice. If granted, any contravention of the injunction would be punishable by all the means available to the court, including imprisonment for contempt of court. An injunction is usually an unwanted restriction on the ability to progress the works, and is to be avoided.

There may be personal consequences for ignoring the provisions of a notice. CPA 1974 provides that where the person causing or permitting the offence is a corporate body, an officer of that body (such as a director or a manager) may also be liable[13]. CPA 1974, s 87(2) adds that where the commission of an offence by any person is due to the act or default of another person, that other person is also guilty of an offence.

CPA 1974 also provides for the establishment of noise abatement zones. The purpose of these zones is to allow an authority a mechanism for preventing deterioration in environmental noise levels[14]. If the construction work is taking place within a noise abatement zone, the Project Manager should be aware of additional noise restrictions the project may be under.

PRACTICAL CONSIDERATIONS

In conclusion on the issue of noise pollution, Project Managers should pay careful attention to the scope of their work under the conditions of their appointment. Under standard forms of building contract, the responsibility and cost of complying with the relevant statutory obligations normally falls upon the Contractor (for example, clause 6 of the JCT Standard Form of Building Contract with Contractor's Design Agreement 1998). That is not to say, as explained above, that the Employer/ Developer, or even the Project Manager himself, might not be found liable for breach of statutory responsibilities. In any event, it will always be in the interests of the Employer/Developer for the Project Manager to ensure compliance with statutory regulation and the smooth progress of the works.

Where the Project Manager is contractually responsible for environmental issues, one of the matters he should ensure are carried out is to ascertain the noise

12   CPA 1974, s 74(1).
13   CPA 1974, s 87(1).
14   CPA 1974, ss 63–67.

requirements of the local authority. He should have regard to the site layout and types of machinery likely to be used, and consider whether alternative techniques would achieve less noisy operations. If possible, an application for the local authority's consent under CPA 1974, s 61 should be made, bearing in mind that it affords a defence to any prosecution for contravention of a relevant s 60 notice.

Where a s 60 notice has been served, it is useful to keep the Environmental Health Department of the local authority informed of the progress of the works and particularly of noisy operations that are to take place. The local authority is then more likely to be sympathetic to the builder when faced with complaints by local residents, and more willing to grant informal relaxations from the terms of the notice when these are requested. It is equally important to establish links with the local community to induce potential complainants first to make their complaints direct to the Project Manager, Clerk of Works or the builder, rather than the local authority. It is obvious, therefore, that any steps that can be taken to minimise or avoid noise, especially in advance when the progress of works is not affected, should be taken.

(b) Waste on land

Waste on the site, whether already obvious on site, discovered on taking possession, or generated during the works, is both costly to deal with and subject to a great deal of recent government intervention. EPA 1990, Pt II regulates what is categorised as 'controlled' or 'special' waste. The former covers most type of waste, including that arising from construction, demolition or excavation. It is an offence to deposit controlled waste on any land or to keep it without a waste management licence[15]. There are specific duties on those controlling the works to avoid causing pollution to the environment and a specific duty of care in respect of waste[16]. Waste management licences may be revoked or suspended. No one can now deal in waste without complying with this Act and its regulations.

'Special' waste is material designated by regulations, which is considered to be so dangerous or difficult to treat, keep or dispose of that special treatment is required for dealing with it[17]. Where special waste is discovered on land, regulations require the owner to make provision either for its safe retention on the site or for its lawful removal. EPA 1990 makes general provision for a public register of information concerning waste, for inspectors with powers of entry and taking records, samples etc, for requiring information to be furnished by those carrying out work, and for powers to deal with imminent danger of serious pollution[18].

---

15 EPA 1990, s 33.
16 EPA 1990, s 34.
17 EPA 1990, s 62.
18 EPA 1990, ss 64–71.

If land is or becomes contaminated, for example with noxious chemicals, the statutory framework is even stricter. Project Managers should act with diligence, working with local authorities to ensure that the contamination is dealt with promptly and lawfully. The powers of local authorities are significant and it must be in the best interests of the employer/developer to keep local authorities informed and 'on-side'. EPA 1990, Pt IIA[19] deals with contaminated land. The Act provides for every local authority to inspect and identify contaminated land (ie land on or under which are substances that create a significant possibility of harm being caused, or of pollution of controlled waters), and to keep a permanent register of such land[20]. The local authority has a further duty to require remediation works by serving notice on the person who caused or permitted the contamination, or, if he cannot be identified, on the owner or the occupier[21]. Where the substances are likely to cause 'serious' harm or pollution, the land is to be designated a 'special' site, subject to further regulations[22].

PRACTICAL CONSIDERATIONS

The treatment and disposal of waste and contamination is a specialist field, with great potential cost implications, and takes place against a back-drop of a detailed regulatory framework. The Project Manager should consult with the Contractor or waste disposal sub-contractor about the most cost-effective and time-efficient compliance with the regulations. The local authority should, if asked, give guidance about local provision for commercial waste disposal. As the Project Manager will usually want to conserve time, keeping the local authority fully informed is usually a good idea.

3 Building control

The Building Regulations issued under the Building Act 1984 impose requirements on persons carrying out almost all substantial building work in England and Wales. All designers of building work should be fully cognisant of the requirements of the Building Regulations. The Project Manager's role is therefore usually secondary, and limited to overseeing that the regulations are referred to and adhered to. Nevertheless, Project Managers should have a good general awareness of the types of work to which Building Regulations apply, and should know where to find the detail of approved behaviour should it be necessary for them to carry out quick research.

19 Introduced by Environment Act 1995, s 57.
20 EPA 1990, ss 78E and 78R.
21 EPA 1990, ss 78E and 78F.
22 EPA 1990, s 78C.
23 Building Act 1984, s 121.
24 Powell-Smith and Billington The Building Regulations (10th edn, 1995) p 12.

The Building Act 1984 has a wide application to 'permanent or temporary building … any other structure or erection of whatever kind or nature[23]' … This definition is thought to include many structures which might not otherwise be thought of as buildings, such as fences, radio towers, silos, etc[24].

The Building Act 1984 empowers the Secretary of State to make regulations about the design and construction of buildings and the provision of services, equipment and fittings in connection with buildings. Building Regulations themselves are issued by statutory instrument fairly frequently. The Building Regulations 2000 have replaced and consolidated all previous amendments[25]. At the date of publication there have been two further amending regulations. The Building Regulations are the rules by which Project Managers must monitor compliance.

Supplementing the Building Regulations are the Approved Documents, which give *'practical guidance with respect to the requirements of any provision of building regulations'*[26]. The Architect or Designer of a project should have copies of the Approved Documents and the Project Manager should ensure that the details in the Approved Documents have been properly adhered to. The Approved Documents and the focus of any local authority building control scrutiny (and therefore where the Project Manager should take interest) are in the following areas of work:

A   Structure.

B   Fire safety.

C   Site preparation and resistance to moisture.

D   Toxic substances.

E   Resistance to the passage of sound.

F   Ventilation.

G   Hygiene.

H   Drainage and waste disposal

J   Heat producing appliances.

K   Protection from falling/collision/impact,

LI   Conservation of fuel and power.

M   Access and facilities for disabled people;

N   Glazing – safety: impact/opening/cleaning,

R7   Materials and workmanship.

25   SI 2000/2531.
26   Building Act 1984, s 6.

For a useful readable initial guide to the Building Regulations, the Stationery Office issues a *Manual to the Building Regulations*, which is now on its third edition.

It is for local authorities to enforce the Building Regulations[27]. A local authority officer has the right to enter premises to ascertain whether there is or has been a contravention of the Building Regulations as well as for other specified purposes[28]. Such entry can be gained at reasonable hours on 24 hours' notice to the occupier of the premises (save in the case of a factory or workplace), and the officer should, on request, provide a document proving his authority. To refuse him entry where all the formalities have been complied with is an offence. In any event, it will always, we think, be in the best interests of all parties involved in progressing works to be co-operative with officers of the building control department of the local authority.

It is often easier (and is the more usual practice) for an employer to require the contractor to deal with Building Regulations submissions and the monitoring of compliance. However, the responsibility, at least for monitoring, may well be given to the Project Manager. It is therefore useful to describe to some degree the processes that the Project Manager is likely to encounter. Where it is intended that there is to be building work or a material change of use, it will be necessary to supply to the local authority a building notice (reg 13) or full plans (reg 14). Full plans are needed where it is intended that the work will include the erection of a building fronting on to a private street.

(a) Building Notice (reg 13)

A Building Notice must state:

1   The name and address of the person intending to carry out the work and signed by that person or on the company's behalf.

2   A statement that it is a Building Notice for the purpose of reg 12(2)(a).

3   A description of the proposed building work or material change of use.

4   The location and use or intended use of the building to which the notice relates.

If the building work to be carried out involves the erection or extension of a building, the Building Notice should be accompanied by:

5   A plan to scale of not less than 1:1250, showing the size and position of the building, or the building as extended, and its relationship to adjoining boundaries, the external boundaries of the plot of land upon which the building is found,

27 Building Act 1984, s 91.
28 Building Act 1984, s 95.

and the size, position and use of every other (proposed) building within that plot and the width and position of any street on or within the boundaries of the plot.

6   A statement specifying the number of storeys of the building.

7   Details of the drainage design, of precautions taken in building over a drain, sewer or disposal main, and of the steps to be taken to comply with any regulations imposed by the local authority.

There are also specific additional requirements where the work involves the insertion of insulating material into the cavity walls of a building, and in certain circumstances where the building work involves the provision of a hot water storage system[29].

(b) Full Plans (reg 14)

If the Full Plan submission is required it should include:

1   A statement that the plans are deposited for the purpose of reg 12(2)(b).

2   Full Plans in duplicate (or a single copy if the work relates to a house or flat). 'Full Plans' is defined as a description of the work and everything otherwise required for a Building Notice.

3   Other plans to show that the work complies with the regulations.

4   A statement notifying whether the building will be put to a designated use under the Fire Precautions Act 1971.

A Building Notice expires three years from submission. If the works have not yet started, a further Building Notice is required[30].

(c) Other notices

The Building Regulations generally require that building control be kept well informed about the progress of the works. There are requirements that notice should be given to the local authority at various stages of the works. Specifically:

1   When the work is to start (at least two days before work starts)[31].

29 Building Regulations 2000, SI 2000/2531, reg 13(3), (4) respectively.
30 SI 2000/2531, reg 13(7).
31 SI 2000/2531, reg 15(1).

2   Prior to covering up any excavation for a foundation, any foundation, any damp proof course or any concrete or other material laid over a site (at least one day before the covering up).[32]

3   Covering up of a drain or sewer (at least one day before the covering up).[33]

4   Within five days of completing the building work (or the completion of certain drainage works)[34].

5   At least five days before any part of the building is to be occupied if the building is not completed[35].

The sanction for failing to provide notice is that the local authority may require that the works be cut into, laid open or pulled down so that the local authority can check whether the regulations have been complied with[36]. This will obviously be a serious set-back to the progress of the works. However, the Project Manager should be aware that all is not lost if one of the stages of notice is omitted. Regulation 21 deals with what is known as unauthorised building work. As soon as the Project Manager notices that the Contractor or other individual has failed to comply with the regulations, he should ensure that the owner applies in writing to the local authority for a Regularisation Certificate, sending with this application[37]:

1   a statement stating the application is made in accordance with reg 21;

2   a description of the unauthorised work;

3   a plan of the unauthorised work; and

4   a plan showing additional work needed to be carried out to ensure that the unauthorised work complies with the Building Regulations.

In these circumstances the Project Manager should know that the local authority is more or less permitted to make whatever investigations it thinks appropriate.

The local authority may make such tests of drains or sewers as are necessary to establish whether the works comply with the drainage and waste disposal requirements, and take samples of materials to be used in the works to ascertain whether they comply with the regulations[38].

32 SI 2000/2531, reg 15(2)(a).
33 SI 2000/2531, reg 15(2)(b).
34 SI 2000/2531, reg 15(4), (3) respectively.
35 SI 2000/2531, reg 15(5).
36 SI 2000/2531, reg 15(6).
37 SI 2000/2531, reg 21(3).
38 SI 2000/2531, reg 18 and 19 respectively.
39 SI 2000/2531, reg 17.

The local authority shall give completion certificates on request[39]. The Project Manager should be aware that these may be needed as part of the conditions of sale of the property (if it is being sold by the Project Manager's Employer) or for building insurance purposes, and should ensure that he gets a copy.

For more information on environmental legislation, we recommend reference to a website produced by the Environment Agency at address *www.environment-agency.gov.uk/netregs/*. This is the only British website designed to help small businesses navigate through the maze of environmental legislation.

4 European procurement legislation

The Project Manager may be involved advising the Employer prior to contract. Where he does so, and where the Employer falls within a defined category of public employer ('contracting authority' – defined below), he must have full reference to a host of EC directives generally referred to as public procurement legislation.

European legislation is directed at the harmonisation and transparency of public procurement throughout the EU. The aim is to further the EU objectives of the free flow of goods, persons and services between Member States and to further the principle of non-discrimination on grounds of nationality. Since implementation by three sets of UK regulations, the EU legislation has a broader role in law as the potential focus for challenging procurement decisions by public bodies regardless of any inter-state element[40]. The UK regulations also implement the requirements of the EU Remedies Directive[41]. When advising a 'contracting authority' during the tendering process, a Project Manager must ensure that the Employer treads very carefully.

(a) Contracting authorities

The Regulations define and list those bodies that constitute a contracting authority and must comply with the requirements of the regulations. A contracting authority includes government ministers and departments, the Houses of Parliament, fire and police authorities, and local authorities[42]. The Regulations apply whenever a

---

40 Public Works Contracts Regulations 1991, SI 1991/2680; Public Supply Contracts Regulations 1995, SI 1995/201; and Public Services Contracts Regulations 1993, SI 1993/3228.
41 Directive 89/665 'on the co-ordination of the laws, regulations and administrative procedures relating to the application of review procedures to the award of public supply and public works contracts'.
42 The Public Works Contracts Regulations 1991, SI 1991/2680, reg 3. All the references to Regulations in this section of the chapter are to SI 1991/2680; however, the requirements of all three regulations are very similar.

contracting authority seeks offers in relation to a proposed public works contract[43]. A public works contract is defined as a contract for the carrying out of a work or works for a contracting authority, or under which a contracting authority engages another to procure such works[44].

(b) The regulations

Generally speaking, the regulations set out specific requirements as to the criteria and procedure used to award contracts. They only apply where the contracting authority has sought offers for such contracts. They do not apply where an authority decides not to put work, supplies or services out to tender. Also, they only apply where the estimated value of the contract comes above certain thresholds. For example, in relation to public works contracts the threshold is €5,000,000.

The regulations require technical specifications to be included in the contract documents[45]. Such technical specifications must be defined by reference to relevant European standards where these exist and are appropriate. Technical specifications which would tend to favour a particular contractor cannot generally be included.

There are three procedures for tendering which are permitted by the regulations: open, restricted and negotiated[46]. The contracting authority, on the Project Manager's advice, may choose between them, save that the negotiated procedure can only be used in exceptional circumstances, such as where the nature of the works or their risks do not permit overall contract pricing. The open procedure involves advertising the intention to contract generally and comparing each tender received. Under the restricted procedure, the authority is allowed to choose from those persons expressing an interest in tendering from which it will actually invite a formal tender.

The regulations also lay down the criteria on which Contractors' tenders may be rejected without having to consider their bids on the merits[47]. These include tenderers that are or have been bankrupt or guilty of a criminal offence or an act of grave misconduct in business, for example. A lack of technical capacity can also rule out a Contractor.

Once the authority has gathered its range of non-excluded bids under whichever procedure, it must award the contract on the basis of the offer made. The award must either be an acceptance of the lowest price or an acceptance of the offer most

43   SI 1991/2680, reg 5.
44   SI 1991/2680, reg 2.
45   SI 1991/2680, Pt II.
46   SI 1991/2680, Pt III.
47   SI 1991/2680, Pt IV.

'economically advantageous'. 'Economically advantageous' involves consideration of a range of factors that should be specified to the tenderers, depending on the type of contract involved – for example, the period for completion, running costs, profitability and technical merit.

(c) Sanctions

If a contracting authority fails to comply with the extensive provisions of the regulations, a relevant contractor may seek remedies against the authority[48]. Such Contractor would be one which sought, or seeks, or would have wished, to be the Contractor to whom a public works contract is awarded, and is a national of an established member state of the EU. The Contractor must show that it has suffered or risks suffering loss or damage. This requirement is not, however, a difficult one to satisfy, as it merely requires a genuine interest in participating in an award from which the Contractor has not been lawfully excluded. The remedies which may be awarded are damages where the contract has already been awarded to another contractor, or suspension of a non-compliant procedure, or setting aside of an illegal decision falling short of the award of the contract or damages[49].

The famous case of *Harmon* shows graphically what expensive errors can be made by an ill-advised contracting authority[50]. It demonstrates why Project Managers involved in the tender process for a contracting authority must have regard for the detail of the public procurement legislation. The common law also provides more limited protection for tenderers, and the Project Manager should be aware that even when advising any employer in relation to a tender process the process should be transparent and, once published, should be followed.

CASE LAW

Tendering pursuant to EU Procurement Regulations

Harmon CFEM Façades (UK) Ltd v Corporate Officer of the House of Commons[51]

This case related to the fenestration of Portcullis House, the annexe to the Houses of Parliament, constructed to make more office space for MPs. The House of Commons, when seeking tenders, set out its criteria for awarding the contract as 'overall value for money' without specifying further what this

---

48 SI 1991/2680, reg 31.
49 SI 1991/2680, reg 31(6), (7).
50 *Harmon CFEM Façades (UK) Ltd v Corporate Officer of the House of Commons* (1999) 67 Con LR 1.
51 *Harmon CFEM Façades (UK) Ltd v Corporate Officer of the House of Commons* (1999) 67 Con LR 1.

meant. This criterion was not allowed under the regulations. Authorities may award to the lowest priced tender or the most 'economically advantageous', but only if the criteria of the latter were made transparent. In this case, in the absence of further specifying the tender criteria, the House of Commons was bound in law to accept the lowest priced tender without regard to other factors. It failed to do so and awarded the contract to a partly British Contractor which had not returned the lowest tender. Harmon were awarded millions of pounds in damages.

5 Housing Grants, Construction and Regeneration Act 1996

It is fair to say that most Contractors operate within a small profit margin, and many work in such a way that on a snapshot view, at any given time, they could be regarded as technically insolvent. They are very dependent upon regular cashflow. One of the purposes of the Housing Grants, Construction and Regeneration Act 1996 (Construction Act) was to try to minimise the cash-flow difficulties which face Contractors and to give them protection against employers keeping back payments for whatever reason. This statutory intervention succeeds, at least in part, in weighing the scales more in favour of the Contractor than the Employer. For example, in certain circumstances the Construction Act imposes payment terms upon the Employer and, where the Employer fails to pay in accordance with the payment terms, allows the Contractor to suspend work legally, without repudiating the contract. The Project Manager, as the Employer's agent, should therefore be well aware of the pitfalls that the Construction Act presents for employers.

The Construction Act provisions apply only to construction contracts as defined[52]. Broadly, construction contracts must be evidenced in writing, relate to the carrying out of construction operations in England, Wales and Scotland, and cannot be contracts where one of the parties is or intends to be a residential occupier[53]. Andrew Davies (see Chapter 10) describes the provisions in relation to applicability in more detail, specifically dealing with contracts which are excluded, and this should be referred to wherever there is uncertainty as to whether the Construction Act applies[54].

---

52 Construction Act 1996, s 104.
53 Construction Act 1996, ss 104(6) (b), 107 & 106.
54 Page 183 below.

(a) Payment terms

Apart from short-term construction contracts (of less than 45 days), the Construction Act requires that a Contractor is entitled to payment by instalments[55]. The Employer and Contractor are free to agree the amounts of the payments and the intervals at which, or circumstances in which, they become due[56]. However, in the absence of such agreement the relevant provisions of the Scheme for Construction Contracts (the Scheme) apply[57].

1 AMOUNT

In the absence of agreement, the Scheme provides that the sum payable is the amount equal to the value of any work performed in accordance with the construction contract to the end of the relevant period (together with payment for materials, where provided for in the contract, and any other sum provided for in the contract), less the amount already due (and paid)[58].

2 INSTALMENTS

Where the parties have failed to agree the intervals by which instalments should be paid, the Scheme provides that a stage payment becomes due simply on the making of a claim by the Contractor[59]. This could potentially cause an Employer great cashflow difficulties himself, so the Project Manager should always advise the employer prior to contract to agree the intervals by which payments are to be made. The Construction Act further provides that every construction contract shall provide a final date for payment in relation to any sum that becomes due[60]. The Employer and Contractor are also free to agree the final date for payment and the Project Manager should encourage them to do so. In the absence of such agreement, the Scheme again steps in, requiring payment to be made, at the latest, 17 days from the date the payment becomes due[61]. There are also provisions as to when the final instalment falls due, namely, 30 days following completion of the work or the making of a claim by the Contractor, whichever is the later[62].

---

55 Construction Act 1996, s 109(1).
56 Construction Act 1996, s 109(2).
57 Construction Act 1996, s 109(3); Scheme for Construction Contracts (England and Wales) Regulations 1998, SI 1998/649, Schedule, Pt II, paras 2–4.
58 SI 1998/649, Schedule, Pt II, para 2.
59 SI 1998/649, Schedule, Pt II, para 4(b).
60 Construction Act 1996, s 110(1)(b).
61 SI 1998/649, Schedule, Pt II, para 8.
62 SI 1998/649, Schedule, Pt II, para 5.

3 NOTICES

The Construction Act also requires an employer to respond promptly to claims made by Contractors and imposes a system of notices. The Project Manager should be alive to the very quick response required by the Construction Act, especially if he receives claims on behalf of the Employer. First, the Act provides that the Employer should provide what has become known as a 's 110 Notice' to the Contractor not later than five days from when the payment in relation to a particular claim becomes due[63]. The s 110 notice should set out how much the Employer proposes to pay and the basis upon which the amount is calculated. Secondly, and more importantly, if the Employer intends to withhold payments and not to comply completely with the Contractor's application, then he must serve what has become known as a 'Withholding Notice'[64]. To be effective, this notice must specify the amount which is to be withheld and the ground or grounds for withholding payment[65]. If more than one ground is cited the notice must also specify the amount of money attributable to each ground. A valid Withholding Notice must also be issued by the Employer before the prescribed period before the final date for payment. The parties are free to agree what the prescribed period is to be; alternatively, the Withholding Notice must be given not later than seven days before the final date for payment[66]. The s 110 Notice may double as a Withholding Notice so long as it contains the required detail[67]. It is certainly simpler to advise the Employer to consider what his position will be on payment well before the deadline for service of a Withholding Notice.

The Employer should be advised that the Contractor has the right, where a sum due under a construction contract is not paid in full by the final date for payment, and in the absence of an effective Withholding Notice, to pursue the Employer for the full sum in adjudication or to suspend works on the contract lawfully[68]. This latter course of action is permitted subject only to the Contractor giving the Employer at least seven days' notice of intention to suspend, and setting out the ground or grounds for suspension in the notice. A suspension by the Contractor will be lawful (and will not amount to a repudiation of the contract) even where the Employer has a valid set-off, if it has not been raised in a valid Withholding Notice[69]. The right of the Contractor to suspend work ends when the Employer makes payment in full of the amount due[70].

---

63 Construction Act 1996, s 110(2) and SI 1998/649, Schedule, Pt II, para 9.
64 Construction Act 1996, s 111(1).
65 Construction Act 1996, s 111(2).
66 Construction Act 1996, s 111(3) and SI 1998/649, Schedule, Pt II, para 10, Part II.
67 Construction Act 1996, s 111(1).
68 Construction Act 1996, ss 108 and 112.
69 *Levolux AT Ltd v Ferson Contractors Ltd* [2002] BLR 341: no set-off could be raised in the absence of a valid Withholding Notice, so the sub-contractor was entitled to suspend the works.
70 Construction Act 1996, s 112(3).

Below is a table which provides two examples of the application of the provisions of the Construction Act and the Scheme. It simply demonstrates that it is better for the Employer to agree payment terms, and the Project Manager should advise him accordingly:

Table of dates for payment under the Scheme

Stage	Parties have agreed monthly instalments but nothing more	No agreement on any payment terms
Payment application made	1 January	1 January
Monies due	8 January	1 January
Latest date for Employer to specify sums to be paid[71]	13 January	6 January
Latest date for Employer (or Project Manager on his behalf) to serve a withholding notice[72]	18 January	11 January
Final date for payment	25 January	18 January
Date Contractor may issue adjudication proceedings on basis of non-payment and/or give 7 days' notice of intention to suspend the works	26 January	19 January
Lawful suspension of works by Contractor	3 February	27 January

4 PAY WHEN PAID CLAUSES

In accordance with the general scheme of the Construction Act, it also prohibits conditions of contract which impose a *'pay when paid'* obligation on the Contractor.[73] A term making payment to a Contractor or Sub-contractor under a construction contract conditional on the paying Employer or Contractor receiving payment from a third person (the ultimate employer) will be ineffective, save in very limited circumstances. A Project Manager should advise his client that they cannot rely on such clauses.

71 Section 110 notice.
72 Construction Act 1996, s 111.
73 Construction Act 1996, s 113.

5 ADJUDICATION

The Construction Act also provides for any party to refer a dispute pertaining to a construction contract to an adjudicator at any time[74]. This is a short timetable dispute resolution procedure which should result in a decision which is binding and enforceable in the courts until the dispute is finally determined by legal proceedings, by arbitration or by agreement[75]. An adjudication decision will be enforceable irrespective of challenges to the merits or validity of the adjudicator's decision[76]. It is thus a powerful tool for a party who is properly geared up for the rigours of this swift resolution procedure. As a result, it is our view that Project Managers unfamiliar with the procedure and seeking to use adjudication, or on the receiving end of a notice to refer to adjudication, ought to seek specialist advice, whether from experienced lawyers or claims consultants. Project Managers should also note that it is possible to use the payment provisions contained in the Construction Act and statutory adjudication to secure payment of their own fees relating to construction operations[77].

6 Contracts (Rights of Third Parties) Act 1999

The Contracts (Rights of Third Parties) Act 1999 (C(RTP)A 1999) allows third parties, those who are not party to a contract, to enforce certain terms. Andrew McCormack, in Chapter 3, has addressed what effect C(RTP)A has on the role of a Project Manager with reference to liability for design and workmanship. The scope of C(RTP)A is, however, potentially wide, encompassing aspects of the Project Manager's work that might not be anticipated, far beyond the range of collateral warranties.

The enforceable rights, self-evidently, arise from contracts. The only excluded contracts are to be found in C(RTP)A 1999, s 6 and they do not include construction contracts but do include contracts of employment. Thus if a Project Manager is employed under a contract of employment, C(RTP)A operates so as to exclude any right on a third party to enforce any term of the contract of employment against the Project Manager[78].

C(RTP)A 1999 provides that a third party may enforce terms not only where the contract *expressly* provides that the third party may, but also where the term '*purports*

---

74 Construction Act 1996, s 108.
75 Construction Act 1996, s 108(3).
76 *Macob Civil Engineering Ltd v Morrison Construction Ltd* [1999] BLR 93.
77 *Gillies Ramsay Diamond v PJW Enterprises Ltd* [2003] BLR 48, Ct Sess: a letter containing conditions of appointment of a consultant (contract administrator) was a construction contract under the Construction Act.
78 C(RTP)A 1999, s 6(3).

to confer a benefit' on the third party, in which case the third party must be expressly identified in the contract as a member of a class or answering a particular description (but need not be in existence when the contract is entered into[79]). Risks to the Project Manager are presently compounded because the courts have not given a view on what is meant by 'purporting to confer a benefit'. When a Project Manager is administrating the construction contract he must consider a whole additional dimension of potential rights that may be given inadvertently or otherwise to third parties.

In practice, this may be of more concern to the Contractor than to the Employer (or his representative, the Project Manager). For example, where the Contractor has contracted with the Employer not to cause dust, noise or other disturbance to local residents, the local residents may pursue a claim directly against the Contractor in the event of noise or other disturbance. In this case, the Contractor has apparently agreed to confer a benefit on the local residents (one of whom would be a member of a class expressly identified in the contract to be the beneficiaries of a term – therefore falling within C(RTP)A 1999, s 1). The C(RTP)A might, however, also make the Project Manager more accountable to the Contractor. Where, for example, the Project Manager's terms of appointment identify various tasks he is to carry out in relation to (and for the benefit of) the Contractor, the Contractor may then seek to enforce those terms against the Project Manager. For example, where the Project Manager has agreed with the Employer to make prompt provision of certain information or drawings in his control to the contractor (planning approvals, existing services drawings etc), the Contractor might successfully pursue a claim and seek specific performance of this term against the Project Manager.

Another area which is potentially of great importance to the Employer is the potential rights of a third party to veto the variation or rescission (premature end) of the contract by the parties[80]. If the variation to the works is such that it would extinguish or alter the third party's entitlement under that right, it would, in certain circumstances, be necessary to obtain the consent of the third party affected before the variation or rescission could become valid. One example of a situation where this might occur is where an employer, developing a public building, varies the scope of works by which a provision in the specification for a disabled lift or lavatory is varied to be one for able-bodied persons only. A disabled person, in certain circumstances (where he has effectively registered his right with the Employer), will have to give his assent or else the variation will not be valid[81].

The risks are potentially wide, and the true scope of C(RTP)A 1999 is presently untried in the courts. The solution which has become accepted in the construction industry, and which would seem advisable for the Project Manager to adopt when

---

79 C(RTP)A 1999, s 1(1), (3).
80 C(RTP)A 1999, s 2.
81 C(RTP)A 1999, s 2(1)(a).

in contractual negotiations for his own terms of appointment, as well as the construction contract, is to exclude the effect of the C(RTP)A as much as possible[82]. The Joint Contracts Tribunal (JCT) has adopted a policy that all JCT Standard Forms of Building Contract should contract out of C(RTP)A 1999 by use of the words: 'Notwithstanding any other provision of this Contract nothing in this Contract confers or purports to confer any right to enforce any of its terms on any person who is not a party to it.' Given the unseen risks, it would seem to be prudent to adopt wording such as this and to be circumspect when expressly identifying in a contract anyone other than the parties contracting.

7 Limitation Act 1980

The Limitation Act 1980 (LA 1980) will not be of frequent relevance to a Project Manager's operations, but is something for a Project Manager to bear in mind when faced with or considering legal proceedings. Put shortly, LA 1980 puts a time cap on when a party can pursue damages for negligence, breach of contract or some other action in legal proceedings. For example, where a Project Manager has a responsibility for securing planning permission, and he successfully obtains planning permission but not for the intended building. The Employer's intended building (without permission) is constructed, but the local authority later requires the Employer to pull down the building because it has no planning permission. The Employer might then seek to recover his losses by pursuing legal proceedings against the Project Manager. If the action is brought sufficiently long after the events have occurred, the Project Manager can bring a limitation defence which could be a complete bar to the claim being brought.

There are different limitation periods for different kinds of action and in different circumstances, and this chapter is too short to set out all the possible permutations. In broad terms, LA 1980 provides that the limitation period for actions for breach of contract run from six years when the breach of contract occurs[83]. In the above example, the limitation time period therefore starts when the Project Manager makes the wrong application in breach of terms of his contract, even though no damage has yet been suffered as a result. The normal six years' time period is extended to twelve years if the contract has been entered into as a deed (also referred to as being 'under seal'). For tortious actions such as negligence, the time-clock is also (in relation to Project Manager's usual duties) generally six years, generally running from when the damage has been suffered[84]. In the above example, this might be only when the Employer has to pull down his building. The rule that the time clock in negligence

---

82 As permitted, in part, by C(RTP)A 1999, s 1(2).
83 Limitation Act 1980, s 5.
84 Limitation Act 1980, s 2.

only starts when damage is caused creates some serious difficulties in construction cases, because damage (particularly a latent defect) which is caused in the process of building works is often not discovered until some time after the building is completed. For this reason there is an extension to the limitation period where the damage is discovered over three years after it has been caused, of three years from when the claiming party discovered the damage (subject to a long-stop of fifteen years from the date of damage)[85]. There are also exceptions which may be applicable, such as where the claim is based on the defending party's fraud or where the claimant seeks relief from the consequences of a mistake (as defined)[86].

If a party is concerned about leaving himself open to future liability in relation to a contract, he is free (subject to the provisions of UCTA 1977) to try to get the contracting parties to expressly provide for a limitation period in the contract and so cut down the period of exposure that would otherwise apply under LA 1980.

The Law Commission has recently produced proposals for reform of LA 1980 which aim at simplifying the numerous and complicated rules determining limitation periods and, at the same time, hope to improve the injustices resulting from those current principles[87]. The proposals stipulate a three-year limitation period (the 'primary period'), to apply to tort and contract, to run from the date of 'discoverability', with an overall maximum claim period of ten years (the 'long-stop') from the tortious act or breach of contract. The Law Commission hopes that those proposals will make the system easier to understand and protect claimants who might otherwise be unable to pursue a claim before they even discover the problem.

Bibliography

Blount K (gen ed) *Knight's Guide to Building Control Law and Practice* (9th Issue, 2000), Tolley.

Blount K (gen ed) *Knight's Building Regulations (with Approved Documents)* (6th Issue, 2000), Tolley.

Bruce A 'Problems of building site noise and how to avoid them' (1998) 142(35) *Solicitors Journal* 834–835.

Dugdale A (ed) *Clerk and Lindsell on Torts* (18th edn, 2000) Sweet and Maxwell.

Freshfields Construction & Engineering Group *Management Contracting, Law and Practice* (1994) Cavendish Publishing.

85 Limitation Act 1980, ss 14A and 14B.
86 Limitation Act 1980, s 32(1)(a) and (c).
87 Law Com No 270 (2001).

Harris D, Smith C and Wiseman A (ed) *Garner's Environmental Law* (2002) Butterworths.

Manual to the Building Regulations (3rd edn, 2001) The Stationery Office.

Murdoch J and Hughes W *Construction Contracts, Law and Management* (3rd edn, 2000) Spon Press.

Parisotti M 'Decent proposals', *Building Magazine*, 17 May 2002, p 55.

Polley S *Understanding the Building Regulations* (2001) Spon Press.

Powell-Smith V and Billington M *The Building Regulations* (10th edn, 1995) Blackstone Press.

Ramsey V and Furst S (ed) *Keating on Building Contracts* (7th edn, 2001) Sweet and Maxwell.

Speaght A and Stone G *Architect's Legal Handbook* (7th edn, 2000) Architectural Press.

Uff J *Construction Law* (8th edn, 2002) Sweet and Maxwell.

Waite AJ 'Statutory Controls on Construction Site Noise' (1990) 6 Const LJ 97.

Wignall G 'Handling Nuisance Claims: Noise' (1998) 142(31) *Solicitors Journal* 744–745.

CHAPTER 7

Health and safety for Project Managers

By Kathryn Gilbertson

Summary

Health and safety is a huge legal topic, and this chapter simply seeks to give an overview of various health and safety issues which affect Project Managers day to day.

The chapter covers:

- Introduction to health and safety in the UK and the powers of the Health and Safety Commission and Health and Safety Executive.

- Introduction to the key provisions of the Health and Safety at Work etc Act 1974 (HSW):
    - Applicability of Approved Codes of Practice ('ACOPS')
    - Review of the enforcement powers of the authorised inspector
    - Explanation of what enforcement action is likely to be taken
    - Summary of who can be prosecuted and the penalties that can be imposed and, in particular:
    - prosecution of directors
    - corporate manslaughter.

- Review of the Management of Health and Safety at Work Regulations (1999):
    - Key pointers on the measures to prevent or control exposure to safety risk
    - What is meant by certain key terms:
        - competent advisers
        - emergency plans
        - training and information
        - co-operation and co-ordination.

- What a risk assessment is, the types of risk assessment and the standard terms used in risk assessments.

- Requirements under the Health and Safety (Consultation with Employees) Regulations 1996.

- Guidance on when you should report an accident or a dangerous occurrence, together with whom to report to and what must be reported.
- Some tips on specific safety issues for Project Managers:
  - permits to work
  - manual handling
  - lifting equipment
  - working at height.
- Introduction to the Construction (Health, Safety and Welfare) Regulations 1996 and duties under those regulations.
- Introduction to the Construction (Design and Management) Regulations 1994 ('CDM Regulations'), including:
  - establishing who the client is
  - the role of planning supervisor
  - the role of the designer
  - the role of the principal contractor
  - the requirement to keep a Health and Safety plan
  - the requirement to keep a Health and Safety file
  - what is meant by competent and adequate resources
  - what is meant by Employee Consultation and the CDM Regulations.

1 Introduction

Project Managers can be considered as employers on many construction sites or within the field of managing a given task or project. They will have detailed knowledge of the work being undertaken and so, with skill and care, will be able to advise the appropriate safety management strategies, assess the hazards and risks of work being undertaken, investigate the causes of accidents and supervise work tasks.

In this chapter we provide an overview of the relevant safety legislation which will be applicable to the Project Managers, together with some specific safety rules that require detailed knowledge.

2 Health and safety law in the UK

(a) Health and Safety at Work etc Act 1974 (HSWA 1974)

This applies to all persons at work, whether employer, employee or self-employed. HSWA 1974 also protects persons not at work, such as the general public, where their health or safety may be affected by any work being undertaken.

The Act aims: to secure the health, safety and welfare of people at work; to protect other people from risks arising out of work activities; and to control how equipment is designed, manufactured and supplied for use in the workplace.

(b) Health and Safety Commission (HSC)

The HSC is the national authority for all health and safety at work matters. It is the policy-making body responsible to the Secretary of State for Work and Pensions and makes arrangements to implement HSWA 1974 itself. It has as its mission statement 'to ensure that risks to people's health and safety from work activities are properly controlled'.

Its goals are: to continue to reduce injury rates; to continue to reduce work-related ill health and consequent days lost from work; to continue to improve the working environment; and to prevent major incidents with catastrophic consequences occurring in high hazard industry.

The HSC submits proposals for new regulations, has the power to direct the Health and Safety Executive or others to investigate accidents or dangerous occurrences, and makes reports on an annual basis as to the status of safety performance in the UK.

(c) Health and Safety Executive (HSE)

The HSE is the executive wing of the HSC and acts in accordance with directions and guidance given by the HSC. The HSE undertakes the major enforcement activity of safety legislation.

3 Health and Safety at Work etc Act 1974

(a) Section 2: duties of employers to employees

Employers must, so far as is reasonably practicable, protect the health, safety and welfare of their employees. To do this they need to provide:

*   safe plant and safe systems of work;
*   arrangements for safe use, handling, storage and transportation of articles and substances;
*   adequate information, instruction, training and supervision;
*   safe places of work including safe access/egress;
*   safe working environment with adequate welfare facilities.

5546545554554555555555555555

Employers with five or more employees must prepare a written health and safety policy statement which details the arrangements for safety, and they should bring this to their employees' attention. Employers must also consult with their employee representatives when making safety arrangements.

(b) Section 3: duties of employers to others

Employers must, so far as is reasonably practicable, conduct their business to ensure that people who are not their employees are not exposed to health and safety risks. This duty extends to visitors, contractors and members of the public. Individuals who are self-employed are placed under a similar duty and must take care of themselves.

(c) Section 4: duties relating to premises

Where organisations share or control work premises then they must, so far as is reasonably practicable, ensure the health and safety of all non-employees who work there.

Therefore, landlords and managing agents are responsible for the safety of those working in the common parts of the building, for example cleaners, maintenance staff, lift engineers etc. Non-domestic tenants are also responsible for safety in those areas covered by their lease.

(d) Section 6: duty of manufacturers

Anyone who designs, manufactures, imports or supplies articles for use at work must ensure, so far as is reasonably practicable, that those articles are safe for their intended use.

(e) Section 7: duty of employees

While at work, employees have a duty:

- not to endanger themselves or others through their acts or omissions.
- to co-operate with their employer by following safe working practices, wearing protective equipment etc.

(f) 'Reasonably practicable'

Most health and safety duties require the duty holder to do everything so far as is reasonably practicable. This places an obligation on the duty holder to show that it has done everything that is reasonably practicable in the circumstances. Thus there is a balancing act of risk to health and safety against the cost of overcoming that risk and the methods available to undertake it.

The Court of Appeal case of *Davies v Health and Safety Executive*[1] confirms that the obligation is on the employer to show that the work it undertook was reasonably practicable, and so employers should record their decision to implement and reject certain safety measures if they wish to make use of this defence.

Safety measures must be proportionate to the risk, and thus the crux of the safety hierarchy is to identify and assess the risk and then identify and assess the available control measures. After an incident, it is usual for an employer or an inspector to identify another control measure that should have been used to prevent the accident occurring. Therefore, it is imperative that a duty holder contemplate a work task from all perspectives before determining whether the time and cost involved to control it is disproportionately high in comparison to the risk involved.

Guidance is often available from the Approved Codes of Practice, HSE specific guidance, relevant British Standards or specific industry protocols.

(g) Approved Codes of Practice (ACOPs)

ACOPs have a special status in law. They are not statutory requirements in themselves but may be used in criminal proceedings as evidence that statutory requirements have been contravened. Where a prosecution is for the infringement of a regulation and there is an appropriate ACOP linked with that regulation, it is for the defendant company or person to show that the provisions of the ACOP were observed, or that what was done was equally effective or better than that proposed by the ACOP.

In most circumstances, persons are better advised to follow the ACOP than to deviate from it.

(h) Enforcement

Only authorised inspectors are able to carry out the functions set out under HSWA 1974. Thus for construction sites, factories and heavy industry, HSE inspectors will undertake the inspection, interview and the bringing of proceedings, while offices, shops, and light industrial units will be inspected by the local authority environmental officer.

---

1   [2002] EWCA Crim 2949, [2003] IRLR 170.

Inspectors have a wide range of powers enabling them to undertake investigations. Contraventions will positively require certain works to be undertaken. Inspectors are also able to enter premises, seize evidence, and question witnesses. In particular, their powers include the following.

1 POWERS OF ENTRY

Inspectors can enter premises where they believe it is necessary to do so to carry out their duties. These visits can be at any time. Often such visits will be by appointment where it is imperative that the inspector speaks to certain individuals. It is an offence to obstruct an inspector who is attempting to exercise these powers. Inspectors should show their identification details or 'warrant card' before gaining entry or exercising their powers. Thus it is recommended that employers always seek to ascertain the authority of the inspector by viewing the warrant card. Once on the premises, the inspector can carry out examinations, ask that evidence is left undisturbed, or take photographs and make other records of the circumstances during their investigation.

2 SEIZURE OF EVIDENCE

An inspector can collect physical evidence including samples to test for environmental hazards. They may also dismantle equipment and detain it so that it can be preserved for use in proceedings.

3 DOCUMENTARY EVIDENCE

Inspectors can require the production of documents which they deem necessary to see for the purposes of their investigations. These will include formal records kept in accordance with statutory requirements (such as an accident book, lift reports etc) but also any company papers such as a safety manual, correspondence, internal memoranda, or any audit reports on safety. It is not possible to refuse an inspector such documents on the grounds of confidentiality or trade secrets.

4 INTERVIEW

An interview under HSWA 1974, s 20 is unusual in that there is no 'right to silence' for a company or individual under investigation. Therefore an individual must respond to all questions asked of them by an inspector. Most s 20 interviews follow a written question and answer pattern which is then signed by the individual to confirm that the content of their answers is correct to their knowledge and belief.

The inspector is able to ask any person who he believes can give information relevant to an enquiry to answer questions as necessary. The person being interviewed is entitled to have a nominated person to be present with him. The nominated person may be a lawyer (although not always). Such interviews are often used in proceedings against a person's employer. The inspector will rely on those answers to conclude their investigations and determine whether any safety provisions have been breached.

On many occasions an inspector will rely on the more usual interview under the Police and Criminal Evidence Act 1984. During this type of interview an inspector will generally caution the interviewee: 'You do not have to say anything. But it may harm your defence if you do not mention when questioned something which you later rely on in court. Anything you do say may be given in evidence.'

(i) Enforcement action

Inspectors are able to use their discretion over how they deal with non-compliance issues. On many occasions they will take informal action via a letter requesting that action be taken within a certain time period. Such correspondence tends to confirm the deficiency identified and recommend certain works to be undertaken referring the individual to guidance documents that have been issued. However, an inspector can also serve one or two types of enforcement notice under HSWA 1974.

1 IMPROVEMENT NOTICE

Where an inspector is of the opinion that one or more statutory provisions have been contravened, he may issue an Improvement Notice requiring the responsible person to take necessary action to remedy the contravention within a specified time period. The notice will specify the provision which the inspector believes has not been complied with, give the reasons why the inspector is of that opinion, and specify the time period in which the work is to be carried out. This must be not less than 21 days. The inspector may specify the action that the inspector believes is necessary to remedy the contravention.

2 PROHIBITION NOTICE

Where an inspector forms an opinion that an activity is being carried out (or is likely to be carried out) that will involve a serious risk of personal injury, he may issue a Prohibition Notice requiring the activity to be stopped. The Prohibition Notice may be 'immediate' or may be 'deferred' by coming into effect at the end of a specified period. The inspector may specify the action to be taken to remedy the cause of the risk or the contravention. If this is done the directions will be issued in a schedule attached to the notice.

Example of an Improvement Notice

Improvement Notice

Health and Safety at Work etc Act 1974 – Sections 21, 22 and 24

Name

I, ...

Address

Trading as

Inspector's full name

Inspector's official designation

One of Her Majesty's Inspectors of being an inspector appointed by an instrument in writing made pursuant to Section 19 of the said Act and entitled to issue this notice

Official address

of

Telephone no:

hereby give you notice that I am of the opinion that

Location of premises or place of activity

at

You, as an employer/self-employed person/person wholly or partly in control of the premises/other are contravening/have contravened in circumstances that make it likely that the contravention will continue or to be repeated* the following statutory provisions:

The reasons for my said opinion are

and I hereby require you to remedy the said contraventions or, as the case may be, the matters occasioning them by

(and I direct that measures specified in the schedule which forms part of this notice shall be taken to remedy the said contraventions or matters)*

Signature   Date

*an improvement notice is also being served on

of

related to the matters contained in this notice

Environment and Safety Information Act 1988

This is a relevant notice for the purposes of the Environment and Safety Information Act 1988 YES/NO*

This page will only form the register entry*

Signature   Date

*delete as appropriate

(j) Appeal

An appeal can be made to an industrial tribunal against the terms of an Improvement Notice or Prohibition Notice. The appeal must be lodged within 21 days of the notice. The appeal can seek to have the terms varied (for example increase the time limit allowed for the Improvement Notice) or can challenge the issue of the notice.

Details of an enforcement notice will be included in the public register unless it relates solely to the protection of persons at work. It is possible to find details of enforcement notices served on the HSE website at www.hse.gov.uk/enforce/index.htm.

(k) Prosecutions

Employers, employees and the self-employed can be prosecuted under HSWA 1974, s 33 if they commit an offence of failing to discharge their duties under the Act. Such prosecutions will initially be heard in the magistrates' court (or sheriff's court in Scotland). The maximum penalty for failing to comply with an Improvement Notice or Prohibition Notice or with a remedy order made by the court under HSWA 1974, s 42 is a fine of £20,000 or term of imprisonment of up to six months, or both. Breaches of HSWA 1974, s 2–6 are subject to a maximum fine of £20,000, while other offences, including breach of health and safety regulations, tend to be subject to a maximum fine of £5,000. Where cases are referred to the Crown Court, either for sentence or for trial, and the defendant is found guilty, then the penalty will be an unlimited fine or up to two years' imprisonment or both.

An analysis of the enforcement statistics compiled by the HSE in their annual report 2002 shows that they have a success rate of about 80% for prosecutions. This is because the duty under health and safety legislation is onerous, and when an accident has occurred the courts are prepared to consider that insufficient steps have been taken to prevent such an occurrence.

(l) Prosecution of directors

Under HSWA 1974, s 37, if it is proved that an offence was committed by a company with the consent or connivance of, or was attributed to neglect on the part of, a director, manager, secretary or other similar officer, then that person as well as the company can be prosecuted.

(m) Corporate manslaughter

Whenever there is a workplace death the police and the HSE will undertake a joint investigation. This will include work-related road traffic accidents. This investigation will be in addition to the coroner's inquest, which will investigate all cases of sudden death to determine the identity of the deceased, and when, where and how they came to their death.

The coroner may adjourn the inquest until any prosecution for manslaughter is over, which tends to be several years after the accident. In cases where an inquest goes ahead prior to prosecution, the verdict may lead to consideration by the Crown Prosecution Service (CPS) for proceedings of corporate manslaughter/manslaughter. Certainly a verdict of unlawful killing would lead the CPS to reconsider their evidence.

For a company to be convicted of corporate manslaughter, a director must be convicted of gross negligence manslaughter. Only if that director is prosecuted can the company in turn be convicted of corporate manslaughter. This is because of the need for the company's directing mind to be shown to have committed the offence. The effect of a manslaughter prosecution would be an unlimited fine for the company and a term of imprisonment up to life for individuals. Charges under health and safety legislation can also carry penalties of up to two years' imprisonment and/or an unlimited fine.

An individual is guilty of gross negligence manslaughter if a jury is satisfied that:

*   the individual owed a duty of care to the deceased;

*   the individual breached that duty of care; and

*   the breach was grossly negligent.

While there has been an increase in the number of prosecutions being brought for manslaughter/corporate manslaughter following workplace incidents, these are unusual. However, in the future such prosecutions will become more common as the HSE/CPS decide to rely on the courts to determine whether in fact the failure of a company and its directors in their duties towards their employees has brought about an individual's death.

For the courts to convict a company of corporate manslaughter, a director/senior manager must be convicted of gross negligence manslaughter and the convicted director/senior manager must represent the directing mind of the company in relation to that death.

For large companies it is often difficult to find a director or senior manager who can be shown to be the company's directing mind and have sufficient involvement in day-to-day activities to be guilty of manslaughter. Thus many of the successful prosecutions have been brought against the smaller organisations.

The Government proposes a new offence of corporate killing, which will make it easier to convict large companies and other organisations following workplace deaths. Such an offence will require proof:

*   of a management failure within the organisation which is one or more of the causes of death; and

*   that this failure represented conduct falling far below that which could be expected of the organisation in the circumstances.

However, these proposals still require inclusion in the Queen's Speech and employers should now consider whether their management systems are sufficiently robust to ensure that they will not be the subject of this future liability.

Other changes proposed by the corporate killing legislation will include a new offence of killing by gross negligence, in which an individual can be convicted where their conduct unintentionally led to someone's death. It is proposed that this will have a penalty of up to ten years' imprisonment.

4 Management of Health and Safety at Work Regulations 1999 (MHSWR 1999)

MHSWR 1999 apply to all work activities, with the exception of those in seagoing ships. They are accompanied by an approved code of practice which gives guidance on compliance with the regulations and specific guidance on young persons at work. It should be noted that the Construction (Design and Management) Regulations 1994 (CDM Regulations) are to be read in conjunction with MHSWR 1999. CDM Regulations place specific duties on clients, planning supervisors, designers and contractors which are in addition to the duties under MHSWR 1999 on a construction project.

The requirements of CDM Regulations include risk assessment (reg 3), health and safety arrangements (reg 5), health surveillance (reg 6), information for employees (reg 10), employees' duties (reg 14) and the protection of young persons (reg 19).

MHSWR 1999 require employers to provide employees with understandable and relevant information on risks to their health and safety, as well as information on how to avoid those risks. When dealing with individuals who have little or no understanding of spoken or written English, employers will need to make special arrangements.

On construction sites there are often conditions which require quick reactions to verbal commands. The inability to speak or understand English could create a particularly high risk to health and safety. However, the blanket refusal to consider non-English employees for any vacancies or work activity would be in breach of the Race Relations Act 1976, and employers need to consider how to communicate effectively with those individuals who do not speak and/or understand English. It may be that small groups of non-English speakers could work together with a supervisor/ganger who could act as their interpreter. This individual would need to stay with the gang at all times in order to deliver induction and briefings, relay instructions and act as their liaison. These arrangements would need to be contained within the health and safety plan so that any work place hazard could be reduced to its lowest level.

(a) Measures to prevent or control exposure to safety risks

(See specific risk assessment section on p 202.)

MHSWR 1999, Sch 1 sets out the principles to use when considering measures to prevent or control exposure to risks. These are:

- avoid risks where possible;

- evaluate risks that cannot be avoided;

- combat risks at source;

- adapt work to the individual, by reviewing design of workplace, choice of equipment, working methods etc;

- adapt to technical progress through regular reviews of risk assessment;

- replace dangerous with non-dangerous or less dangerous (for example substituting chemicals);

- develop a coherent overall prevention policy;

- give priority to collective measures over individual protection (that is, protect all those persons exposed to the risk).

- give appropriate instruction and training.

(b) Competent advisers

Every employer must appoint a competent person to advise in relation to compliance with health and safety requirements. A person is competent if he has sufficient training and experience, or knowledge and other qualities. While there is no requirement for formal qualifications, employers must be satisfied that the person is properly able to assist them.

Preferably the competent person should be an employee within the organisation rather than an external consultant.

(c) Emergency plan

Employers must develop procedures to deal with serious and imminent danger. These emergency plans should consider fire, bomb threats and public disorder.

Employers should maintain a contacts list of the necessary emergency services (police, fire, ambulance services) and make appropriate contacts with them.

(d) Training and information

Employers must provide their employees and others with comprehensive information on the risks to their health and safety (those identified by risk assessment) together with the relevant protective measures (again identified by risk assessments).

Employees should be trained on induction and whenever working arrangements or conditions change. There should also be regular refresher training. By maintaining detailed training records signed by the individual employee upon completion of the appropriate course, employers can be satisfied that they have provided sufficient training for the tasks in hand.

(e) Co-operation and co-ordination

Where two or more employers share work premises they must co-operate with each other to ensure the safety of all persons working on site. Thus where contractors are working in one area they should nominate a person to co-ordinate the joint health and safety arrangements so that all persons are aware of fire safety arrangements, etc.

Employers must make a suitable and sufficient assessment of the risk to the health and safety of their employees and others affected by their activities. Risk assessments should be reviewed on a regular basis and certainly after any accident or incident. The assessment should be revised as appropriate.

(f) Risk assessment

1 WHAT IS A RISK ASSESSMENT?

A risk assessment is a check of what could harm persons at work or affect others by that work. It is generally accepted that a risk assessment should involve five steps:

- assess the actual work task;
- identify the potential hazards involved;
- evaluate the seriousness or severity of those hazards;
- decide upon the control measures necessary to reduce the likelihood of harm being caused;
- record, monitor and review the assessments.

2 TYPES OF RISK ASSESSMENT — GENERIC

These are general assessments covering repetitive work tasks. The intention is that with the necessary control measures in place, the residual risk should be considered low.

3 SITE-SPECIFIC RISK ASSESSMENTS

These are specific to the premises and would take into account any additional hazards that might be present due to work conditions, location or time constraints.

There is always a difficulty with generic risk assessments, in that the compiler or user can be complacent. Thus it is essential that the control measures in place are sufficient to control the risks.

The assessment should be clear and concise, since it is essential that it is understood and used.

4 HIERARCHY OF RISK CONTROL

The competent person carrying out the assessment should consider measures to reduce the risk by taking into account the following hierarchy:

*   **Stop undertaking the task** – design improvements or change the process.

*   **Substitute** – use less hazardous materials.

*   **Minimise the risk** – by limiting exposure to individuals, such as through job rotation.

*   **Control measures** – barriers, warning signs etc.

*   **Personal protective equipment** – this must be used as a last resort since it only protects the individual.

5 TERMS USED IN RISK ASSESSMENT

*   **Harm** – death; bodily injury; damage, physically or mentally.

*   **Hazard** – potential for anything to cause harm.

*   **Risk** – likelihood of harm actually occurring.

*   **Severity** – consequences of that harm occurring.

*   **Control measures** – action to be taken to remove or minimise risk.

Specific risk assessments are required for:

Risks	Regulations
Asbestos	Control of Asbestos at Work Regulations 2002, SI 2002/2675
Chemicals	Control of Substances Hazardous to Health Regulations 1999, SI 1999/437
Design (work for construction and engineering)	Construction (Design and Management) Regulations 1994, SI 1994/3140
Lead	Control of Lead at Work Regulations 1998, SI 1998/543
Manual handling and lifting	Manual Handling Operations Regulations 1992, SI 1992/2793
Noise	Noise at Work Regulations 1989, SI 1989/1790
Personal protective equipment	Personal Protective Equipment at Work Regulations 1992, SI 1992/2966
Pregnant and new mothers	Management of Health and Safety at Work Regulations 1999, SI 1999/3242
VDUs/work stations	Health and Safety (Display Screen Equipment) Regulations 1992, SI 1992/2792
Young persons	Management of Health and Safety at Work Regulations 1999, SI 1999/3242

5 Health and Safety (Consultation With Employees) Regulations 1996

Where employees are not represented by trade union safety representatives under the Safety Representatives and Safety Committees Regulations 1977 [2], employers are required to consult with them on significant health and safety issues. This may be directly with individual employees or with elected employee representatives. Employee representatives are entitled to time off with pay to carry out these functions and to undergo training.

(a) Reporting of accidents or dangerous occurrences

Employers are required to report accidents, injuries or dangerous occurrences under the Reporting of Injuries, Diseases and Dangerous Occurrences Regulations 1995

2 SI 1977/500.

(RIDDOR 1995). Approximately two construction workers are killed every week, and the HSE and local authorities use this information to identify trends, investigate serious accidents and target their resources accordingly.

1 REPORTING PROCEDURE

There is a central reporting facility known as the Incident Contact Centre (ICC) based in Caerphilly. Reports can be made to them by telephone, fax or on the Internet via email. The reports are forwarded from ICC to the relevant inspector for processing. ICC will also forward a copy of the incident report to employers, giving them the opportunity to amend any errors. Employers are required to keep a copy of that report for inspection by visiting inspectors.

2 REPORTING DETAILS

Post-incident Contact Centre, Caerphilly Business Park, Caerphilly, CF83 3GG.

Telephone: 0845 300 9923 (8.30 am to 5.00 pm)

Fax: 0845 300 9924

Email: riddor@natbrit.com.

Website: www.riddor.gov.uk or www.hse.gov.uk – using the Riddor link.

3 WHAT MUST BE REPORTED: DEATH OR MAJOR INJURY

- **Death** – as a result of an accident at work. HSE must be notified immediately.
- **Major injury** – fracture of skull, pelvis, spine, fracture of any bone in arm or wrist, leg or ankle, loss of sight, amputation, loss of consciousness etc.
- **Over three-day injury** – where an employee or self-employed person has three consecutive days off work (excluding the day of accident but including weekends), or where they are unable to undertake their usual working task for over three days.
- **Work-related disease** – poisons, lung diseases, skin cancers, hepatitis etc.
- **Dangerous occurrence** (something that had the potential to result in a reportable incident but not on this occasion) – collapse or failure of lifting equipment, an electrical incident causing fire or explosion, collapse of scaffolding, collapse of a structural building etc.

In order to investigate an accident properly, employers are recommended to keep records which can then be made available to insurance companies or inspectors investigating the incident. Such records can be kept in any form but should include the day and time of the event, details of the persons involved, description of the incident, and any witnesses. Further, employers should keep records confirming the date and method of reporting this accident/incident to ICC.

5 DUTY TO REPORT INJURIES, DANGEROUS OCCURRENCES OR DISEASES

Reportable event	Injured person	Responsible person
Death, specified major industry, over three-day injury or scheduled disease.	Suffered by an employee. Suffered by a self-employed person working under the control of the contractor.	The employer. The person in control of the premises (normally the principal contractor).
Specified major injury, over three-day injury or case of disease.	Suffered by a self-employed person in premises under his own control.	The self-employed person (or someone acting for him).
Death, or injury requiring removal from site to hospital for treatment or major injury occurring in a hospital.	Suffered by a person who is not at work (a member of the public) but who has been affected by the work of someone else.	The person in control of the premises where the accident occurred.
A dangerous occurrence.		The person in control of the premises.

(b) Some specific safety issues for Project Managers

1 PERMITS TO WORK

MHSWR 1999 require permits to be used to control high risk activity where specific hazards could be present. Such work activities that should be covered by a permit may include hot works, roof works, working in confined spaces, lift works, work on scaffold towers or mobile working platforms, demolition works etc.

Key features

1   Permits can only be issued by someone who understands the risks and necessary control measures that are put in place, namely the authorising person.

2   Any person who controls premises could be required to enforce the use of a permit to work system.

3   The permit has to be task specific. The permit should not be viewed as a replacement for risk assessments and method statements since these still need to be done.

4   The permit should be for a limited time period only, clearly dated with specific conditions attached.

5   Permits should not be transferable.

6   The permits should state any safety precautions required before work is done, for example isolation of electricity, discharge of pressurising systems etc.

7   The authorising person should only sign and date the permit when he is satisfied that all necessary precautions have been taken.

8   A permit should not be issued if the risks are too high – for example, bad weather or other dangers.

9   A permit register should be used to prevent conflicts in work activities. Each permit should have a unique number for easy reference and thus enable the authorising person to identify when several permits are operating at once.

10 All permits should be retained for three years by the authorising person.

Typical control measures to be considered when issuing a permit for roof works would include:

- testing of the fragility of the roof structure;

- provision of edge protection;

- prevention of falls of materials/objects;

- adequate means of access – roof ladders, crawling boards etc;

- personal protective equipment.

- Monitoring of climatic conditions.

2 MANUAL HANDLING

The Manual Handling Operations Regulations 1992[3], apply to all construction work and other work which involves an element of manual handling. These regulations

3   SI 1992/2793.

aim to control the risk of injury to workers when handling loads, particularly the risk of back injury. Manual handling operations are defined as any transporting or supporting of a load, including the lifting, putting down, pulling, pushing, carrying and moving by hand or by bodily force.

The regulations place a duty on the employer to avoid, so far as is reasonably practicable, the need for employees to undertake manual handling operations at work which involve a risk to their being injured. When it is not reasonably practicable to avoid the need for manual handling which involves the risk of injury, the employer should:

• assess the risk of all such manual handling operations;

• take appropriate steps to reduce the risk of injury to the lowest practical level.

Employers should take steps to provide employees with general indications of the weight of each load.

Employees also have duties to make use of any system of work provided by their employers. Manual handling assessments should be site specific in order to prevent twisting and lifting actions which cause considerable injury. Furthermore, the working environment may pose particular difficulties because of space constraints preventing good posture, uneven or slippery surfaces affecting the individual's capability to undertake the task.

3 LIFTING EQUIPMENT

• Provision and Use of Work Equipment Regulations 1998[4].

• Lifting Operations and Lifting Equipment Regulations 1998[5].

These regulations have particular impact when working with lifts, forklift trucks, vehicle hoists, mobile elevated work platforms, piling frame, cranes, hoists, winches etc. The regulations place basic requirements on the lifting equipment itself and specific requirements where the equipment is being used to lift individuals.

They require all lifting equipment to be examined by a competent person before it is put into service for the first time and require the equipment to be examined at least at every 12 months to ensure that it is operating correctly (equipment must be examined every six months if it is being used to lift people).

4   SI 1998/2306.
5   SI 1998/2307.

The examination must be undertaken by a competent person who must make a report to the employer containing specific details of any defects. Furthermore, should they find any defects that present an existing or imminent risk to serious personal injury, a copy of that report will be forwarded to the enforcing authority.

Reports should be kept for a period of two years. In the main, copies are served upon an employer's insurance company. Where any defect is identified, the equipment cannot be used until the defect has been rectified.

When hiring lifting equipment, both the hirer and the hire company have responsibilities in respect of that equipment. The hire company must ensure that the equipment is maintained, inspected and tested and provide all necessary information to the hirer. The person responsible for hiring the equipment must ensure that they have selected suitable equipment and that it complies with the relevant legislation.

4 WORKING AT HEIGHT

- Construction (Health, Safety and Welfare) Regulations 1996[6].
- Workplace (Health, Safety and Welfare) Regulations 1992[7].

The legislation requires that suitable and sufficient steps must be taken to prevent a person from falling a distance of two or more metres or any distance likely to cause injury. This is because of the number of workers suffering fatal falls and others who suffer less serious injuries as a result of working from heights. In particular, regard should be had to ladders, scaffolding and roof work.

Ladder accidents tend to be caused because there was something wrong with the ladder or with the way in which the ladder was being used. Employers can ensure safe use of ladders by regular inspection, maintenance and training.

Scaffolds may only be erected, altered and dismantled by competent persons. Scaffolding must be inspected on a regular basis, and in particular upon its completion, after a period of not more than seven days, after alteration, after adverse weather, and after anything that is likely to have affected its safety.

Scaffolds can only be inspected by a competent person, and a record of the findings must be kept and sent to the person in control within 24 hours of inspection. Accidents involving scaffolding include people falling, materials falling, or the scaffold itself collapsing.

6   SI 1996/1592.
7   SI 1992/3004

There are specific rules in relation to scaffolding for the provision of guard rails, toeboards and other edge protection. These must be adhered to, since deviation will result in immediate Prohibition Notices being served by an inspector, thus preventing use until the scaffold has been rendered compliant.

Most roof work fatalities could have been prevented by the provision and use of appropriate equipment. There are systems available to prevent operatives from falling from sloping roofs – namely roof edge barriers, special working platforms below eaves level, normal scaffold platforms and the use of roof ladders. Specialist advice should be sought when constructing and maintaining roofs, and in particular fragile roofs.

6 Construction (Health, Safety and Welfare) Regulations 1996 (C(HSW)R 1996)

These regulations are designed to preserve the health, safety and welfare of anyone who carries out construction work, as well as protecting others affected by this work. They lay down detailed requirements for construction work.

They only apply to construction work being carried out by a person at work. Here construction work is defined as 'the carrying out of any building, civil engineering or engineering construction work'. In particular, the regulations deal with activities such as precautions against falls, work on structures and matters such as traffic routes, emergency procedures and weather protections.

A construction site is defined as a 'work place where the principal work activity being carried out is construction work'.

(a) Who has duties under these regulations?

- Employers whose employees are carrying out construction work.
- Self-employed person carrying out construction work.
- Every person who controls the way in which construction work is carried out.
- Every employee who carries out construction work.
- Every person at work who has a duty to incorporate and report defects to ensure compliance.

(b) Regulation 5: the general duty

This imposes a duty so far as is reasonably practicable, to ensure a safe place of work and a safe means of access to and from that place of work without risk to health and safety of any person at work there. The duty relates to the management and supervision of construction work. To achieve these obligations the following should be done.

REGULATION 28: TRAINING

To reduce the risk of injury, every person carrying out construction work should possess the necessary training and technical knowledge or experience. Alternatively, they should be under such a degree of supervision by a person having such training, knowledge or experience as may be appropriate having regard to the nature of the activity.

REGULATION 29: INSPECTION

This provides that the following places of work shall only be used to carry out construction work if they have been inspected by a competent person:

- the working platform or any personal suspension equipment;
- excavations;
- coffer dams and caissons.

Where a place of work includes any of the above, an employer or other person having control shall ensure that the scaffold, excavation, coffer dam or caisson is stable and of sound construction and that the safeguards required by the regulations are in place before employees first use that place of work.

REGULATION 30: REPORTS

When an inspection is required, the person who carries out that inspection shall prepare a report which includes particulars specified by the regulations.

(c) Summary of regulations

Duty	Regulation
Safe places of work	5
Cautions against falls	6 and 7
Falling objects	8
Work on structures, demolition or dismantling explosives	9, 10 and 11
Excavations, coffer dams or caissons	12 and 13
Prevention of drowning	14
Traffic routes*	15
Doors and gates	16
Vehicles	17
Prevention of risk from fire	18
Emergency routes, exits and procedures*	19 and 20
Fire detection and fire fighting*	21
Welfare facilities (toilets, washing facilities, drinking water, rest areas, areas to change and store clothes)*	22
Provision of fresh air	23
Temperature and weather protection	24
Lighting	25
Good order of construction site*	26
Training	28
Inspection	29
Reports	3

* denotes regulations which apply to construction work carried out on a construction site only.

7 Construction (Design and Management) Regulations 1994 (CDM Regulations 1994)

The regulations place duties on five key individuals to a contract: client; designer; planning supervisor; principal contractor; and contractors.

(a) Do the CDM Regulations 1994 apply?

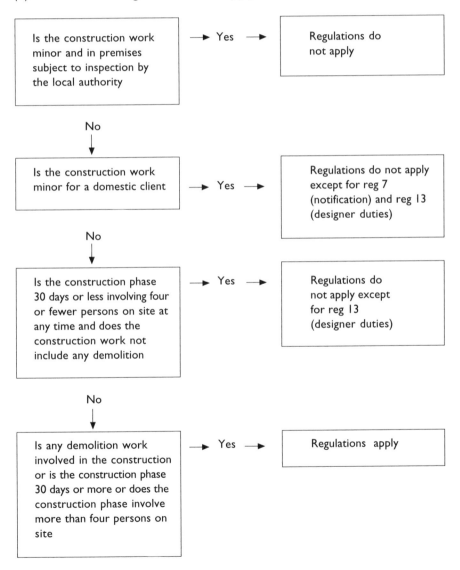

Is the construction work minor and in premises subject to inspection by the local authority	→ Yes →	Regulations do not apply

No ↓

Is the construction work minor for a domestic client	→ Yes →	Regulations do not apply except for reg 7 (notification) and reg 13 (designer duties)

No ↓

Is the construction phase 30 days or less involving four or fewer persons on site at any time and does the construction work not include any demolition	→ Yes →	Regulations do not apply except for reg 13 (designer duties)

No ↓

Is any demolition work involved in the construction or is the construction phase 30 days or more or does the construction phase involve more than four persons on site	→ Yes →	Regulations apply

(b) Procurement process – who is the client?

For the purposes of CDM Regulations 1994, the identity of the client is a crucial decision. The owner of the site can be the client. However, in today's increasingly complex construction site the management can be outsourced to a major contractor who could be the client.

The most important role for the client is the appointment of a planning supervisor and the principal contractor. The client must also ensure that the health and safety plan is completed before construction work starts.

(c) The role of the planning supervisor

The planning supervisor is usually a construction professional who specialises in planning supervision work. However, this is not necessarily the only person who can assume this role, and many others will make contributions to the project.

The main responsibilities of the planning supervisor are as follows:

1 Completion of notice to the HSE.

2 To ensure so far as is reasonably practicable that the design of any structure includes adequate regard to:
 (a) avoidance of foreseeable risks;
 (b) combating risks at source;
 (c) giving priority to measures that will protect all persons at work.

3 Provision of adequate information by the designer.

4 Communication between designers.

5 Arranging preparation of health and safety plan.

6 Creation or updating of health and safety file. This document should always be included in the information provided to designers and made available to all interested parties. It is not unreasonable to overstate the serious commercial and technical consequences of omitting to pay regard to the health and safety file.

(d) The designer

The designer is defined as a person who 'prepares a design' in the course of his work. This will include any employee or other person at work under the designer's control preparing the design for him.

214

The designer's duties include:

* making the client aware of his duties;

* having adequate regard to the health and safety in the design;

* providing adequate information about the health and safety risks of the design to those who need it (CDM Regulations 1994, reg 13(2)(b)).

* co-operating with the planning supervisor and, if appropriate, other designers.

(e) Principal contractor

The appointment of the principal contractor is mandatory for all construction work covered by CDM Regulations 1994. Contracting includes management of construction. To the extent that a Project Manager also manages construction works, the role of a planning supervisor, designer and principal contractor can all be rolled up into that person's remit. Until site work starts, the role of a designer and planning supervisor is an intellectual one. Doing the work brings risk assessments to the fore, and so it is not surprising that the principal contractor has a list of obligations and requirements which include:

1 Completion of the health and safety plan.

2 Introduction of procedures to ensure co-operation between contractors.

3 Ensuring compliance with rules in the health and safety plan.

4 Control of access to site of authorised person.

5 Displaying a notice including particulars of the work as provided to the HSE.

6 Provision of further information to the planning supervisor for inclusion on the health and safety file.

7 Management of the site, including directions to other contractors and make of rules.

8 Bringing to the attention of persons who may be affected by the rules in the health and safety plan.

9 Training in health and safety.

10 Arrangements of feedback from employees and self-employed persons.

(f) The health and safety plan

CDM Regulations 1994, reg 15 sets out the requirements of the health and safety plan which covers the pre-tender and pre-construction stages. The plan should contain detail in proportion to the nature, size and level of health and safety risks involved. The plan requires skill in drafting, since to achieve an adequate health and safety plan requires genuine understanding and expertise in identifying hazards and the associated risks. Furthermore, it is essential that the plan is read and understood.

The safety plan is the key to the entire health and safety management of the scheme. CDM Regulations 1994, reg 10 states:

> Every client shall ensure, so far as is reasonably practicable, that the construction phase of any project does not start unless a health and safety plan complying with Regulation 15(4) has been prepared in respect of that project.

Thus it is essential that the health and safety plan is appropriate for the work.

(g) The health and safety file

This is a very important document. The file should be reviewed and updated to accommodate changes to the property, which in turn may affect hazards and risks for future maintenance, including ultimately demolition. A failure to maintain this document so that it is available to all interested parties, and in particular to planning supervisors, is a criminal offence.

The commercial consequences of failing to have an adequate health and safety plan can affect the future sale value of the building and also the ability to raise finance if appropriate.

(i) Competence and adequate resources

CDM Regulations 1994 require that all parties to a construction project should be competent and have adequate resources to perform the functions and obligations created by the regulations.

There is no prescriptive formula as to whether or not a person is competent and has sufficient resources. However, the regulations compel the parties to address the issues of competency and resources. The obvious knowledge of safety practice gained by attendance on courses, an individual's skills and experience, and an understanding of the regulations all serve to assist in ensuring that the parties have sufficient competence for the work proposed.

(j) Health and safety plan reg 15

I PRE-TENDER HEALTH AND SAFETY PLAN

(a) Description of the project:
    (i) Project description and programme details.
    (ii) Details of clients, designers, planning supervisor and other consultants.
    (iii) Extent and location of existing records and plans.

(b) Client's considerations and management requirements:
    (i) Structure and organisation.
    (ii) Safety goals for project and arrangement for monitoring and review.
    (iii) Permit and authorisation requirements.
    (iv) Emergency procedures.
    (v) Site rules and other restrictions and contractors/suppliers and others.
    (vi) Activities on or adjacent to site during work.
    (vii) Arrangement for liaison between parties.
    (viii) Security arrangements.

(c) Site risks:
    (i) Safety hazards, including boundaries and access adjacent land use, existing storage of hazardous materials location of services and conditions of existing structures.
    (ii) Health hazards such as asbestos, contaminated land, existing storage of hazardous materials.

(d) Significant design and construction and construction hazards:
    (i) Design assumptions and control measures.
    (ii) Arrangements for co-ordination of ongoing design work and handling design changes.
    (iii) Information on significant risks identified during design (health and safety risk).
    (iv) Materials requiring particular precautions.

(e) The health and safety file

2 CONSTRUCTION PHASE HEALTH AND SAFETY PLAN

(a) Description of project:
    (i) Project description and programme details.
    (ii) Details of client, planning supervisor, designer, principal contractor and other consultants and contractors.
    (iii) Extent and location of existing records and plans.

(b) Communications and management of work:

(i) Management structure and responsibilities.

(ii) Safety goals for the project and arrangements for monitoring and review of health and safety performance.

(iii) Arrangements for:
- regular liaison between parties on site, consultation with the workforce, exchange of design information between client, designers, planning supervisor and contractors;
- handling design changes;
- selection and control of contractors;
- exchange of information between contractors in respect of health and safety matters;
- provision and use of common means of access and places of work;
- security and the exclusion of unauthorised people;
- site induction and on site training;
- welfare facilities and first act;
- RIDDOR 1995;
- production and approval of safe working practices;

(iv) Site rules.

(v) Fire and emergency procedures.

(c) Arrangements for controlling significant site risks:

(i) Safety risks:
- services – water, gas and electricity – including temporary electrical installations;
- preventing falls;
- work with or near fragile materials;
- lifting operations;
- maintenance of plant and equipment;
- traffic routes and segregation of vehicles/pedestrians;
- storage of hazardous materials;
- ground conditions and unstable structures.

(ii) Health risks removing asbestos, dealing with contaminated land, manual handling, use of hazardous substances, noise and vibration reduction, other significant health risks.

(d) Health and safety file arrangements for collecting and gathering of information. Consideration of that information and incorporating the same into review of risk assessments. Storage of information.

(j) Employee consultation

CDM Regulations 1994 place an obligation on the principal contractor to ensure that workers (including the self-employed) are able to discuss and offer advice in safety related issues and to ensure that there are arrangements for co-ordination of the views of the workers or their representatives. Where employees are not represented by a trade union then employers are required to consult with them on significant health and safety issues.

(k) Civil/common law

Anyone who suffers ill health or injury as a result of a workplace activity can bring a personal injury claim against those responsible. This claim is in negligence. To be successful the claimant must prove:

- the defendant owed him a duty of care;
- that duty was breached;
- the injury was a foreseeable result of this breach.

The existence of a duty of care is easy to prove in an employer/employee context since, by common law, the employer has a duty to provide:

- safe plant and equipment;
- safe systems of work;
- competent fellow workers.

These common law duties mirror the duties under HSWA 1974, s 2. However, health and safety provisions do not give an automatic right of civil action when breached, although such a breach is good evidence of a breach of the equivalent common law obligations.

(l) Vicarious liability

An employer is responsible for the wrongful acts of employees carried out in the course of their employment. Where the act results in an injury, a claimant can sue the employer under normal negligence principles on the basis of vicarious liability.

(m) Civil claim

Personal injury claims must be brought within three years from the date of knowledge that the claim could be made. In negligence, this would be the date when the claimant knew or should have known that there was a significant injury and this was caused by the defendant's negligence. However, for those claiming occupational hearing loss or asbestosis, then the date of knowledge may be several years after exposure. In these claims Courts have held that the three-year limit runs from the date of diagnosis by a medical consultant.

Successful claimants receive money as damages which are assessed. These would include loss of earnings, damage to clothing, property etc, pain and suffering, medical and nursing expenses, and the inability to pursue social activities or interests.

Most personal injury claims are paid out of insurance (an employer's liability) or public liability insurance subject to exclusions and excesses. Employers are required under the Employers' Liability (Compulsory Insurance) Act 1969 and the Employers' Liability (Compulsory Insurance) Regulations 1998 to hold a minimum of £5m insurance cover for such actions.

CHAPTER 8

Professional indemnity insurance

By Sarah Hannaford

Summary

This chapter looks at two aspects of insurance that Project Managers need to be aware of: the important issue of professional indemnity insurance, and typical insurance provisions and the standard forms of building contract.

The chapter covers:

Professional indemnity insurance

- The effect of the proposal form.

- What is meant by utmost good faith.

- Duty of disclosure and consideration of actual and deemed knowledge and what facts are considered material, including a review of facts that need not be disclosed.

- Penalties for breaches of the duty to disclose.

- Explanation of the two types of insurance policy:
  - occurrence based policy
  - claims made policy.

- Limitations on cover.

- Consideration of whether policies cover legal costs and what costs are included in that.

- Tips on how to make a claim.

- Timing of the notification of the claim.

- What information and assistance is needed.

- Explanation of what the Queen's Counsel clause is.

Typical insurance provisions in the standard form of building contract

- In the light of the decision in *Pozzolanic Lytag Ltd v Bryan Hobson Associates*, it is clear that Project Managers need to be familiar with insurance regimes. This section outlines:
  - the insurance provisions under the JCT 1998 Contracts and in particular insurance against injury to people and property other than the works;
  - what is meant by joint names insurance and how it works;
  - the problems caused by joint insurance.

---

1 Introduction

This chapter covers two issues relating to insurance. First, it considers professional indemnity insurance in the context of Project Managers. Secondly, it deals with typical insurance provisions in standard forms of building contract.

Following years of a relatively 'soft' market for the purchasing of insurance, the market has collectively hardened in concert for the first time since the late 1960s. There are a number of factors that have contributed to the change in market conditions. While some industry observers may point to September 11 as the catalyst, in fact the tide was already turning prior to that point, particularly in respect of professional indemnity insurance. The legacy of underwriting losses throughout the 'soft' market could no longer be sustained, and, against a background of low interest rates and quicker claims settlements through the Woolf reforms (Civil Procedure Rules), major surgery was required to return to profitability and maintain capital support and investment within this insurance sector.

Rates and premiums started to harden in 2001, with further increases in 2002. These rate increases are likely to be maintained in 2003 and possibly 2004. Increased rates and premiums are only one product of a 'hardening' market, and the levels of self-insurance have increased, due to higher excesses and the imposition of wording restrictions by insurers. Examples of these include: removal of aggregate excesses; aggregate indemnity limits; defence costs and expenses included in the indemnity limit and excess; and asbestos, terrorism and toxic mould exclusions.

2 Professional indemnity insurance

(a) The proposal form, utmost good faith and disclosure

The application for insurance begins with the proposal form and other accompanying information which is the basis of the insurance contract. The completion of that document and the process of negotiation raise the issues of good faith and the duty of disclosure. This section covers these key issues.

1 THE PROPOSAL FORM

The proposal form, supplied by the insurer and filled in by the prospective insured (at this stage known as the proposer), is the application for insurance. In the case of professional indemnity insurance for Project Managers, a proposal form will include questions relevant to the nature of their business, experience and professional qualifications, and their claims history. Often this requires additional information for clarification, and sometimes supplementary questions are asked by insurers. All this information forms part of the 'proposal' and amounts to the proposer's offer to enter into a contract of insurance with the insurer.

The 'proposal' is obviously an important document. The questions and answers will be crucial to the insurer's decision as to whether to provide insurance and on what terms.

To reflect the importance of the statements made within the 'proposal', the proposer is generally required to make a declaration on the form confirming that the statements made are true. Such a declaration may typically be in the following terms:

> I believe the above statement and particulars together with any other information supplied is true and I have not suppressed or misstated any material fact. I agree this declaration shall be the basis of the contract between the underwriters and me.

The proposal form will often be expressly incorporated into the insurance contract. Even if it is not, the words 'the basis of this contract' show that the proposer is warranting the accuracy of his statements, and the warranty effectively becomes a term of the insurance policy. A warranty is of great importance in insurance law, since its breach will discharge the insurer's liability on the policy from the time of the breach. As is explained in the next section of this chapter, 'materiality' is an important concept in insurance law. However, materiality is not relevant to breach of warranty. Hence, if the warranty is in fact untrue, the insurer can repudiate liability on the policy, even if the untrue or inaccurate facts were not material.

2 UTMOST GOOD FAITH

Insurance contracts are subject to a higher standard of good faith than many other contracts. They are described as contracts of 'the utmost good faith' or, in the traditional Latin, 'uberrimae fidei'. The duty arises separately from the contract of insurance itself and is an independent legal principle: see the recent House of Lords decision in *The Star Sea*[1].

1   [2001] UKHL 1, [2001] 1 All ER (Comm) 193.

The requirement of the utmost good faith applies to both the insurer and the insured. It is the requirement on the insured that will be of the most interest to the Project Manager and is considered in the following paragraphs.

In the period leading up to entering into the insurance contract, the requirement of the utmost good faith includes an obligation to disclose material facts and to refrain from making untrue statements. This duty of disclosure is dealt with in more detail below. However, this is not the whole of the duty of good faith. There is also a rather more limited duty during the currency of the policy to act in good faith. There have not been many instances in which the courts have held that the duty applies post-contract. Examples include where a term of the policy requires the insured to provide the insurer with information during the policy term, and in the making of claims – where the duty includes the duty not to make dishonest or fraudulent claims.

3 THE DUTY OF DISCLOSURE

The insured is required to disclose to the insurer, before the contract of insurance is formed, every material circumstance which is known or deemed to be known to the insured. The insured is deemed to know every circumstance which ought, in the ordinary course of business, to be known by him.

There are a number of important introductory points. First, it is important to appreciate that the duty of disclosure does not just mean that the insured must answer direct questions truthfully. Obviously, the insured must disclose information in answer to direct questions. For example, he may be asked to reply to questions on the proposal form (see above). However, this is not the limit of the information which he must disclose.

Secondly, an insured can be in breach of the duty without being dishonest or fraudulent. It is an absolute duty to disclose, and forgetfulness or innocent non-disclosure are not defences.

The third important introductory point is the time at which the duty arises. It exists during negotiations for the placing of the contract of insurance and continues up to the date when the contract is formed. It also arises on each renewal of the policy and, where a variation to the policy is sought by the insured, on that variation. There is no continuous duty to disclose material facts or facts affecting the risk during the currency of the policy. Nor is there a duty of disclosure in the making of claims, although the duty of good faith applies to the making of claims (see above).

With this introduction, there are a number of issues to be considered:

1 Actual knowledge;

2   Deemed knowledge;

3   The circumstances which are material;

4   Any facts which need not be disclosed;.

5   The penalty for breach of the duty.

(i) Actual knowledge

The insured must, subject to the test of materiality, disclose facts known to him. He need not disclose inferences which he has drawn from those facts.

Where the insured is a company, identifying the company's actual knowledge may be more difficult. There may, for example, be material facts known to an employee which are not known to the person placing the insurance. It seems likely that the actual knowledge of the company would be limited to the directors/managers or the 'directing minds' of the company, rather than include knowledge of each individual employee.

(ii) Deemed knowledge

The insured is deemed to know every circumstance which ought, in the ordinary course of business, to be known by him. This does not mean that he has to make specific enquiries. However, ignorance through incompetence or turning a blind eye will not prevent an insured being deemed to have the relevant knowledge. It may be that an insured company will be deemed to know facts known to an employee which would not be within its actual knowledge if the directing minds ought to have been informed of such facts during the ordinary course of business.

(iii) Materiality

The principle is straightforward (although application to the facts of an individual case may be somewhat more difficult). The principle is that every circumstance is material which would influence the judgment of a prudent insurer in fixing the premium or determining whether he will take the risk.

The view of the insured at the time as to whether a fact was material is not relevant. The question is what the notional 'prudent insurer' would have thought.

Important points to bear in mind include:

- It is not necessary to show that the insurer would have reached a different conclusion if he had known. It is sufficient that it would have influenced his thought processes.

225

- It does not matter that there is no connection between the undisclosed fact and the circumstances of the loss.

- The date on which to judge whether a circumstance is material is the date the insurance contract was made and not the date of the loss.

It is not possible to give an exhaustive list of material circumstances. It can safely be assumed that the answers to questions posed on a proposal form are considered to be material. Whether or not specific questions are asked of the insured, it would be safe to assume that the following areas are material to the placing of insurance of the value of the premium for a Project Manager:

- Previous losses and claims under other policies.

- Any changes of name.

- (Possibly) previous refusals of insurance by other insurers or, more likely, the reason for such refusals.

The questions asked on a proposal form may limit the proposer's duty to disclosure. For example, the form may ask how many claims have been brought in the last ten years against the proposer. It may then be implied that the insurer does not consider that claims brought outside that period are material. However, it would not be safe to assume that the insured did not need to disclose any facts other than those which form the subject of questions on the proposal form.

(iv) Facts which need not be disclosed

The list of facts which need not be disclosed is not large. However, the insured's duty to disclose does not cover facts known or presumed to be known to the insurer, facts which diminish the risk, or facts of which the insurer waives knowledge.

Insurers obviously cannot rely on a failure to disclose facts of which they were aware, since the purpose of the duty is to prevent them from being misled or induced to enter into a policy as a result of not being informed of a material fact. For similar reasons, it is self-evident that the insurer cannot complain that he was not told of facts which diminish the risk. The insured, of course, is likely to want to inform the insurer of facts likely to diminish the risk in the hope of reducing his premium etc.

The questions of presumed knowledge and waiver are more difficult. An insurer will be presumed to be aware of the business which he is ensuring (in this case, project management). Waiver is not likely to be easy to show. However, if an insurer was told facts which should have put him on enquiry about other facts or circumstances but made no enquiry, he may well be held to have waived such information.

(v) Penalty for breach of the duty to disclose

The result of material non-disclosure can be very serious. The insurer is entitled to 'avoid' the policy. This means that he has no liability under the policy in the future. It also means that he is treated as having no liability in the past. Hence, if the insurer has previously paid out on a claim, he is entitled, if he avoids the policy for non-disclosure at a later date, to reclaim money paid out under the earlier claim. A matter which is likely to be of limited consolation is that the insured will be entitled to repayment of the premiums.

As can be seen from the above, the insurer has a choice of whether to avoid the policy. He may choose not do so. Alternatively, he may act in such a way that a court would interpret his conduct as waiver of the right to avoid the policy or affirmation of the policy. In order to be held to have affirmed the policy, the insurer must have had actual knowledge of the non-disclosure, and a reasonable time to decide what to do and communicate (by words or conduct) the choice to affirm to the insured: see *Insurance Corporation of the Channel Islands v Royal Hotel Ltd* [2]. The last criterion is the most difficult. Mere delay or inaction is unlikely to be sufficient. On the other hand, acceptance of a premium or payment of a loss is likely to be enough.

Of more comfort to the insured professional is the fact that it is not uncommon for insurance policies to contain a provision that the insurer will not avoid if the failure to disclose was innocent or inadvertent and free from fraudulent intent. In the current 'hardening' market such clauses are not as freely available as previously, and in certain areas cover has been restricted.

(b) The policy and claims

This section covers various key issues relating to the type and extent of cover and the making of claims under a professional indemnity policy.

I THE TYPE OF COVER — A CLAIMS MADE POLICY

There are two types of insurance policy:

- an occurrence based policy;
- a claims made policy.

If insurance is on an occurrence basis, the policy that will respond to a claim is that which was in force at the time of the negligent act. If insurance is on a claims made

---

2   [1998] Lloyd's Rep IR 151.

basis, the policy that will respond is the one in force at the time the claim is made (which may, of course, be some time after the negligent act occurred). Professional indemnity policies are almost invariably on a claims made basis. This basis is therefore considered in more detail in the following paragraphs.

In order to determine which of a succession of policies will respond to a claim by the insured (or whether the claim is covered by an insurance policy), it is necessary to establish when the 'claim' was 'made'. The relevant 'claim made' is the third party's claim against the insured. The Court of Appeal in *Robert Irving and Burns v Stone*[3] decided that a claim is not made until the third party notifies the insured of the claim. Hence, where a writ was issued but not served within the period of insurance, the insurers were not liable. as no claim had been notified to the insured within the period.

However, claims made policies tend not just to cover situations where a third party actually makes a claim within the policy period. They usually also cover the situation where a circumstance which may or is likely to give rise to a loss or claim arises during that period. The policy may therefore require the insured to give notice, not only of the actual claim, but also if he becomes aware of any circumstance which 'may give rise to', 'might give rise to' or is 'likely to give rise to' a loss or claim. The policy in force at the date of notification of the circumstance will then be deemed to be the policy which will respond if the third party subsequently makes a claim against the insured.

The important question for the insured faced with such a policy term is when a circumstance may give rise or is likely to give rise to a claim. In this context, 'likely' has been held to mean at least a 50% chance of a claim being made: *Layher v Lowe*[4]. The word 'may', however, involves a lesser degree of probability. It has been held that this means a claim was 'at least possible': see *Rothschild v Collyear*[5].

There are a number of potential difficulties with a claims made policy of which the Project Manager needs to be aware:

- Renewing the policy is crucial. Otherwise a third party may make a claim in relation to a negligent act which occurred some years earlier but there will be no policy to respond. Run-off cover must be maintained when a firm ceases to trade to cover this very eventuality.

- The limits and terms of the policy which will apply to the claim are those that were in force when the claim or circumstance was first notified.

- It is very important to notify circumstances and claims, for two reasons. First, to ensure that cover is accepted under the relevant policy; secondly, to ensure that,

3   [1998] Lloyd's Rep IR 258.
4   (1996) 58 Con LR 42.
5   [1999] Lloyd's Rep IR 6.

if a change is made in insurers with whom a policy is placed, the claim does not fall between policies. Subsequent insurers will be very likely to exclude liability for claims arising from circumstances of which the insured is already aware.

2   LIMITATIONS ON COVER

It is obviously of crucial importance to ensure that adequate professional indemnity insurance is maintained to reflect the risks of the work undertaken. The last thing with which a professional wants to be faced is a substantial element of the claim which is uninsured and has to be met, in the case of a sole practitioner or a partnership, out of personal assets.

The amount that the insurer will pay in relation to a claim can be limited in three ways. First, there is likely to be an upper limit on the amount of each claim which the insurer will pay. Secondly, the policy limit may be for an aggregate amount for all claims or circumstances notified in the policy period. Thirdly, at the other end, there may be an excess which is the insured's responsibility and is the figure below which the insurer has no responsibility. Policies may also include geographical limitations.

Both the limit on the indemnity and the excess may be expressed as an amount per claim or for each policy period. If the limit is for the policy period, it may be expressed as 'in the aggregate' or 'any one claim and in all'. If the limit is for each claim, it is likely to be described as 'each and every claim' or 'any one claim' during the period.

The difference between the two limits is obviously of importance. An aggregate upper limit is likely to be of concern. So, for example, if the upper limit is £250,000 per policy period and three claims of £250,000 are received during the policy period, the insured will potentially face being uninsured in relation to the second and third claims. This problem will not arise if the limit is per claim.

The problem is the reverse where the excess is concerned. If the excess is in the aggregate rather than for each claim, the insured has only to contribute it once during the policy period. An insured facing three claims in a policy period will therefore have to contribute more if the excess is expressed to be per claim.

A further potential difficulty with limitations on the indemnity can occur when a maximum indemnity is to be paid for 'any one occurrence' or a number of claims arising from one single incident or event. This has been interpreted as being more restrictive than 'any one claim' in that a number of claims may arise out of only one occurrence. Again, the reverse problem arises with the excess. So if the excess is to be paid for 'each and every claim', the insured may end up having to contribute a considerable amount from his own pocket.

As to geographical limitations, Project Managers should be aware that there may well be a limitation or exclusion in the policy in relation to claims made or suits brought in the USA and/or Canada or contracts under USA and/or Canadian law. This limitation could be in the form of reduced indemnity limit. Alternatively, no cover at all may be provided for such claims/contracts.

3 COSTS

Another important issue is whether the policy covers legal costs. A defendant to proceedings can face two possible types of legal costs:

1   those incurred by the claimant in successfully prosecuting a claim against the insured; and

2   the costs of defending the claim.

It is usual for the policy to expressly provide for payment of costs. For example, it may contain an agreement to indemnify the insured against all costs and expenses of litigation (a) recovered by any claimant from the insured and (b) incurred with the written consent of the insurance company. The first item covers the claimant's costs. The second covers the costs of defending the claim.

The wording of such clauses needs to be looked at carefully. For example, if the costs for which the insurer provides an indemnity are expressed to be 'all costs and expenses incurred with the insurer's written consent', this will only refer to the defence costs. The words 'all costs and expenses payable by the insured' has been held to mean only the costs of the claimant and not the defence costs.

If there is no express term providing for an indemnity in relation to costs, they may be recoverable as part of the general indemnity. However, if the general indemnity limit is low, the risk is that the claim and costs may exceed it. In such a case, the insured will have to meet the costs once the limit of indemnity is exceeded.

A halfway house occurs in some policies that provide that when judgment is given against the insured for more than the limit of the indemnity, the insurer will also indemnify the insured against the proportion of the costs (determined by the relationship between the indemnity sum and the judgment amount).

(c) Making a claim

I NOTIFICATION OF THE CLAIM

The insured is generally obliged to notify his insurers as soon as any claim is made against him. As we have seen, it is also likely that the policy will require him to notify any circumstance arising which may give rise to a claim. If these notification clauses are conditions precedent to liability under the policy, and an insured fails to notify within the time specified, the insurer is entitled to avoid liability for the claim.

However, professional indemnity policies often contain clauses which mitigate the harshness of this obligation by providing that the insurers will only be entitled to avoid the policy for non-disclosure if there was a fraudulent intent or if the failure could be deemed to be reckless or grossly negligent. Alternatively, it may be possible to argue that the insurer has waived his right to rely on the notice clause. This may occur, for example, if the insurer induces the insured to incur further trouble or expense in relation to the claim in the belief that the insurer was not relying on the notice provision. On the other hand, the mere carrying out of investigations by the insured, without inducing the insured to incur expense etc, may be insufficient to amount to a waiver.

2 INFORMATION AND ASSISTANCE

The insured is also usually required to give such information and assistance to the insurers as they may require in the conduct of his claim. Clauses requiring particulars of the claim can also be conditions precedent to liability under the policy. If the insured fails to comply, again he may have no recovery under the policy. However, as with notification, the insurer may in fact waive the requirement for details.

3 QUEEN'S COUNSEL CLAUSE

A clause which is found only in professional indemnity clauses is a Queen's Counsel (QC) clause. This provides that the insured is not required to defend any legal proceedings unless a QC advises that such proceedings should be contested. It is likely to be in the following format:

> The insurer will pay any such claim or claims which may arise without requiring the assured to dispute any claim, unless a Queen's Counsel (to be mutually agreed upon by the underwriters and assured) advise that the same could be successfully contested by the assured and the assured consents to such a claim being contested, but such consent not to be unreasonably withheld.

This means that an insured cannot be forced by his insurers to contest a claim. Defending a claim may have implications for a professional's reputation which he may wish to avoid.

3 Typical insurance provisions in standard forms

In the light of the recent decision of *Pozzolanic Lytag Ltd v Bryan Hobson Associates*[6] (see Chapter 9), it is clear that Project Managers need to be familiar with the insurance regimes and be proactive in ensuring that the insurance adequately protects the employer.

The following paragraphs therefore describe in outline the insurance regime of the JCT 1998 standard form of contract, which contains a typical although not entirely straightforward insurance regime. Consideration is then given to the potential problem for the professional team created by joint insurance, and the Project Manager's duty in relation to the insurance provisions in the light of *Pozzolonic Lytag*.

(a) The insurance provisions under JCT 1998

The JCT 1998 standard form of building contract provides for two types of insurance: first, insurance against injury to people and property (other than the Works) and, secondly, Insurance of the Works and (where relevant) existing structures.

I INSURANCE AGAINST INJURY TO PEOPLE AND PROPERTY OTHER THAN THE WORKS

Clause 21 covers the first type of insurance. In order to understand this clause, it is necessary to refer back to clause 20. The Contractor is obliged, under clause 20.1, to indemnify the Employer against claims, losses etc arising from personal injury and death except where this is due to acts of neglect of the Employer or persons for whom the Employer is responsible. Under clause 20.2, the Contractor is obliged to indemnify the Employer against losses, claims etc in respect of loss, injury or damage to property (other than the Works).

Clause 21.1 then obliges the Contractor to take out insurance in relation to his liability under clause 20. The amount of the insurance cover (except in relation to employees where legislation is relevant) is to be set out in the Appendix to the form of contract.

Clause 21.2 requires further – limited – insurance to be taken out by the Contractor. This is only required if so stated in the Appendix. It is to be taken out in the joint

---

6   [1999] BLR 267.

name of the Employer and Contractor. It relates to damage to any property other than the works caused by collapse, subsidence, heave vibration, weakening or removal of support of lowering of ground water arising out of the Works. This insurance is limited by the existence of nine exceptions, including design errors and reasonably foreseeable inevitable damage.

2 JOINT NAMES INSURANCE OF THE WORKS

The insurance to be taken out under clause 22 relates to the Works. Clauses 22A and B apply where the Works comprise new buildings. Clause 22C applies where the Works are to existing structures or extend existing structures.

Under clause 22A and B, the cover is to be for all risks, which is defined in clause 22.1 as 'any physical loss or damage to work executed and site materials', subject to a number of identified exceptions. The insurance is to be taken out in the joint names of the Employer and the Contractor. Joint names insurance is defined as a policy of insurance which includes the Employer and the Contractor as the insured, and under which the Insurers have no right of recourse against any person named or recognised as an insured. Nominated Sub-contractors are to be recognised under the joint names policy (or the policy is to include a waiver of the insurers' right of subrogation against these Sub-contractors). The insurance is to be taken out by either the Employer or the Contractor, depending on whether clause 22A or 22B is chosen. The amount of the insurance is the full reinstatement value of the Works plus a percentage stated in the Appendix for professional fees.

Under clause 22C, the insurance is to be taken out by the Employer. Again the insurance is to be in joint names. It is to cover the 'specified perils'. These perils are defined in clause 1.3 and include fire, lightning, floods, earthquakes etc. The amount of the insurance is the full cost of reinstatement, repair or replacement of loss or damage to the structures and contents for which the Employer is responsible.

(b) The problem caused by joint insurance

JCT standard forms of insurance include provisions for insurance to be taken out in the joint names of the Employer and the Contractor. As explained above, in the JCT 1998 standard form a Joint Names Policy is defined as a policy of insurance which includes the Employer and the Contractor as the insured and under which the Insurers have no right of recourse against any person named or recognised as an insured. The contract goes on to provide that nominated Sub-contractors are to be recognised under the joint names policy or that the policy will include a waiver of the insurers' right of subrogation against these Sub-contractors.

A common situation therefore is for the Employer, Contractors and Sub-contractors to be jointly insured (or recognised) for all risks in relation to damage to the Works. The JCT scheme does not include the professional team in the insurance cover.

This means that, for example, in the event of a fire the Employer's Insurers cannot sue the Contractor or nominated Sub-contractor to recover the amounts paid out to the Employer to reinstate the damage. However, if the fire was also caused by negligence of the professional team, they are not protected from a subrogated claim by the Employer's Insurers. The question which then arises is whether the professional team can claim a contribution towards the damages they have to pay the Employer from the Contractors (who also caused the damage).

This situation was considered by the House of Lords in *Co-operative Retail Services Ltd v Taylor Young*[7] (see also Chapter 3). The property had suffered from a fire during the course of construction. The Employer had sued the Architects and Engineers (but not the Contractor or Sub-contractor who were jointly insured with the Employer) for negligently causing the fire. The professional team sought to claim a contribution from the Contractor and Sub-contractor under the Civil Liability (Contribution) Act 1978.

For the purposes of the issues heard by the court, it was assumed that the fire was caused by the breaches of contract of the professional team, the Contractor and the Sub-contractor. The House of Lords decided that the professional team were not entitled to a contribution from the Contractor or Sub-contractor, since the latter would have had a defence to any claim made by the Employer, namely the existence of the joint insurance. The Contractor and Sub-contractor would therefore not have been 'liable for the same damage' as the professional team. There can be no claim for a contribution under the Act unless:

1   the party claiming the contribution and

2   the party against whom the contribution is claimed

are liable to the Employer 'for the same damage'.

This situation is harsh for the professional team, who are then left to bear the claim alone.

There are, however, possible alternative methods of insurance which are becoming more common. For example, latent defects insurance could cover the first ten or twelve years of the life of a building, usually relating to structural defects and the building envelope, and in certain instances five years' cover is available for some aspects of the building services. The attraction is that it is the building that is being

7   [2002] UKHL 17, [2002] BLR 272.

insured rather than simply certain of the parties involved in the construction. Alternatively, single project insurance would cover not only the Employer, Contractor and Sub-contractor but also the design team. However, this option is very difficult to insure in the current market conditions, and even if insurance were available the period would be too short to provide adequate protection. These alternatives are not yet catered for within the JCT schemes.

(c) The need for adequate insurance

It is also important for the Project Manager to be familiar with the insurance provisions provided by the standard forms and to be aware of the need to ensure that the insurance arrangements are adequate and in place. See Chapter 9 and the case of *Pozzolanic Lytag Ltd v Bryan Hobson Associates*[8].

---

8   [1999] BLR 267.

CHAPTER 9

Areas likely to give rise to a dispute including a review of current cases

By Charles Brown

Summary

This chapter reviews recent case law that has examined the role of the Project Manager and his liability.

The chapter covers:

- The Project Manager's duties in respect of communication and the duty to warn:
  - *Chesham Properties Limited v Bucknall Austin Project Management Services Limited*
  - *Pride Valley Foods Limited v Hall & Partners.*

- Review of the duty to warn in respect of delays and cost overruns:
  - *Royal Brompton Hospital NHS Trust v Hammond (No 6)*
  - *Copthorne Hotel (Newcastle) Limited v Arup Associates & Others.*

- The Project Manager's duty to supervise:
  - *George Fischer Holdings Limited v Multi Design Consultants Limited, Davis*
  - *Langdon & Everest and Others*
  - *Pratt v George Hill Associates.*

- The Project Manager's duty to identify the client's requirements and the dangers of the Project Manager acting outside his field of expertise:
  - *Pozzolanic Lytag Limited v Bryan Hobson Associates*
  - *St Albans City and District Council v International Computers Ltd.*

- Project Manager's duties to contractors:
  - *J Jarvis & Sons Limited v Castle Wharf Development Limited and Others.*

- Review of specific concerns that multi-disciplinary consultancies may have when acting as Project Managers.

- Loss flowing from the Project Manager's breach.

1 Introduction

Until 20 to 25 years ago construction projects were managed without a professionally qualified consultant with the title 'Project Manager', and most of the roles undertaken by today's Project Manager were undertaken by other consultants. Inevitably, in what is a relatively litigious industry, the performance of those roles, whether undertaken by architects, engineers or surveyors, has over the years been scrutinised by the courts in detail. With the emergence in the last 20 to 25 years of the Project Manager and the resultant transfer of some of the roles previously undertaken by other professions in the management of construction projects, the judicial spotlight has focused on Project Managers.

It is a somewhat perverse and backhanded compliment to the professional status of the Project Manager that the courts have little difficulty seeing him in precisely the same terms as the older traditional construction professions!

In this chapter we concentrate on the recent decisions which identify specific difficulties and areas of dispute which have affected Project Managers and will continue to do so. However, many of the applicable authorities come from earlier decisions, when what we now accept as project management services were provided by other professions.

This chapter will consider the specific areas that are likely to give rise to a dispute, including:

* communication;

* warning;

* giving advice;

* failure to identify requirements;

* cost monitoring and reporting;

* delay and certification;

* poor supervision, and

* multiple roles.

However, to understand the authorities we must first review the way in which the English courts look at the duties and obligations where professional services are provided.

2 The basis of the Project Manager's liability

As will become apparent, clear and effective drafting of the contract between Project Manager and client can minimise the likelihood of disputes. However, the respective obligations and responsibilities must be unequivocally identified, because if the Project Manager is subsequently in breach of the contractual obligations the client may be entitled to recover the loss resulting from the breach.

(a) Contract and tort

As we stated in Chapter 2, the usual remedy for breach of contract is an award of damages. The measure of damages in contract is still governed by the decision in *Hadley v Baxendale*[1]. The intention is to put the 'injured' party in the position it would have been in had there been no breach. Where there is no contract, the Project Manager nevertheless has a continuing duty in tort. The Project Manager's duty in tort is in negligence, and the duty is owed to anyone who the Project Manager can reasonably foresee will suffer physical damage.

The Project Manager will often have a concurrent liability in contract and tort. The critical starting point in any claim is to look at the services the Project Manager agreed to provide, and then consider the standard of competence expected of the Project Manager on this project. The general rule is that the standard of skill and care is that of the average reasonably competent practitioner.

3 The specific duties

(a) Communication and a duty to warn

Few would dispute that a Project Manager is the client's 'eyes and ears' on site. Whether in the express services to be provided or as a term implied to give business efficacy to the relationship, a Project Manager has a responsibility to communicate any matter of significance and to warn of any matter that can reasonably be said to be important to the client. Important areas include everything relating to progress, cost, and the quality of the construction.

The Project Manager is responsible for reporting to the client, and a lack of communication can at best lead to inefficiency and misunderstanding and at worst have a disastrous effect on the project. Project Managers should set up co-ordinated systems to ensure that all relevant parties are updated at regular intervals. From the outset such systems need to be agreed with the client as to both form and frequency of reporting. A Project Manager has a duty to communicate, report and warn. This implies a duty to hold meetings at regular intervals. Minutes should be taken and

---

1   (1854) 9 Exch 341.

circulated by the Project Manager to ensure that action points are followed up and problems identified and resolved.

While all of this may seem simple and obvious, there have been a number of decisions which illustrate all too clearly what happens when the lines of communication and reporting break down. When this happens, the Project Manager runs a real risk of failing to warn of problems in sufficient time for steps to be taken to avoid or minimise the client's loss.

In the case of *Chesham Properties Ltd v Bucknall Austin Project Management Services Ltd*[2] Bucknall Austin were members of Chesham's team of professional advisers. Chesham made a number of complaints against the members of the team, including the structural engineers, the architect, the quantity surveyors and finally Bucknall Austin, the Project Manager. The activities of the Contractor and, in particular, its claims against Chesham constituted a significant part of the damages which Chesham sought to recover from the various professional consultants.

Chesham alleged that the Project Manager had an express or implied obligation to advise and/or warn and/or inform at any time of its own actual or potential deficiencies in performance and/or the actual or potential deficiencies in performance of the other professional advisers. The deficiencies were those which the Project Manager knew or ought to have known about. They had contributed to the defect in the design, increases in the time required by the Contractor to complete the development, including the granting of extension of time awards, and an increase in the cost to Chesham of completing the development. The costs included the loss and expense payable to the Contractor by reason of the extended contract period.

Expanding upon this, the judge, Judge Hicks QC, explained that Chesham considered that the Project Manager had failed to advise or warn Chesham that the extensions of time granted to the Contractor were caused by deficiencies of performance on the part of one or more of the other consultants, or of the likelihood that they were so caused, or of the need to investigate the conduct of the consultants to establish that likelihood. The Project Manager, it was alleged, had negligently prepared progress reports and financial statements and had failed to advise that sums due to the Contractor for prolongation and loss and expense were due by reason of deficiencies of the performance of one or more of Chesham's team.

Finally, it was alleged that the Project Manager had wrongfully granted extensions of time and awards of loss and expense to the Contractor and had failed to advise or warn of the need to commence arbitration proceedings against the Contractor.

2   [1996] CILL 1989.

In his decision, the judge explained that what made this case unusual was the distinction between breaches of Bucknall Austin's duty to carry out their primary professional functions of design, calculation, measurement, management and the like with due care and skill, and the more unusual concept of a Project Manager being under a duty to warn or inform of the negligence of themselves or the other professionals in Chesham's team.

After reviewing a number of earlier authorities, Judge Hicks QC identified the express terms of the Project Manager's contract, particularly the requirement that the Project Manager:

> ... implement and maintain all monitoring procedures including the performance of the Contractor on site and all consultants and ensure that any difficulties including contractual problems which may prevent the successful outcome of the project are highlighted in good time and that corrective measures are taken whenever possible;

and again:

> ... receive any applications for extension of time, discuss implications and implement corrective action where possible. Approve response and the issue of any certificate for extension of time where unavoidable.

The judge concluded:

> In my view the Project Manager was plainly under a duty ... to report to the plaintiff on deficiencies in performance on the part of its co-defendants. The key provision, as I see it, is the obligation to 'implement ... all monitoring procedures including the performance of ... all consultants'. Monitoring in such a context cannot sensibly be confined to passive observation. It must include reporting to the principal on the performance being monitored by reference to the standards which should be achieved.... similar considerations would lead me to find that a term to the like effect is necessarily to be implied in order to give effect to the obvious intention of the parties and business efficacy to the contract as a whole.
>
> There was a concurrent common law duty to exercise due professional care and skill within the field of the contractual duty.

However, Judge Hicks QC stopped short of the most radical suggestion of Chesham, deciding that:

> ... the allegation that there was any duty on the part of the Project Manager to report on its own deficiencies must be rejected.

A number of similar issues arose in *Pride Valley Foods Ltd v Hall & Partners*[3].

Pride were the manufacturers of speciality breads from a purpose-built factory in which a fire started in one of the oven flues. Owing to the use of highly combustible expanded polystyrene panels in the ceiling around the flue, the fire was able to spread into the ceiling and throughout the building. The factory was destroyed.

Hall were the Project Managers and Pride alleged that the fire was caused by their breach of contract and/or negligence. In a nutshell, Hall should have ensured that the specification for the ovens did not include the panels around the flue and/or should have ensured that it included adequate compartmentation; alternatively, they were aware but failed to advise Pride that the panels were highly combustible and/or that adequate compartmentation was necessary.

The judge at first instance found that Hall were in breach of duty and had failed to advise Pride about the panels and the risk of the spread of fire of which they were aware. However, the judge also held on the balance of probabilities that, although the fire would not have occurred if the advice had been given and accepted, Pride's claim should nevertheless be dismissed because he concluded that if Hall had given the advice it would not have been accepted by Pride and would not therefore have been implemented.

The Court of Appeal judgment was given by Dyson LJ, who noted that Hall's appointment included a 'Schedule of Project Design and Management Services', the objective of which was 'to achieve through successful management from inception through design construction, commissioning and hand-over a building which is delivered within the agreed time, cost and quality parameters'. The schedule comprised some 23 specific services, including the development of requirements into a design brief and the preparation of appropriate employer's requirements, specifications and drawings from which the contractors could design the structure. There was, they concluded, a clear duty on the evidence for Hall to warn Pride of the danger from the panels and the lack of compartmentation, and that it was by no means clear that Pride would (as the judge at first instance found) have rejected such advice if given. It followed that Pride's loss (the destruction of the factory by fire) was caused by the failure of Hall to warn of the need to avoid the use of the panels and to create appropriate fire-stopping compartments. The first instance decision was overturned and Hall, who were a well-known local firm of chartered quantity surveyors and estate managers, were held responsible for the destruction of the factory due to their failure to pass on to their client the knowledge they had received from others about the risk of fire.

---

3   [2001] EWCA Civ 1001, 76 Con LR 1.

It is worth mentioning that Hall themselves had no particular expertise in the field of fire risk and fire prevention, nor of the use of particular construction materials. However, the express wording of the services they undertook to provide was their undoing once the Court of Appeal had removed the surprising finding of the judge at first instance that Pride's possible rejection of the warning should excuse the failure to warn.

(b) Duty to warn – delays and cost overrun

In *Chesham Properties v Bucknall Austin* one of the Project Manager's duties was to 'receive any applications for extensions of time, discuss implications and implement corrective action where possible. Approve response and the issue of any certificate of time where unavoidable'. Similarly, in *Pride Valley Foods v Hall* the stated objective of the schedule of services was 'to achieve through successful management ... a building which is delivered within the agreed time, cost and quality parameters'. In *Chesham* this duty led to allegations about the advice given regarding subsequent extensions of time, awards of loss and expense and ultimately arbitration with the contractor, about which the judge observed, 'I have not yet canvassed the question whether these amendments disclose an arguable cause of action, but it suffices to say that in my view they plainly do.'

In *Royal Brompton Hospital NHS Trust v Hammond (No 6)*[4] the hospital brought a professional negligence claim against a number of parties including the Project Manager and Architect in connection with the construction of a new hospital. They contended that the Project Manager, in failing to ensure that the Architect performed his contractual duties to a proper standard, had been negligent and was in breach of contract. The court concluded that it was virtually impossible to reach a finding of professional negligence against a Project Manager in such circumstances, since in the absence of plain factual error there would always be ample scope for a genuine divergence of opinion between professionals. It followed that the hospital had failed to prove that the extensions of time had been granted negligently.

The 'genuine divergence of opinion' in the *Royal Brompton* case involved a complete analysis of critical and concurrent delays by a multitude of parties and causes upon which the Architect/Project Manager had to finally make a determination and certify, but a plain factual error on a matter which has a time and cost impact can, in certain circumstances, lead a Project Manager into trouble.

The duty to warn is of course part of the overall duty to advise with reasonable skill and care. Some advice may amount to a warranty – a promise of some definite

---

4   (2000) 76 Con LR 131.

measurable performance. The promise may be given before the Project Manager is in contract with the client. The promise may be a factor, even the deciding factor, in the decision to appoint the Project Manager and, if subsequently found to be false, it may be a misrepresentation.

In *Copthorne Hotel (Newcastle) Ltd v Arup Associates*[5] Copthorne wanted to develop a hotel in Newcastle but, in order to obtain planning permission and a development grant, the developer was required to abandon the original design of a local firm and to approach a national firm to provide a multi-disciplinary service including project management. They approached Arup and after discussions appointed them. The total out-turn cost of the hotel was £21.2m, of which construction costs were £15.2m, against an original cost which Copthorne expected of only £8m. Copthorne issued proceedings against Arup, claiming that they had been given inaccurate cost estimates, had failed to design within the costs advised and had failed to control the cost of the project.

On the evidence, the judge found that Copthorne had failed to prove that Arup had agreed at their first meeting to design the hotel for £8m, or advised that they could do so, and therefore failed to establish a breach of contract or negligence (to the extent the alleged cost estimate had been given pre-appointment). In the course of the judgment, however, the court observed that even if representations had been made prior to the creation of the contractual relationship between Arup and Copthorne, there was nevertheless a duty to inform Copthorne of facts of which they subsequently became aware and which falsified what was originally a true statement. As soon as there was also a contractual relationship, then the duty to advise required that it be discharged with due care and skill.

A number of commentators have suggested that the cases establish that a Project Manager who by a representation warrants that a project can be designed and constructed for a specific price is thereafter under an obligation to complete the project on time, to a specified standard and to a definite price. In the opinion of this author, such an interpretation goes beyond both *Copthorne* and *Royal Brompton Hospital NHS Trust v Hammond*, where the difficulty in establishing the Project Manager's liability for time-related issues, and particularly in relation to the grant of an extension of time, was said to make it 'virtually impossible to reach a finding of professional negligence (against a Project Manager) in the absence of plain factual error since there is ample scope for a genuine divergence of opinion between such professionals'. This view is also supported by the decision in *Bolam v Friern Hospital Management Committee*[6].

5   (1996) 12 Const LJ 402.
6   [1957] 1 WLR 582 (see Chapter 2).

What can be said with more certainty is that a Project Manager who expressly warrants the time, price or quality in the wording of the services to be provided runs a significant subsequent risk of facing a claim if there is delay, or cost overrun, and will then have to stake all on resisting the evidence of breach.

(c) The duty to supervise

In the *Copthorne* and *Royal Brompton* decisions referred to above and the *George Fischer* decision (below), the duty to supervise was part of the services the Project Managers undertook to provide. This general obligation is often developed in a schedule of services which sets out more specific duties and obligations.

In *George Fischer Holdings Ltd v Multi Design Consultants Ltd, Davis Langdon & Everest*[7] DLE amongst others faced claims for breach of contract arising out of roof defects on a construction project. The first defendant, MDC, was the designer of the project. DLE, a firm of quantity surveyors, were engaged by a written contract ('the Supervisory Contract') as the Employer's Representative for the contract. The roof of the building when completed suffered from a number of defects, including leakages arising partly from faulty workmanship and partly from design fault. The issues between George Fischer and DLE were:

1   whether DLE was in breach of its duties under the Supervisory Contract (Project Management) in:
    (a) allowing without comment a variation to the roofing design from which leakages became inevitable; or
    (b) failing adequately to supervise the workmanship of the sub-contractor; and

2   whether DLE was in breach of duty in issuing a certificate of practical completion before the project was satisfactorily completed so that George Fischer lost its right of recourse against the performance bond provided by the Contractor.

Judge Hicks QC concluded that DLE was under a duty to appraise and approve the design, and the defects arising from design faults amounted to a breach of that duty. They were also under a duty to supervise and inspect the work of the roofing Sub-contractor, and defects arising from faulty workmanship were a breach of that duty. In addition, DLE had made an error and should not have issued a certificate of practical completion when they did. They were therefore liable for any loss caused to George Fischer by the premature issue of such a certificate.

In *Pratt v George Hill Associates*[8] George Hill was retained as the Architect. Their duties included advising upon tenders from builders. Two builders were recommended by the Architect as being 'very reliable'. Pratt took this advice and entered a contract

7   (1998) 61 Con LR 85.
8   (1987) 38 BLR 25.

with one of the builders, who in the event proved to be very unreliable and failed to carry out the work properly. Pratt finally commenced proceedings against the Architect, claiming damages for negligence in recommending the Contractor and in the performance of their duties as Architects in relation to the work done. The judge at first instance held that George Hill were in breach of their duty to recommend a suitable reliable builder and that the builder's lack of suitability and reliability led to the disastrous execution of the work. The Court of Appeal upheld this part of the decision, finding that Pratt's damage was suffered as a result of the Architect's incompetent work and arose directly from the misrepresentation negligently given by the Architect which caused Pratt to contract with highly unreliable builders.

The important point to note in this case is that the Architect had expressly recommended the builders as reliable, but even if he had not said so in such express terms he would still have been under a duty to take reasonable care to select tenderers who were competent, or else expressly advise (warn) his client that he could give no undertaking as to their reliability.

To the extent that the Project Manager accepts an express obligation to advise on the suitability of tenderers (by no means an uncommon obligation), he can expect to be held responsible following *Pratt v George Hill* where the builder subsequently proves to be unreliable.

(d) Identifying the client's requirement and the dangers of acting outside a Project Manager's field of expertise

An example of both parts of this topic is the 1998 decision before Dyson J (as he then was) in *Pozzolanic Lytag Ltd v Bryan Hobson Associates*[9]. In this case Pozzolanic acted as a middle man, buying pulverised fuel ash from power stations for sale on to the construction industry for use in concrete. As part of the purchase of ash from a power station in 1990, it was necessary for Pozzolanic to be able to store the ash on site at the power station. In 1991 Bryan Hobson, a firm of civil and structural engineers, was engaged by Pozzolanic to carry out services in relation to the design and construction of handling and storage facilities, which included the construction of a dome for the storage of the ash. Bryan Hobson wrote to Pozzolanic setting out the terms of their engagement, which included the provision of consultancy services covering any necessary negotiations with the Contractor and 'contract and project management' of the subsequent construction contracts.

The construction contract which Bryan Hobson then had to supervise was a JCT standard form of contract 'With Contractor's Design'. It included the requirement in clause 21A for the requisite insurance policies to be in place, and the further

9   [1999] BLR 267.

requirement that when requested by the Employer the Contractor should produce for inspection documentary evidence that the insurance required was in place and was being properly maintained.

Bryan Hobson advised the Employer that the design sub-consultants to the Contractor 'have probably got professional indemnity cover which meets this specification' but critically did not satisfy themselves that the Contractor itself had the cover.

Pozzolanic subsequently requested the Contractor to complete a certificate relating to insurance and to provide evidence of adequate insurance to cover the design risks. Subsequently, the dome collapsed as a result of design defects which would ordinarily have been covered by the indemnity insurance of the type required under clause 21A, but it transpired that the Contractor had no assets and the only relevant insurance in place was the sub-consultant's. Pozzolanic alleged that Bryan Hobson had been negligent and/or in breach of their contractual duty of care in failing to ensure that indemnity insurance was in place to cover any liability of the Contractor.

Among the issues the judge had to decide was whether Bryan Hobson owed a duty of care to Pozzolanic to take reasonable care to ensure that, as required under clause 21A, there was insurance which would cover the Contractor's liability in respect of his obligations, and, assuming (as was the case) that there was no insurance in place, whether the real or effective cause of the loss was Pozzolanic's own failure to ensure that the relevant insurance was in place.

Dyson J concluded that Bryan Hobson was appointed as Project Manager and was obliged to ensure that the clause 21A insurance was in place, and that Pozzolanic's failure to ensure that the insurance was in place was not the cause of the loss. The judge explained that the starting point was the terms of engagement put forward by Bryan Hobson. Both parties called expert evidence which was directed to the question whether an engineer appointed to undertake contract and project management had a duty to ensure that all insurances required of the Contractor by the contract documents were in place. The judge concluded that 'the duties which by the letter of 6 June BHA offered to undertake included the duty of ensuring that the insurance required of the Contractor by the contract was in place'.

It follows from this decision that a Project Manager's duties may include a requirement to ensure that the Contractor's insurance policies are in place, and this despite the fact that a structural engineer can by no stretch of the imagination be described as holding himself out as an expert in insurance matters. Commenting on the evidence of Mr Rhodes of BHA which had been provided on this issue, the learned judge said:

> BHA, [Mr Rhodes] said, did not have the expertise necessary to assess the adequacy
> of the proposed insurance. I cannot agree with the opinion of Mr Rhodes. If a Project
> Manager does not have the expertise to advise his client as to the adequacy of the

insurance arrangements proposed by the Contractor, he has a choice. He may obtain expert advice from an insurance broker or lawyer. Questions may arise as to who has to pay for this. Alternatively, he may inform the client that expert advice is required, and seek to persuade the client to obtain it. What he cannot do is simply act as a 'postbox' and send the evidence of the proposed arrangements to the client without comment.

A further example of the dangers of a Project Manager going outside their normal sphere of expertise is to be found in a 1996 Court of Appeal decision, *St Albans City and District Council v International Computers Ltd*[10]. This was an information technology case involving the supply of software from ICL to St Albans City and District Council for assessing and administering the Community Charge. The software contained an error which overstated the relevant population of the area, causing a loss of revenue. The judge found that ICL's Project Manager gave an assurance that the figures were correct and that he did not have the technical knowledge to give such an assurance.

At the trial ICL ran a number of 'technical' legal defences. One was that the assurances given by ICL's Project Manager were negligent misrepresentations and that ICL was not responsible for them because the Project Manager had breached the terms of his service agreement with St Albans by so doing. The defence was ultimately rejected.

(e) Duties to contractors

The Court of Appeal decision in *J Jarvis & Sons Ltd v Castle Wharf Development Ltd, Gleeds Management Services Ltd and Franklin Ellis Architects Ltd*[11] found that employers and their Project Managers could have certain duties to Contractors.

Castle Wharf was the developer and Gleeds was retained to co-ordinate the development and manage the tender process. Jarvis was the Contractor on the project, an office development in Nottingham. The development was a prominent and sensitive one over which the local authority was exercising close control by the strict imposition of planning permissions. These permissions were a source of continuing negotiation between the authority and the defendants, as a number of variations to the project were proposed from time to time but only some were actually approved by the authority.

The dispute related to Jarvis's losses due to costs wasted and delays caused by an enforcement notice issued by the local authority due to unapproved variations. Jarvis claimed that, during the tender period, Gleeds negligently misstated the situation

10   [1996] 4 All ER 481.
11   [2001] EWCA Civ 19, [2001] NPC 15.

regarding the planning permissions. Jarvis said that they relied on those misstatements and hence Gleeds was liable for damages.

The trial judge found in favour of Jarvis, but the Court of Appeal did not, because in the circumstances they decided that 'inferences' were made rather than actual misstatements, and also that there was no reliance.

However, the Court of Appeal did say that there was no reason *in principle* why an employer, *or his Project Manager*, could not be liable for negligent misstatement made to a contractor to induce him to tender. (See Chapter 2 on misrepresentation.)

(f) The multi-disciplinary consultancy as Project Manager

The extent of the project management role accepted by a substantial consultancy as seen in the *Copthorne* case may, it is alleged, have encouraged the suggestion from a number of commentators that if a Project Manager represents that a project can be completed for a specific sum of money, this in turn implies a warranty as to progress, cost and quality. Although, as previously noted, the court in that case was not prepared to extend the Project Manager's liability as far as this, it nevertheless demonstrates the potential dangers where a consultancy appears to be offering a 'multi-discipline one-stop service'. The authorities suggest that if a Project Manager (particularly a substantial multi-disciplinary consultancy) represents that a project can be undertaken for a specific sum, this may constitute a warranty as to the cost of the project. If, following his appointment, the Project Manager produces cost plans and regular financial updates and these prove to be inaccurate or untrue, then the Project Manager is likely to be in breach. In *Copthorne* the case failed because, on a balance of probabilities, the claimant's evidence was not sufficiently persuasive, not because there was no cause of action against the Project Manager.

(g) Proving loss

It should not be assumed that, simply because a duty is identified and a breach established on a balance of probabilities, substantial damages will be awarded against a Project Manager. In practice there are substantial difficulties in establishing the existence of recoverable damages, particularly in claims for sub-standard cost reporting.

Even if the Project Manager is negligent in underestimating the final cost, the client still has to demonstrate as a matter of fact and evidence that if it had been given the proper cost information it would not have committed itself to the extra expenditure or to the level of such expenditure.

The client or employer will have to establish that, even though it would have gone ahead with the project, if it had been given the correct cost information at an appropriately early stage steps could have been taken to avoid or reduce the extra expenditure, such as the acceleration, disruption, prolongation cost that was in fact incurred.

There is also an argument that once the client has incurred the cost, albeit involuntarily, there may be a benefit or value derived from this expenditure. The client may have extra value for the work undertaken. If this is the case, the additional value will be brought into account when assessing the damages recoverable.

The courts will always look at the facts of each case, and although the authorities provide useful guidance for Project Managers there will always be an element of uncertainty, since the test to be applied is that of the reasonably competent Project Manager exercising the appropriate skill and care in the provision of the particular project management services.

CHAPTER 10

Dispute resolution

By Andrew Davies

Summary

Whilst many Project Managers, we hope, will not need a detailed understanding of the dispute resolution processes available in the UK, this chapter provides a helpful summary in the event that the Project Manager does need to have some knowledge. In particular this chapter covers:

Litigation

- The basic procedure.

- Introduction to the Civil Procedure Rules.

- Introduction to pre-action protocols and in particular the pre-action protocol for construction and engineering disputes.

The procedure for commencing court proceedings:
  - County Court procedure
  - High Court – Technology and Construction Court.

Arbitration

- Introduction to the Arbitration Act 1996.

- Explanation of when a dispute can be referred to arbitration.

- Introduction to the extent of the arbitrator's power to hear a dispute.

- Explanation of the arbitration procedure.

- A brief look at how international arbitrations are resolved.

Adjudication

- Introduction to statutory adjudication and the Housing Grants, Construction and Regeneration Act 1996.

- How an adjudicator is appointed.

- A brief summary of the adjudication procedure.

Alternative Dispute Resolution

- A brief summary of the forms of ADR available:
  - mediation, conciliation and negotiation, neutral evaluation and facilitation.

- The Court's approach to ADR.

- A more detailed look at the mediation process.

A comparison of the types of dispute resolution process for construction disputes

---

1 Introduction

In Chapter 9 we outlined when and where disputes are likely to arise during a construction project. It is of paramount importance to the success of a project that any disputes that arise are resolved as soon as reasonably practicable. This chapter discusses the procedures for the most popular methods of dispute resolution used in construction disputes, with which Project Managers need to be familiar.

Knowing these procedures and how they work can help the Project Manager in two ways:

- assisting the client if he becomes involved in a dispute during the project; and

- helping to protect himself if he becomes involved in a dispute.

If a problem arises on site there should not be automatic recourse to formal dispute resolution: there are other methods that can and should be explored. The parties should get together informally and try to resolve the dispute. The Project Manager may have a duty under the terms of his appointment to assist the client, but he can still facilitate a meeting between the parties.

If the informal procedure, which is increasingly being encouraged by the court (see below), fails for whatever reason, then formal dispute resolution should be considered. At this stage the Project Manager can advise the client on his options. These options may to a certain extent be set out in the contract, for example a requirement for early neutral evaluation or arbitration or even both (see later), but the Project Manager should be aware of what rights the client (or the Project Manager if in dispute with the client) has outside the contract.

The main forms of dispute resolution discussed in this chapter are:

- **Litigation.** This involves parties presenting their cases in court before a judge who will give a binding decision.

- **Arbitration.** If the contract provides for arbitration, this process involves parties presenting their cases to an arbitrator (or panel of arbitrators) in a private and confidential setting, to achieve a binding decision.

- **Adjudication.** All parties to a 'construction contract' have the right under the Housing Grants, Construction and Regeneration Act 1996 (the Construction Act) to refer a dispute to adjudication. This is a quick (usually 28 days) process where an adjudicator hears the parties' views on a dispute and reaches a confidential binding decision. The decision can be set aside later by the court or an arbitrator.

- **Alternative Dispute Resolution (ADR).** ADR is the term for all methods of resolving disputes other than litigation. Given the increasing popularity of arbitration and adjudication, we have devoted sections to each, using ADR as an umbrella term given to all other methods of resolving disputes, from informal meetings of directors through to structured mediations. These methods are confidential and the parties can choose whether to be bound by the decision.

2 Litigation

Litigation involves the parties to a dispute putting their case, on paper in the form of statements of case and witness statements and in oral evidence at trial, to a judge in court. The ultimate result which the party bringing the claim, the claimant, hopes to achieve is an enforceable judgment against the unsuccessful party, the defendant.

Regardless of the size of claim, court procedure is governed by the Civil Procedure Rules (CPR). The CPR were introduced in 1999, following Lord Woolf's 'Access to Justice' report and replaced the old and different County Court Rules and Supreme Court Rules, which governed County Court and High Court procedure respectively.

Under the CPR an action worth less than £25,000 is commenced in the County Court. An action above £50,000 in value is commenced in the High Court. There is discretion as to whether claims between the £25,000 and £50,000 are heard in the County Court or High Court. If a claim involves issues or questions which are technically complex, a specialist judge of the Technology and Construction Court (TCC) is required to hear the case. It will be heard in the TCC, which is a division of the High Court.

Project Managers will be involved with projects and disputes of varying sizes and therefore the procedures in both the County Court and the TCC are discussed here.

(a) Pre-Action Protocols

The aim of the CPR is to reduce the number of cases that reach the courts. The CPR tries to achieve this aim by requiring parties to litigation to have attempted ADR before issuing proceedings (see below) and also by requiring parties to follow Pre-Action Protocols.

The aim of the protocols is to encourage the early exchange of full information about the prospective claim, to enable the parties to settle the claim before proceedings are commenced and, if settlement cannot be achieved, to manage the litigation effectively. These protocols relate to different types of claims, and there is a protocol specifically for construction and engineering disputes. Project Managers should be aware of how the protocol operates.

The Pre-Action Protocol for Construction and Engineering Disputes (the protocol) applies to all construction and engineering disputes, specifically including professional negligence claims against architects, engineers and quantity surveyors. While the protocol does not specify that professional negligence actions against Project Managers are included, we consider that Project Managers and any other construction professional may be caught by the protocol.

The protocol is not compulsory. The court may, however, penalise a party on costs at the conclusion of proceedings if they fail to comply with the steps set out in the protocol.

The first step under the protocol is the letter of claim, which the claimant must send to the defendant. The letter must set out: the claimant's full name and address; the full name and address of the defendant; a clear summary of the facts of the claim; the basis of each claim, including terms of the contracts or statutes relied upon; the nature of relief claimed (money damages or specific performance – where the claimant asks the defendant to carry out or to stop carrying out a particular activity); whether the defendant has previously rejected the claim when put to him; and the names of any experts whose opinion supports the claim.

The defendant has 14 days to respond in writing, giving the name of his insurer (if any). If no response is received in 14 days the claimant may commence proceedings. Within a further 14 days (or up to four months if the parties agree), the defendant must provide a full response to the letter of claim, stating any facts that are agreed and the basis upon which any facts or claims are rejected. The defendant must state in this letter whether he intends to counterclaim against the claimant. The claimant has an equivalent period of time to respond to any counterclaim as is given to the defendant to respond to the claim.

As soon as possible following the exchange of letters, the parties should meet to agree the main issues in the case and consider how they may be resolved without the need for litigation, or, if litigation is inevitable, how the litigation can be completed quickly with the minimum of cost. The meeting will be 'without prejudice', meaning that what each party said during the meeting cannot be disclosed to the judge in a later court hearing. The judge can only be told that a meeting took place, the date of the meeting and the parties who attended.

(b) Procedure for commencing court proceedings

Proceedings in both the County Court and the High Court are commenced by issuing a claim form and particulars of claim. These must be issued by the court and served upon the defendant, either by the court or by the claimant. The particulars of claim can be served up to 14 days later than the claim form, but the claim form must in these circumstances state that the particulars are to follow.

The claim must be sufficiently detailed to allow the defendant the chance to assess the case against him and to prepare a defence. If the claim is badly drafted or has no substance, further information can be requested. If this further information is not provided, or an answerable case is still not set out, the defendant can apply to have the claim struck out, meaning that the claimant cannot proceed with their claim and a judgment is given in favour of the other party, often with adverse consequences as to costs. The claimant cannot usually bring a further claim for the same relief on the same facts after having been struck out.

The defendant has 14 days from receipt of the claim form and particulars of claim (or the particulars of claim if served separately) to serve an acknowledgment of service confirming that he has received the claim and indicating whether the claim will be admitted, contested in part, or contested fully. This acknowledgment of service needs to be filed at the court and served upon the claimant.

The defendant has 14 days from serving his acknowledgment of service to prepare and file a defence. This allows a maximum of 28 days following receipt of the particulars of claim. If the defendant wishes to include a counterclaim to recover or set-off money owed against that claimed from him, he can do so at this stage without the permission of the court or the claimant.

Third parties, known under the CPR as Part 20 defendants, can also be joined into the proceedings at the time of service of the defence without permission. Both counterclaims and 'third party' claims are known as Part 20 claims. If a Part 20 claim is not made at this stage, the consent of the other party is required, failing which an application needs to be made to the court at a later date for permission.

The claimant has the option of replying to the defence. If he does not serve a reply, he is not taken to admit what is set out in the defence. Where there is a Part 20 counterclaim the claimant will serve a reply and defence to counterclaim, answering the allegations set out in the counterclaim. This must be filed at court at the same time as the allocation questionnaire, which the court sends out upon receipt of the defence, to be returned within 14 days. The reply must be served upon the defendant, and it is good practice for parties to exchange allocation questionnaires.

A typical timetable for the exchange of statements of case, in both the County Court and High Court, will be as follows:

Document	Party serving document	Time limit for service
Claim form	Claimant	Usually 6 years from breach of contract or discovery of negligence (see Chapter 2)
Particulars of claim	Claimant	14 days after serving claim form (day 14)
Acknowledgment of Service	Defendant	14 days from receipt of particulars of claim (day 28)
Defence	Defendant	14 days after serving acknowledgment (day 42)
Part 20 Claim	Defendant/Part 20 claimant	With defence, or at any time with court's permission or claimant's consent (day 42)
Part 20 Defence	Claimant/Part 20 defendant	14 days after Part 20 claim (day 56)
Reply	Claimant	14 days after defence (day 56)

The subsequent events in the progress of a case differ whether the case is in the County Court or High Court, so we will deal with the remainder of the procedure separately.

I COUNTY COURT PROCEDURE

There are three different tracks in the County Court where case management will be carried out differently, according to the value and complexity of the case:

- small claims track;

- fast track; and

- multi-track.

Claims worth less than £5,000 (or £1,000 if a claim for personal injury is involved) are allocated to the small claims track. Once allocated to this track, there will be no case management conference (CMC), due to the simplicity of the issues, and the matter will proceed to a final hearing before a district judge. Costs here are fixed to a maximum of £80 plus disbursements (limited to £200) and court fees. Any costs incurred by either party over and above these levels are not recoverable, regardless of whether they succeed.

On the fast track, a district judge hears claims worth between £5,000 and £15,000. There will be a CMC and limited directions. Costs are not limited here (although the Lord Chancellor's Department is, at the time of publication, considering whether to limit fast track costs). The level of the costs recoverable should be proportionate to the amount in dispute. For example, if a party were successful in recovering £10,000, costs of £20,000 would not be proportionate and would usually be disallowed, leaving the successful party to pay the balance of his legal fees.

The multi-track is for cases worth over £15,000. Judges here can deal with cases in excess of £25,000 if they are not referred to the TCC. A CMC will be held on this track, where directions will be set for all stages of the procedure through to the ultimate conclusion of the matter at trial.

On the fast track and multi-track in the County Court, an allocation questionnaire will need to be completed after the defence has been filed. This document will tell the judge important information about the case and how it should be managed through to trial. A list of suggested directions should be filed with the questionnaire, in which the parties will set out the steps they think need to be taken before the case is ready for trial.

Directions are usually made to provide for disclosure of documents by way of lists, inspection of documents, exchange of witness statements and for expert evidence, if required. Deadlines will be given for these milestones to be met at reasonable intervals up to the trial window (a period of two to four weeks, the dates for which are set at the CMC) that will be allocated for the final hearing. Any departure from this timetable will incur the wrath of the judge, who has the power to manage the progress of the case as opposed to allowing the parties and their representatives to set the timetable, the idea being to process cases more quickly at a lower cost.

If an initial deadline is missed, strict alternative deadlines may be set by the court which, if missed, may result in the defaulting party's case being struck out. If for any reason the court does not pick up on defaults by a party, it is open to the other party to apply to the court for an order to make the defaulting party comply. The usual order given is that, unless the defaulting party complies with a deadline, their case will be struck out.

(i) Trial

A trial in the County Court will take place before a district or circuit judge with experience of hearing a variety of cases in different areas. The level of judge depends upon the value and complexity of the case. The trial should last no more than two days unless the issues are extremely complex and require several witnesses of fact. The judge will give a judgment either at the conclusion of the trial or he will reserve judgment to be given a later date, either orally or in writing.

(ii) Costs

The usual rule in relation to costs is that costs follow the event, which means that the unsuccessful party bears his own costs and pays those of the successful party. In the County Court the level of recovery depends on the track the case has been allocated to. The general rule that the costs should be proportionate to the amount claimed applies in both the fast track and the multi-track (as in the TCC). If the costs cannot be agreed, they will be assessed by a costs judge at a separate hearing[1].

2 HIGH COURT — TECHNOLOGY AND CONSTRUCTION COURT

The procedure in the TCC is essentially the same as that for the County Court, but with some important differences. Cases heard by the TCC will be of higher value and more technically complex than the County Court. Frequently this means that the parties will rely on many more documents and require more witnesses of fact and experts. These cases are therefore heard by specialist judges with experience in construction, engineering and technology related matters. Examples of actions normally heard by TCC judges include cases concerning civil or mechanical engineering, building and other construction work generally, and claims for professional negligence against engineers, architects and other construction professionals.

A claim in the TCC is commenced by issuing a claim form and particulars of claim, which must be filed at the court and served on all parties – multi-party litigation is more common in the TCC than it is in the County Court. The claim form should be marked 'Technology and Construction Court'.

I   The procedure for assessing costs is outside the scope of this chapter.

As TCC cases involve disputes of greater value and the projects to which they relate are usually larger and more complex, a feature of TCC litigation is to annex schedules to statements of case. Schedules are a useful means of pleading financial particulars and of setting out claims in columns and figures that would be incomprehensible if explained in words (see further below in relation to Scott schedules).

When a defendant is served with a claim form and particulars of claim, he must acknowledge service of the claim within 14 days (as in the County Court). Where the TCC procedure differs from the County Court is that the TCC, on receiving an acknowledgment of service, will allocate a judge to the case. The allocated TCC judge will hear all CMCs, applications and usually the trial, having become familiar with the issues in the case throughout the proceedings. Within 14 days of receiving a copy of the acknowledgment of service, the claimant must apply to the court for the first CMC. Depending on how quickly the claimant requests the CMC and how quickly the court can arrange a date for this to be fixed, the CMC may take place before the defence is served, which will be no more than 14 days after the acknowledgment of service.

A defence is served in the same way as in the County Court but, as with the particulars of claim in TCC litigation, supporting schedules may be annexed to the defence. It is open to the defendant at this stage to put forward a counterclaim against the claimant. The counterclaim should relate to the original claim and usually arises out of the same contract or allegation of negligence, as otherwise it is unlikely to be linked to the main claim. Non-related disputes should be litigated separately initially, although related actions may be joined. For example, a claim may be brought by the contractor for payments for monies owing under an application for payment, to which the client, as defendant, will issue a counterclaim to set off the claims against him for defective works or delay. The claimant may serve a reply to the defence and a defence to any Part 20 counterclaim. This will be the final statement of case served in the proceedings and is the final opportunity for a party to set out its case.

The first time the parties appear before their allocated judge will be at the first CMC. Before this hearing the parties must complete a case management questionnaire and case management directions form. At the first CMC, the judge will set the timetable for the remainder of the case, based on the information presented by the parties in their case management questionnaires and directions forms. The judge will set a trial date at this CMC that the parties must try and work towards. There will usually be sufficient time in the timetable for all directions to be complied with. It is rare for a trial date to be moved once set.

By way of example of matters discussed at the first CMC, both parties may make representations to the judge as to the number of experts they may require, the time they may require for disclosure of documents, witness statements and any further matters such as Scott schedules. The judge at the first CMC will order a second CMC further along in the timetable, frequently around the time of disclosure and/or witness statements.

(i) Disclosure

The CPR requires parties to disclose all documents that support their case and all documents that adversely affect their case. The usual form of disclosure is for the party disclosing documents to prepare a list of those documents (there is a prescribed form in the CPR). The list will be examined by the other party, who may choose to inspect some or all of the disclosed documents. In TCC cases disclosure is often a lengthy exercise as there are frequently large amounts of documentation to be sifted before disclosure is given and then inspected by the other party.

(ii) Expert evidence

Disputes in the TCC frequently involve technical issues for which the parties and their lawyers need the assistance of an expert in that particular field to help explain their case to the judge. Under the CPR the witness owes his duty to the court and not the party who appoints him. Any reports prepared by the expert must contain a declaration to that effect. Project Managers with sufficient experience may be called upon to give evidence as experts, frequently in professional negligence cases involving other Project Managers. In cases with which they are involved, Project Managers will be called as witnesses of fact (see below), invariably on behalf of the client.

The detail required in the expert's report will depend upon the nature of the dispute. If there are several heads of claim in one dispute, the expert will need to look at all of these, if they are within his field of expertise. The CPR require that the evidence should be restricted to that which is reasonably required to resolve the proceedings. Long reports relating to the value of every item on a final account, for example, should be avoided if only two or three areas are in dispute – the report should be restricted to those areas.

The CPR envisaged that there would be a reduction in the number of experts used in cases, and moved towards single joint experts appointed either by the parties or the courts. Single joint experts have been used frequently in County Court cases, but in the TCC parties still tend to retain their own expert. This may be due to the dispute having developed a long time before proceedings are actually commenced and the fact that both parties have required the assistance of an expert to help their understanding of the issues.

(iii) Witnesses of fact

The CPR requires witness statements to be exchanged between the parties some months before trial. Witness statements in TCC litigation may be lengthy documents, usually supported by several annexes of documents made up, for example, of contemporaneous correspondence, drawings or notes of meetings. The witness statement does not prevent the witness giving oral evidence, but curtails the oral evidence a witness is required to give in response to questions from his own lawyers. The witness's 'evidence in chief' will be his witness statement and possibly one or two supplementary questions. The other party's lawyers are free to cross-examine the witness on his statement, and this may be followed by re-examination by the lawyers for the party who called the witness (i e asked him to give evidence on their behalf).

(iv) Scott Schedules

Scott schedules are common to TCC litigation (and are also used in arbitration). The benefit of Scott schedules is that they allow complex issues to be assembled into an easily readable tabular format, which is easy to produce with current computer software. A Scott schedule is usually prepared by the claimant in columns and rows, with each row dealing with a particular issue. The columns should give each issue a number, explain briefly what the issue is and provide room for each party to set out their position on the issue. The claimant serves the schedule on the defendant who adds their comments on the particular issue on the document in the space allocated for them. This allows the judge to see what each party's position is on a particular issue without having to turn up the relevant paragraph of each party's statement of case. In a complex TCC claim involving many issues this can save a great deal of time at trial.

A typical Scott schedule will look like this:

Item number	Description	Claimant's comments	Defendant's comments	Judge's comments
1	Variation 2	Extra work £10,000	No extra work £0	Some extra work £4,000

(v) Interlocutory applications

In addition to the two CMCs and pre-trial review hearing that are usually arranged in a TCC case, there are frequent 'interlocutory applications', which are made to the judge during the course of the proceedings. In a TCC action an interlocutory application must be made to a TCC judge. In London this should be the judge to whom the case has been assigned. These applications frequently arise out of procedural issues, such as the failure of a party to provide information requested by the other party, requests for extensions of time to comply with a direction, or requests for disclosure of specific documents which one party believes another party has in their possession, but has not disclosed.

If one party, following the service of all statements of case, considers that the other party's case is sufficiently weak that it will not succeed at trial, they may apply for summary judgment. This remedy is available under the CPR to the claimant and defendant. The test in the CPR states that summary judgment will be given against a claimant or defendant if the court considers that the claimant has no real prospect of succeeding on the claim or issue, or that the defendant has no real prospect of successfully defending the claim or issue. The court must also be satisfied that there is no other compelling reason why the case or issue should be disposed of at trial.

An application for summary judgment must state clearly that the application is for summary judgment under CPR, Part 24 and must be supported by evidence that identifies all relevant points of law and states that the applicant believes the other party has no real prospect of succeeding with their claim or defence. The witness statement is usually prepared and signed by the solicitor, but the Project Manager and the client may be asked to give statements in support of such applications. After a hearing of an application for summary judgment in the TCC, the court may grant a variety of orders. The judge may give judgment on the claim, strike out the claim or defence, dismiss the application, or make a conditional order. Such conditions could include permission to proceed with the claim or defence provided that money is paid into court. This means that the party with the weak case must pay a sum of money into the court funds that will be used to pay the other party's costs if the case fails. This may prove a deterrent to a party who has a weak case.

A party may, in the course of the proceedings, wish to make amendments to his statement of case. This frequently arises following disclosure and inspection of documents when new issues emerge that make a party's case stronger or weaker. Either party may wish to amend their case to reflect the developments. The procedure for amending a statement of case is set out in the CPR, Part 17. Once a statement of case has been served, a party may amend it only with the written consent of all other parties or the permission of the court. The party wishing to amend will usually serve a draft of the amended document on the other party when asking for their consent to the amendment. If consent is not given, an application must be made to the court enclosing the draft statement of case and evidence in the form of a witness statement (possibly from the Project Manager but usually by the party's solicitor) setting out why the amendment is necessary. If the court makes an order allowing the amendment it may also make orders for consequential amendments to the other party's statements of case affected by the amendments.

(vi) Summary costs orders

Costs orders are made as a result of these interlocutory hearings, and the successful party's costs are assessed immediately on the basis of schedules provided to the judge and the other parties at least 24 hours before the hearing. These costs usually become payable within 14 days. Costs of CMCs are awarded 'in the case', which means they will be included in the successful party's costs to be assessed after trial.

(vii) CPR, Part 36

Litigation is an expensive exercise to undertake and parties will wish to protect their clients in relation to the costs of litigation. CPR, Part 36 affords the claimant and the defendant the opportunity of obtaining some protection on costs.

A claimant may, in an attempt to settle the proceedings, offer to accept a sum from the defendant to conclude the proceedings. If the offer is expressed as a Part 36 offer, the defendant has 21 days to consider the offer and either accept or reject it. If the offer is accepted, the dispute has been settled. If the parties have not agreed how costs are to be dealt with as part of the settlement, the court will be asked to decide who pays the costs. Costs will normally follow the event. If the Part 36 offer is rejected, the matter proceeds to trial, where the fact that there has been a Part 36 offer is kept from the judge. If the judgment following the trial is for more than the claimant offered to accept in his Part 36 offer, the claimant will be awarded his costs of the proceedings from the date of the Part 36 offer on an indemnity basis (see below) and at a higher rate of interest.

The defendant may also make a Part 36 offer, but he must confirm his intention to settle the claim for the sum offered by paying that sum into court. Again, this is kept from the judge. If the defendant loses the case and is required to pay the claimant, and if the sum he must pay is less than the Part 36 payment into court, the claimant, despite being successful, must pay the defendant's costs of the proceedings from the date of the Part 36 payment.

(viii) Trial

A trial in the TCC can last from anything from two or three days to several months. The judge, after hearing legal argument and oral evidence from witnesses of fact and experts, will reserve his position and produce a judgment (in approximately one to two months' time) that is binding on all of the parties. When the judgment has been written the judge's clerk will release a copy of the judgment to the parties' solicitors to read and to comment on any typographical errors. A few days after the judgment has been released the judge will convene a hearing where it will be formally handed down in court. The judge may (but will not usually) read out his judgment.

After the judgment has been handed down, the issue of costs is to be considered. This hearing is the first occasion upon which a judge will hear whether there have been any tactical offers or payments (Part 36 payments – see above) and decide who should pay the other party's costs and on what basis.

TCC judgments are released into the public domain, usually on the court service website (www.courtservice.org.uk) or to more general publications by one of the parties' solicitors or counsel. The release of TCC judgments is encouraged and another website (www.bailii.org), publishes most TCC judgments.

(ix) Effect of judgment

While the decision of the judge is binding, the parties have a maximum of 14 days in which to consider asking for permission to appeal to the Court of Appeal to re-hear the issues. Appeals are allowed only on matters of law and not on fact. The judge's interpretation of the facts presented to him in witness statements and oral evidence is not capable of being appealed. The judge must have made an error in law for an appeal to be allowed. The issue of costs may be held in abeyance until after the Court of Appeal hearing, where frequently the unsuccessful party is ordered to pay the costs both 'above and below', which means that the party losing the appeal pays for all the costs of the TCC action and the appeal procedure. TCC litigation is an expensive exercise and is usually reserved for large complex multi-party cases.

(x) Costs

The general rule in relation to costs in litigation is that the unsuccessful party bears his own costs and pays the costs of the successful party. The amount of costs paid can either be agreed between the parties or referred to specialist costs judges in the High Court for assessment. There are two bases on which costs are assessed, standard and indemnity. When standard costs are assessed, the benefit of the doubt as to whether they were reasonably incurred is given to the paying party. The level of costs usually recovered on the standard basis is roughly 65%. When costs are assessed on an indemnity basis, the benefit of the doubt goes to the receiving party, who can expect to recover up to 85% of his costs. Indemnity costs are imposed as a sanction against a party for their conduct of the proceedings.

As set out above, a party may protect their position on costs by way of a Part 36 offer or payment. The effective use of Part 36 can have a dramatic impact on the overall sum a party is required to pay following a judgment in the TCC.

3 Arbitration

Arbitration is the only form of dispute resolution apart from litigation where the parties are guaranteed to achieve a final and binding decision. The main difference between litigation and arbitration, and the major advantage for commercial parties, is that arbitration proceedings are held in private and details of the award are not made public. Whereas the trial of an action in court will be heard in public and judgments for most TCC cases are available on the Internet, only the arbitrator, the parties and their representatives are allowed to participate in arbitration proceedings unless all parties and the arbitrator agree otherwise. The public have no right to attend an arbitration hearing.

(a) The Arbitration Act 1996

The Arbitration Act 1996 (AA 1996) has revolutionised arbitration procedure under English law and international arbitrations conducted under English law. AA 1996 applies to all arbitrations commenced on or after 31 January 1997. The object of arbitration as defined by the Act is to obtain 'the fair resolution of disputes by an impartial tribunal without unnecessary delay or expense'. These worthy sentiments may not be reflected in reality, as the arbitration procedure is frequently as lengthy and as costly as litigation.

While arbitration is a suitable alternative venue for dealing with complex disputes (if the parties' contract provides for arbitration), multi-party disputes common in the TCC are more difficult to arbitrate as they require the consent of all the parties. AA 1996, s 35(2) states that 'unless the parties agree to (consolidate proceedings) the tribunal has no power to order consolidation of proceedings or concurrent hearings'. Responding parties can use this provision as a tactical advantage to make a claimant who wishes to pursue several respondents have several separate sets of proceedings. The claimant may try to reduce the impact of this difficulty by having all disputes heard before the same tribunal to lessen the extra burden that may be placed on them by fighting on several fronts.

(b) Agreement to arbitrate

The dispute and/or types of dispute that can be referred to arbitration will be defined in the contract between the parties. The JCT contracts provide for disputes to be resolved by arbitration, as do the RICS Project Management Agreement and Conditions of Engagement (albeit for the latter when adjudication has been ruled out or is unsuccessful). AA 1996, 6(1) states that an agreement to arbitrate is 'an agreement to submit to arbitration present or future disputes'. The agreement must be in writing for AA 1996 to apply. If the agreement to arbitrate is made orally, the provisions in force before AA 1996 define the procedure to be followed. The position prior to AA 1996 is not discussed in this chapter.

AA 1996, s 6(2) states that 'reference in an agreement to a written form of arbitration clause or to a document containing an arbitration clause constitutes an arbitration agreement if the reference is such as to make that clause part of the agreement'. For example, it is common in construction projects for a sub-contract to refer to the terms of the main contract for the method of dispute resolution. This is a valid arbitration agreement under the Act.

(c) Jurisdiction

Jurisdiction is the extent of the arbitrator's power to hear the dispute. The arbitrator's jurisdiction is determined by the agreement to arbitrate and by the reference of the dispute to arbitration. If jurisdiction is not conferred on the arbitrator by either of these methods, AA 1996 allows the arbitrator to decide his own jurisdiction. This decision is, however, subject to challenge by the courts. AA 1996, s 48(3) confers on the arbitrator the power, unless otherwise agreed by the parties, to (a) order a party to do or refrain from doing anything; (b) order the specific performance of a contract (other than a contract relating to land); and (c) order the rectification, setting aside or cancellation of a deed or other document.

Before an arbitration can be commenced, a dispute or difference must have arisen between the parties. AA 1996 states that the word 'dispute' includes 'difference'. A dispute can be generated by one party making the claim or assertion and the other party rejecting it. A claim on its own does not create a dispute.

A problem, disagreement or difference between parties on a project does not become a dispute automatically, however heated the disagreement may become. What amounts to a 'dispute' has been decided by the courts several times in relation to arbitration and particularly in recent years following the introduction of statutory adjudication (see below). In both arbitration and adjudication a 'dispute' needs to have crystallised before the dispute resolution procedure can be entered into. One party needs to make a claim that is rejected by the other party, thus creating the dispute.

Once a dispute has arisen, recourse to the contract would be required to determine the identity of the arbitrator or, in default of an arbitrator being named in the contract, the arbitrator nominating body.

Notice of the reference of a dispute to arbitration must be served by one party (the claimant) on the other party (the respondent) before the reference to the arbitrator can be made.

(d) The tribunal

The contract will state whether there is to be one or more arbitrators that hear the dispute. This is the tribunal, or arbitral panel, however it is composed. The arbitral panel must be impartial. While AA 1996 requires the arbitrator to act 'judicially', the role of the arbitrator differs from that of a judge, in that a judge is appointed by the state and an arbitrator is appointed by the parties. The arbitrator owes a duty to the parties themselves and is not accountable to Parliament or the general public as a judge is. One of the most important differences between an arbitrator and a judge is that the arbitrator may be chosen because of his expertise in the subject matter of the dispute. While TCC judges are legally trained and have gained technical knowledge of construction disputes, an arbitral panel can include experts in the field of the dispute, for example project management or tunnelling.

The JCT and ICE forms of contract refer specifically to one arbitrator and the remainder of this chapter assumes one arbitrator deciding the dispute.

(e) Appointing the arbitrator

The arbitrator or arbitrator appointing body may be named in the contract. In default of either being mentioned, an appointment can be made by agreement between the parties, in which case the claimant will usually suggest names of arbitrators to the respondent, who will either agree or suggest alternative names.

Arbitration proceedings are conducted in a manner that closely mirrors court proceedings. The timetable can require statements of case, disclosure of documents, witness statements and oral evidence, closely following the CPR. Arbitrators do, however, have a very wide discretion as to the way the proceedings before them are conducted, whereas the courts are bound by the CPR. Note that arbitrators may be bound by the rules under which they may act[2].

While there can be a close relationship between arbitration procedure and the CPR, AA 1996 states that intervention by the courts should be restricted. The court is not jealous of the powers conferred on arbitrators and will intervene only when asked to do so.

---

2   There are several rules, for example JCT Rules, ICE Rules, CIMAR Rules.

The arbitrator's authority depends upon the scope of the agreement in the contract and whether that contract refers to any rules or model. The rules or model define the procedure that will be used, subject to the arbitrator's overall discretion.

In all cases the arbitrator's power is that provided for by AA 1996. The arbitrator must also comply with the rules of natural justice and the continuing development of case law affecting arbitration.

It was not until 1999 that TCC judges were held to have the same powers as arbitrators to 'open up, review and revise any certificate' in the JCT arbitration clause[3].This was previously considered to create a power exclusively to be exercised by an arbitrator.

Arbitration also differs from court procedure in relation to joinder of multiple parties. As an arbitration agreement flows from the contract, there is privity of contract between the parties and it is only the signatory to the contract who can be involved in the arbitration dispute. Other parties may only be joined into the arbitration with the consent of all parties. In court, any party may, with permission if out of time, bring in other parties to the proceedings as second or third defendants or as Part 20 defendants.

AA 1996 confers more power on the arbitrator to deal efficiently with proceedings. AA 1996, s 1(b) states that 'the parties should be free to agree how their disputes are resolved, subject only to such safeguards as are necessary in the public interest'. The arbitrator has power to decide all procedural and evidential matters unless the parties have entered into further written agreement separate from the agreement to arbitrate in the contract.

(f) Arbitration procedure

The common procedure is to make an application for the appointment of an arbitrator to the appropriate authority provided for in the arbitration agreement. Once he has been nominated or appointed the arbitrator will contact each of the parties concerned, informing them of his nomination or appointment. This can be an important point in the process, as the referral of a dispute to an arbitrator can cause parties to re-evaluate their positions and enter into settlement negotiations.

If the dispute still remains unresolved, and one or more of the parties wishes to progress the arbitration, a preliminary meeting or case management meeting will be called by the arbitrator, usually at his office or other neutral ground. Directions will be set at this meeting for the remainder of the arbitration procedure.

---

3   *Beaufort Developments v Gilbert Ash NI* [1999] 1 AC 266, HL.

An arbitration may take place either on a documents-only basis or with an oral hearing. In the case of a documents-only arbitration, there is usually provision for leave to apply for an oral hearing. In any event, the arbitrator has the power to call for an oral hearing if, in his opinion, it would assist him with his function. The oral hearing will be the final stage of the arbitration procedure before the award. Like a trial in the TCC, the parties will present legal argument, oral witness and expert evidence to the arbitrator. Simple disputes are ideally suited to documents-only arbitrations, whereas more complex disputes need oral hearings to allow parties to put their case.

Usually the arbitrator will be unaware of the extent and initial detail of the dispute until the initial meeting is held. Both parties to the dispute and the arbitrator should realise from the outset that they are there to help each other, and that the arbitrator is interested in the proper carriage of justice.

Whether the arbitration is on a documents-only basis or is to be by way of an oral hearing, the parties should agree as many facts as possible. Where these are not agreed, the rules of evidence should be applied, or a variation of the rules be agreed or directed. Arbitration on a documents-only basis is often speedier and less costly than an oral hearing.

(g) Evidence

An arbitrator is in charge of his own procedure, but he must of course conduct himself in a proper manner. He must, for instance, have a regard to the rules of evidence, though these may be varied or even disregarded altogether if the parties agree. In so doing, the alteration should be made to assist the arbitration process and not be against the wishes of one or both parties. Furthermore, the arbitrator should give the parties adequate notice of his intended departure from normal procedure.

Only relevant evidence will be admissible, and opinion evidence will be admissible only if given by an expert in a particular field.

Evidence which is privileged, for example correspondence marked 'without prejudice', is not admissible if it relates to the dispute in question and will not be seen by the arbitrator until after he has published his award.

Whereas an arbitrator may take into account his own skill and experience, he is not allowed to take into account evidence which he has gained himself without first notifying the parties and seeking their reaction to it.

AA 1996, s 38(5) states that an arbitrator may insist that each witness is examined on oath or affirmation.

(h) Disclosure

As under the CPR, disclosure may take place in arbitration where either party may examine the documents of the other if it is reasonable to suppose the document contains information to advance a party's own case or to damage that of their opponent. Disclosure must be limited to matters which are in issue.

The arbitrator's powers to order disclosure are contained in AA 1996, s 34(2)(d).

(i) Legal disputes

A legal dispute concerning some aspect of the arbitration may be decided by the court if:

- under AA 1996, s 45 the arbitrator gives consent in that respect; or
- both parties agree to refer it to the court.

Alternatively, the legal dispute may be settled by the arbitrator himself. In respect of this task he will be guided by the lawyers acting for each of the parties to the dispute. In addition, an arbitrator may seek the guidance and assistance of a legal assessor. However, in such a case the arbitrator's decision must ultimately be his own.

Assuming that the legal dispute is referred to the court, the court in deciding the matter would first note whether an agreement exists between the parties which excludes their right to seek an appeal or reasons. Secondly, the court will bear in mind whether the dispute substantially affects the right of one or both of the parties and whether there would be a significant saving of costs. The legal dispute may then be referred back to the arbitrator.

(j) The award

AA 1996, s 47 provides that, unless the parties otherwise agree, the arbitrator may make more than one award at different times on different aspects of the matter to be determined. All that is required of the arbitrator is that the award should specify the issue or claim or part of the claim that is the subject of the award. These awards will usually carry the term 'Interim Award'. The term 'Final Award' is usually reserved to the last award in time and is the award that deals with all outstanding matters.

The award may be a reasoned award or an award without reasons. The parties may wish to have the matter of costs resolved as a separate and later issue. In such a case, the award will be 'Final Save as to Costs' and later a 'Final Award' will be given.

The award should:

- be dated and set out the nature of the dispute;

- give the identity of the parties and their representatives;

- list the documents received;

- mention any inspections that have been carried out and their date;

- summarise the claims of each party;

- state the date and authority of the arbitration appointment or nomination;

- clearly state the award in a way that is unambiguous.

If the award is reasoned, it should also give a decision on each issue and the reasons for the decision and rejection of the alternative view.

Once the award is published, the arbitrator will normally issue it to the parties on payment of his fees in full, but not otherwise. If the award is 'final save as to costs' it will also be accompanied with further directions as to costs, or at least seek confirmation that such directions are still required.

The arbitrator's award should ordinarily be in writing and be carefully drafted and checked by the arbitrator, since it cannot be altered at a later date.

AA 1996, s 48 states that the arbitrator may award the following remedies:

> 48(3) The tribunal may make a declaration as to any matter to be determined in the proceedings.
> (4) The tribunal may order the payment of a sum of money, in any currency.
> (5) The tribunal has the same powers as the Court –
>> (a) To order a party to do or refrain from doing anything;
>> (b) To order a specific performance of a contract (other than a contract relating to land);
>> (c) To order the rectification, setting aside or cancellation of a deed or other document.

(k) Costs

Traditionally, the arbitrator should adhere broadly to the principles adopted in the TCC in relation to costs that the successful party should receive their costs from the unsuccessful party. Where there is a claim and a counterclaim, each must be considered in relation to costs. However, an arbitrator will frequently reflect all cost matters in one global order such as that one party is awarded a proportion of their costs.

These broad principles have now been codified by AA 1996, s 61(2) which states that:

> ... unless the parties otherwise agree, the tribunal shall award costs on the general principle that costs should follow the event except where it appears to the tribunal that in the circumstances it is not appropriate in relation to the whole or part of the costs.

A party may protect their position in relation to costs in one of two ways. First, a party may apply to the arbitrator for a limit to be applied to the amount of recoverable costs in the arbitration. The arbitrator's powers to impose a cost cap are contained in AA 1996, s 65. This cost cap is unique to arbitration and can be a useful tactic for a party to use if their opponent is using a large team of lawyers and experts on a case where, given the amount in dispute, the fees for professional services would be disproportionate.

Secondly, a party may protect their position on costs by making an offer, known as a *Calderbank* offer, without prejudice save as to costs. These *Calderbank* offers cannot be drawn to the attention of the arbitrator until the award has been published and the issue of costs is to be decided. If during the course of the proceedings the unsuccessful party has offered to settle the dispute for a sum of money in excess of that now awarded to the successful party, this can be drawn to the attention of the arbitrator in respect of costs and the traditional costs awards usually made.

Any provision in the arbitration agreement which fetters the arbitrator's discretion in respect of the apportionment and assessment of costs is void in law; however, such agreements may be made once the dispute has arisen. The arbitrator has the discretion to apportion the costs of each of the parties as well as his own costs and fees.

As stated above, the award may be 'final save as to costs' where the arbitrator will receive representations on costs once liability has been dealt with.

The arbitrator also has power to assess the costs that he has apportioned, although it is possible for the arbitrator to ask the High Court to carry out this task. Assessment is a process applied to all fees at arbitration (including the arbitrator's), allowing them to be moderated to what is reasonable in the circumstances.

(l) Appeals on a point of law

The appeal may be made with the consent of all parties to the reference or by leave of the court, subject to the parties not having entered into an exclusion agreement as defined in AA 1996, s 5. AA 1996, s 70 also requires all other appeals or reviews to have been exhausted.

AA 1996, s 69(3) gives guidelines as to when leave to appeal should be given:

- If the rights of one or more of the parties is substantially affected.

- If the original tribunal was asked to determine the question.

- If the decision of the original tribunal is obviously wrong.

- If it is a point of general public importance and the view of the original tribunal is open to doubt.

In all events, it must be, in the view of the court, right and proper for it to determine the question.

Where the parties agree to have an unreasoned award, they automatically agree to exclude their right of appeal on a point of law (AA 1996, s 69(1)).

(m) Challenging the award

A party may challenge an award:

- due to lack of substantive jurisdiction (AA 1996, s 67);

- due to a serious irregularity (AA 1996, s 68).

1 JURISDICTION

The court may dismiss such an application, or declare the award to be either wholly or partly of no effect.

2 IRREGULARITY

AA 1996 sets out what amounts to irregularity and also requires that owing to this irregularity substantial injustice will result.

The grounds are contained in AA 1996, ss 68(2)(a)–(i). They deal with such issues as fraud, failure to deal with all issues, uncertainty or ambiguity of the award, and failure to follow the correct procedure.

If the court is satisfied that there has been a serious irregularity, it may remit the award in whole or part for reconsideration, or set it aside in whole or in part. In all cases, appeals and challenges must be made within 28 days of the date of the award.

(n) Enforcement

An arbitration award does not of itself compel the losing party to comply with its terms. The court must be requested to enforce the award as a judgment[4]. Alternatively, the party seeking to enforce the award may bring an action on the award as a contract if the award is for a sum of money and may seek to enter summary judgment of the amount awarded. The losing party may in either case object to enforcement on grounds such as that the arbitrator had no jurisdiction. Similar challenges are frequently made in relation to adjudication (see below).

(o) International arbitration

International arbitration is arbitration between parties based in different states. Arbitration is the most effective mechanism for resolving international disputes, as neither party will be keen to submit to the jurisdiction of the courts in the other party's country. Arbitration provides flexibility in relation to forum, rules, arbitrators and language that a national court could not provide. Under the New York Convention 1958, to which virtually every country is a signatory, international arbitration awards can be enforced far more easily than foreign judgments. Project Managers should note that the degree to which signatories to the New York Convention have agreed to abide by the rules in relation to enforcement differs from country to country.

The United Kingdom is frequently used as a seat of international arbitration and many disputes are conducted in the English language and under English law. They may be wholly foreign cases, where an English arbitrator may be appointed to act between parties between different states, or one party may be from the UK and another party from another state. Project Managers on large international projects should be aware of the arbitration clause in the contract and note whether the dispute resolution procedure is governed by English law and where the seat of the arbitration is. AA 1996 has unified all English arbitration law, which includes international arbitrations governed by English law.

There are many forms of rules that govern international arbitration and there are in theory four different laws which may affect the conduct of an international arbitration:

1   The law governing the underlying contract, applicable to the merits of the case (substantive law).

2   The law governing the agreement to arbitrate which will be the same as 1 (if contained in the contract).

---

4   AA 1996, s 66.

3   The law governing the arbitration proceedings (the procedural law).

4   The law governing the submission to arbitration (which may in theory be different from 1 to 3 above)[5].

The most popular arbitration clause used in international construction contracts provides for arbitration under the ICC Rules of Arbitration, and we shall concentrate in this chapter on that procedure to illustrate international arbitration.

(p) Arbitration under the ICC Rules

The ICC Court of Arbitration in Paris is the most prestigious international arbitration institution. An ICC arbitration may have arbitrators of any nationality sitting on panels hearing disputes in any part of the world in a variety of languages. The ICC Rules are governed by the ICC Court of Arbitration, which appoints or confirms the appointment of the arbitrators and, in the absence of agreement between the parties, confirms the place of the arbitration. The court sets a timetable for the dispute and scrutinises the format of awards handed down under the procedure.

ICC Procedure

The arbitrator	If the parties do not agree on whether the dispute should be heard by a sole arbitrator or by a panel of three, the court will appoint the arbitrator. The arbitrator must be independent of the parties and, if challenged by either party, the court will consider his replacement.		
Statements of case	The ICC Rules allow for the exchange of statements of case, the timetable for which is as follows:		
	Document	**Party serving**	**Time limit**
	Request for arbitration	Claimant	Subject to limitation
	Answer to request and any counterclaim	Respondent	30 days
	Reply to counterclaim	Claimant	30 days from counterclaim

---

5   *Black-Clawson v Papier werk AG* [1981] 2 Lloyd's Rep 446.

Terms of reference	Before proceeding any further the arbitrator will draft terms of reference which contain a summary of the claims and counterclaims and a list of issues in dispute. The document will also set out procedural rules that must be followed. A meeting may be called after the arbitrator publishes his terms of reference to allow the parties and the arbitrator to achieve a better understanding of the issues. General procedural matters will also be dealt with here.
The proceedings	Article 20(1) of the ICC Rules states that the arbitrator has to establish the facts 'by all appropriate means'. The arbitrator can decide the dispute solely on the documents or may require oral evidence and representations at a meeting. The hearing is in private unless the parties the arbitrator agree otherwise.
The award	The arbitrator may make a partial award (see interim awards above) before he makes his final award, which must be made no later than six months after the terms of reference are approved by the court. The final award has to fix the costs of the arbitration. The award is final and the parties are deemed to have given an undertaking to carry out the effect of the award without delay. There is no form of appeal against an ICC award.

Given the short timetable, the requirement to reach an award within six months of agreeing the terms of reference and the absence of a right of appeal, international arbitrations under the ICC lead to an award far more quickly than their English domestic counterparts. This may account for the five percent increase in referrals to the ICC every year since 1997.

4 Adjudication

We have assumed that most Project Managers reading this book will be involved with managing construction projects. The most important development in construction dispute resolution in recent years is statutory adjudication, introduced by the Construction Act 1996. Any party to a 'construction contract' that relates to construction 'operations' (see below) which includes an agreement to do architectural, design, or surveying work can refer a dispute to adjudication under the Act. The role of the Project Manager may therefore be covered by the Construction Act.

(a) Adjudication and the Project Manager

Project Managers need to be aware of the adjudication procedure because:

- they may be involved in a dispute with the client, or
- the client may be involved in a dispute with which they need to assist,

both of which could be referred to adjudication.

The Project Manager can be a party to an adjudication with the client under both APM and RICS forms of appointment. The Project Manager can be asked to assist the client who more frequently becomes involved in disputes that are referred to adjudication.

(b) The contract

Before we look at the statutory regulations and case law that form the law on adjudication, the Project Manager needs to be aware that the first port of call should be the contract. The statutory right to refer most construction disputes (see below for exceptions) does not apply to some contracts, most importantly for contracts with residential occupiers. This does not mean that the dispute resolution clause in the contract cannot provide for adjudication as the mechanism. Project Managers should consider when entering into a contract with a client whether they wish to have disputes dealt with by adjudication.

I REQUIREMENTS OF THE CONSTRUCTION ACT

The Construction Act states that any party to a construction contract may at any time refer a dispute arising under that contract to adjudication. The party referring the dispute is known as the 'referring party'. The other party is known as the 'responding party'. The contract between the parties must be in writing.

Several types of work that would generally be considered to be construction operations are not covered by the Construction Act. For example, the following are excluded from reference to adjudication under the Construction Act:

- Drilling for oil or natural gas;
- Mining;
- Construction of plant for nuclear processing, power generation, or water or effluent treatment;
- Constructing equipment for the production, transmission, processing or bulk storage of chemicals, pharmaceuticals, oil, gas, steel, or food and drink;

276

- Any contracts for the making, installation and repair of artistic works, such as sculptures, murals and other works that are wholly artistic in nature.

CASE LAW

Interpretation of 'construction operations'

Gibson Lea Interiors Ltd v Makro Self Service Wholesalers Ltd[6]

Was shopfitting a construction operation?

The Construction Act 1996, s 105(1)(c) defines 'installation in any building or structure of fittings forming part of the land' as a construction operation. Judge Seymour QC thought that shopfitting did not amount to a construction operation unless it consisted of the construction of 'structures forming, or to form, part of the land' or 'installation in any building or structure of fittings forming part of the land', as set out in the Construction Act, s 105(1)(a) and (c). None of the shopfitting items supplied by Gibson Lea were held to be fixtures.

The Act did not apply, and as the dispute between the parties should not have been referred to adjudication, Judge Seymour refused to enforce the adjudicator's decision.

CASE LAW

Interpretation of 'construction operations'

Gillies Ramsy Diamond v PJW Enterprises Ltd[7]

A claim for professional negligence against Diamond, who had provided general consultancy services in relation to a building project, was referred to adjudication. It was found that these services included arranging construction operations for others and/or contract administration and therefore the matter could be referred to adjudication, despite the absence of an adjudication clause in the contract.

---

6   [2001] BLR 407.
7   [2003] BLR 48.

The Construction Act requires the parties' contract to allow a dispute to be referred to adjudication. The contract must also provide a timetable ensuring the appointment of the adjudicator and referral of the dispute to him within seven days after the notice of adjudication. The adjudicator must be bound to reach a decision within 28 days of referral, or within a longer period if agreed by the parties (after the dispute has been referred). In the absence of such a clause in the parties' contract, the Construction Act states that the Scheme for Construction Contracts (England and Wales) Regulations 1998 (the scheme) will apply.

In order for a reference to adjudication to be valid, one of the key elements is that there must be a 'dispute'.

CASE LAW

Had the adjudicator heard a fully formed dispute?

Fastrack Contractors Ltd v Morrison Construction Ltd and Imreglio UK[8]

Morrison, the main contractor, had refused to pay Fastrack, the sub-contractor, under their application for payment number 12. Morrison alleged poor performance by Fastrack, which Morrison were intending to ask others to complete. Fastrack believed this was without justification and a breach of contract, and withdrew from the site. Fastrack made a further interim application, number 13, against which Morrison attempted to set-off in respect of its alleged entitlement to damages and additional completion costs of the sub-contract. Fastrack went to adjudication in respect of application number 12, and was awarded £35,199.70.

Fastrack then issued a second notice of adjudication claiming a sum higher than the gross sum forming application number 13. Morrison contended that the second adjudicator had no jurisdiction, as there was no current dispute that could be referred to adjudication. The adjudicator held that he had jurisdiction and awarded £120,601.68 to Fastrack, including the sum of £35,199.70 awarded on the previous adjudication.

Fastrack went to the TCC to enforce the adjudicator's decision. Judge Thornton QC held that whether or not the reference was wholly or partly lacking in jurisdiction would depend on the nature and extent of the dispute that had purportedly been referred to adjudication. A particular dispute could put simply as 'what sum is due?' without any particular sum being included as

8 [2000] BLR 168.

part of that claim. A claim and its submission did not necessarily constitute a 'dispute' for the purposes of the Construction Act, s 108, as a dispute only arose when a claim had been notified and rejected, either by the opposing party refusing to answer the claim or where there had been a bare rejection of a claim.

On the facts, there were disputed issues that had arisen separately from the issue of application number 13, and all were in dispute by the date that the Notice of Adjudication was served. Those disputed issues had been referred by Fastrack to Morrison, had been rejected by Morrison, and had therefore developed into disputes by the time the second Notice of Adjudication had been served. The adjudicator therefore did have jurisdiction to conduct the adjudication and to make an award in favour of Fastrack.

Some contracts may contain a bespoke adjudication procedure, some may refer to a set of rules published by a nominating body, and others will be silent in relation to adjudication. The most popular adjudication procedure, used in default of any mention of a procedure in the contract, is the scheme, and the procedure explained in this section is based on the scheme.

(c) Appointment of the adjudicator

The adjudicator may be named in the contract or selected from a nominating body for his particular expertise in an area. The RICS has a list of adjudicators, as does the Technology and Construction Court's Solicitors' Association (TeCSA). It is for the parties to decide whether they wish a surveyor, an engineer, or a lawyer to hear their adjudication. The nominating body will then select an adjudicator from their list, depending on their availability. Our experience of the TeCSA procedure is that, following a request from the referring party for an adjudicator to be appointed by the nominating body, TeCSA ask a selection of the adjudicators on their list (chosen in alphabetical blocks), to confirm by return of facsimile that they are able to hear the dispute. The first adjudicator to respond saying he is available will be appointed.

The Notice of Adjudication must set out in writing the nature of the dispute and the parties involved, details of where the dispute has arisen, the nature of redress sought and the names and addresses of the parties to the contract. This Notice must be served on every other party to the contract and upon the adjudicator once appointed.

Once the Notice has been served, the adjudicator must be appointed for the procedure to continue. A Notice of Adjudication may be sufficient to bring the other party to the negotiating table and no adjudicator will be needed. The first port of call is the contract, which will either specify a named adjudicator, a nominating body or both. If none of these are contained in the contract, the referring party shall select an adjudicator nominating body and approach that body to appoint an adjudicator.

An individual adjudicator named in the contract must confirm whether he is willing to act within two days. If the adjudicator is unwilling to act or fails to respond, the referring party may request another adjudicator named in the contract to act. If there is no such adjudicator named, the referring party may approach the nominating body (if any) named in the contract. If there is no nominating body named, the referring party may approach any nominating body to select an adjudicator. This person shall indicate whether they can act within two days.

If the adjudicator is appointed by a nominating body, the nominating body must communicate the selection of an adjudicator to the referring party within five days. If no response is given within five days, the referring party can either agree with the responding party the identity of another adjudicator or request another nominating body to select an adjudicator. The new adjudicator shall confirm his willingness to act within two days.

The scheme states that, regardless of how the adjudicator is nominated, the referring party shall serve a Referral Notice, which is his statement of case in the adjudication together with any documents in support of his case, on the adjudicator and the other parties to the dispute not later than seven days from the notice of adjudication.

(c) Adjudication procedure

There is no set timetable for the intervening exchange of the responding party's statement of case or the referring party's reply. These matters are at the discretion of the adjudicator, who under the scheme has the power to give directions as to the timetable of the adjudication, the deadlines for written submissions, the length of those submissions and whether further oral representations will be required. The adjudicator may request a meeting with the parties where he may question any of the parties or their representatives. He may also carry out site inspections, tests and experiments.

(d) The decision

The scheme requires the adjudicator to reach his decision not later than 28 days after the date of the Referral Notice or 42 days after the Referral Notice if the referring party consents. This can be extended further with the agreement of all parties.

If one party requests the adjudicator to give reasons for his decision he must do so. He is not bound to do so if neither party requests.

In the absence of any specific time period in which the parties must comply with the decision, the scheme states that the parties shall comply with the decision immediately.

If a party does not comply with the adjudicator's decision, an abridged summary judgment procedure can be used in the TCC to enforce the decision.

If the paying party wishes to contest the finding of the adjudicator and the TCC judge at the enforcement hearing, the entire dispute may be re-heard by a TCC judge or arbitrator, depending on the contract. The unsuccessful party will however still have to pay the successful party the amount awarded in the decision and the costs of the enforcement process, and be out of funds for the duration of the forthcoming proceedings (in our experience up to 18 months or even longer).

(e) Costs

The scheme states that the adjudicator is entitled to his reasonably incurred fees and expenses, for which both parties are jointly and severally liable. The adjudicator may, however, order how his fees are to be apportioned. The fees may be apportioned 50/50 between the parties, or the unsuccessful party may be ordered to pay all the adjudicator's fees.

Unlike in litigation and arbitration, the adjudicator does not have the power to order either party to pay the other party's legal costs.

This decision does not prevent the parties agreeing that one party will bear all of the costs and the adjudicator's fees.

CASE LAW

Costs in adjudication

Bridgeway Construction Ltd v Tolent Construction Ltd[9]

The parties had agreed in their contract that the party issuing and pursuing a notice of adjudication should bear both parties' costs and the adjudicator's fees. Bridgeway served a notice of adjudication and a decision was made in

---

9 [2000] CILL 1662.

their favour. Tolent paid Bridgeway in accordance with the decision, but the sum paid was the decision less Tolent's costs. Bridgeway contested this matter but Mackay J held that the contract had been freely negotiated between the parties and was not void or voidable. The Construction Act 1996 was of no assistance to the judge, as it is silent on costs.

Project Managers should be aware of any such clauses in contracts that deal with the costs of adjudication proceedings.

(f) Enforcement

Project Managers need to be aware if they are involved in an adjudication that the adjudicator's decision is immediately payable. If the unsuccessful party refuses to pay, the decision can be enforced by an abbreviated procedure in the TCC. The role of the TCC in this procedure is not to re-hear the arguments put before the adjudicator, but to decide whether the adjudication procedure was followed correctly.

It is at the enforcement stage where the challenges to the validity of the adjudicator's decision will first be raised. Several challenges to the validity of an adjudicator's jurisdiction have been raised since 1998 when AA 1996 came into force. Other areas of successful challenge have included bias by the adjudicator and the insolvency of the paying party.

(g) Challenging the decision – jurisdiction

The enforcement procedure following an adjudicator's decision is the first opportunity for an aggrieved party to challenge the adjudicator and the most popular challenge to date has been to his jurisdiction.

The general rule in relation to challenges to the adjudicator's jurisdiction remains that an adjudicator must either step outside the boundaries of the dispute referred to him or act with bias for his decision to be unenforceable.

The first reported challenge to an adjudicator's jurisdiction that went to the Court of Appeal asked the question whether an error made by an adjudicator meant that his decision was void and could not be enforced.

CASE LAW

Challenging the adjudicator's decision

Bouygues UK Ltd v Dahl-Jensen UK Ltd[10]

The test was that if the adjudicator had answered the right question in the wrong way his decision would be binding, whereas if he had answered the wrong question, his decision would be a nullity.

The 'question' is that put to the adjudicator by the referring party at the outset of the adjudication process and determines the scope of the dispute and the adjudicator's jurisdiction.

C & B Scene Concept Design Ltd v Isobars Ltd[11]

In relation to a mistake by an adjudicator that, despite his error, there was 'entire agreement as to the scope of the dispute'. The adjudicator had made an error of law but had not exceeded his jurisdiction. His decision was therefore binding. The Court of Appeal said:

> It is important that the enforcement of an adjudicator's decision by summary judgment should not be prevented by arguments that the adjudicator has made errors of law in reaching his decision, unless the adjudicator has purported to decide matters that are not referred to him.

RG Carter Ltd v Edmund Nuttall Ltd[12]

A dispute arose between the parties when Carter put forward a claim for delay, loss and expense. No settlement was achieved and the matter was referred to adjudication. The adjudicator took into account a report prepared on behalf of Carter that detailed the alleged losses, but differed from their original claim, as the losses detailed in it were slightly lower than originally claimed and were made out under different heads. Carter were successful before the adjudicator and went to the TCC to enforce the decision.

Nuttal argued that the adjudicator's decision was not binding on it and was unenforceable, since they were unaware of the report and the report could

---

10 [2000] BLR 522, CA.
11 [2002] EWCA Civ 46, [2002] BLR 93.
12 [2002] BLR 359.

therefore not have been the subject of a dispute. The question for the court was 'what constituted a dispute?'

Judge Seymour held that an adjudicator had jurisdiction only to determine disputes that were the subject of a notice of referral to him, and could not decide on matters not within such a notice. A dispute was different from a claim. Although a dispute could also be a claim, there was more to a dispute than a mere claim that has not been accepted. 'Dispute' was to be given its ordinary English meaning and an essential feature was the formulation of arguments on both sides. The dispute referred to the adjudicator consisted of the unresolved earlier claims and not those as formulated in the later report on which the adjudicator relied. Although the matters in that report could subsequently have developed into a dispute, they were not part of the dispute as at the time of the adjudicator's decision. Accordingly, the adjudicator had acted outside his jurisdiction and his decision was unenforceable.

CASE LAW

Other challenges to the adjudicator

Austin Hall Building Services v Buckland Securities Ltd[13]

Here a party on the receiving end of an adjudicator's decision against them attempted a challenge to the decision based on the Human Rights Act 1998 (HRA 1998). HRA 1998 enshrines many basic human rights, such as the right to free speech, the right to peaceful family life and the right to a fair trial. It is in relation to a fair trial that the challenge was made. Austin Hall claimed that adjudication did not allow a fair trial, as public authorities cannot act in a way contrary to HRA 1998, which they argued the adjudicator had. Bowsher J ruled that this challenge failed, as an adjudicator was not a public body and not bound by HRA 1998. A judge would be a public body as he gives an enforceable judgment. An adjudicator's decision, on the other hand, requires a further step to become enforceable.

Discain Project Services v Opecprime Developments Ltd[14]

Judge Bowsher QC found that the conduct of an adjudicator who held unilateral telephone conversations with one party and did not report them

13 [2001] BLR 272.
14 [2001] BLR 285.

> to the other party acted in a manner that could be perceived as being biased. As bias was a breach of natural justice, the decision was not enforced.
>
> The perception that an adjudicator was biased, even though he was not, was sufficient for a challenge to an adjudicator's decision to succeed.

Project Managers involved in an adjudication should note that if the adjudicator contacts them unilaterally they should report it to the other party. Failure to do so may lead to them not being able to enforce a decision in their favour.

Statistically, it is the referring party who has been more successful in adjudications to date. The main reason for this is that adjudication is a front loaded process and parties may spend as much time as they like preparing for their adjudication. The responding party is on the back foot from day one, in that they have a strictly limited time period in which to formulate replies to the claims that their opponents have taken some months to formulate.

5 Alternative dispute resolution

Many forms of Alternative Dispute Resolution (ADR) are available to parties to a dispute. In general terms, ADR refers to dispute resolution that produces a non-binding result, where no decisions can be imposed on the parties by a third party, such as a judge, arbitrator or adjudicator.

ADR has become increasingly important since the CPR were introduced, as the courts are seeking to reduce the number of disputes being litigated. Statutory adjudication has further eased the burden on the TCC in relation to construction disputes.

Agreeing to undertake some form of ADR is usually a voluntary arrangement entered into by the parties, but ADR as a first step before either litigation or arbitration is commenced can be prescribed by the contract.

(a) Forms of ADR

There are various forms of ADR, all of which have the common features of an informal procedure conducted by a third party who attempts to assist the parties in achieving settlement of their dispute. The third party may be asked to give a ruling, which will not usually be binding. If the parties wish to be bound by the outcome of the ADR procedure they may enter into an enforceable agreement that ratifies the settlement.

The main forms of ADR used in England and Wales are as follows:

I MEDIATION

Mediation is a non-binding process in which both parties attempt to negotiate the settlement of their dispute assisted by a neutral third party (the mediator).

2 CONCILIATION

This is effectively negotiation between two or more parties assisted by a third party who will try to facilitate a settlement. Mainly public bodies provide this form of ADR and the procedures and rules are governed by statute. The conciliator is more interventionist than a mediator in private disputes.

3 NEGOTIATION

Negotiation does not require a third party to assist. The parties deal directly with each other in attempting to resolve the dispute. This is usually the first step taken in any dispute to try and resolve it, either with the parties acting alone or through their legal representatives. Any settlement reached in negotiation can be formalised in a settlement agreement, which can be an enforceable contract.

4 NEUTRAL EVALUATION

Here a third party selected by the parties is asked to give an opinion on the merits of the dispute. Neutral evaluation gives parties a realistic early and neutral assessment of the strength of their case, as it is a similar procedure to putting a case before an arbitrator or judge. The procedure can be useful in construction disputes where technical issues need to be decided and the parties effectively need a third expert to decide on an issue where, for example, the parties' experts have become entrenched.

A meeting may be held with the evaluator for each party to put their case. In simple disputes the matter can be dealt with on documents only.

5 FACILITATION

A facilitator attempts, as his title suggests, to facilitate settlement between the parties. He does so by assisting the parties with matters such as information gathering, fact finding, chairing round tables meetings and so on. The facilitator does not come to a binding decision, but assists the parties in negotiation.

There is a great deal of overlap between facilitation and mediation, which is discussed in detail below.

(b) Approach of the court to ADR

If the contract allows the dispute to be dealt with by litigation, the CPR encourages ADR to save pressures on court time and unnecessary costs.

CASE LAW

The court's approach to ADR

Dunnett v Railtrack plc[15]

Here the Court of Appeal decided that a party who had refused to mediate a dispute before embarking on litigation should bear their own costs of the proceedings, despite having succeeded in the action. The Court of Appeal held that all steps should be taken to further the overriding objective in the CPR, which requires cases to be settled justly and with minimum expense.

(c) Contracts and ADR

ADR is increasingly stipulated in the contract between the parties as the first stage in the dispute resolution process. This reflects the view of the court under the CPR that the parties should use ADR first. This may appear an expensive hoop for the parties to jump through before they get down to the real fight in court.

The Project Manager should be aware that if he (or the client) decides not to go through the ADR process as a cost-saving measure, there may be a greater cost penalty to pay at the end of the litigation.

CASE LAW

Contract and ADR

Cable & Wireless plc v IBM United Kingdom Ltd[16]

Cable & Wireless (C&W) refused to enter into the alternative informal procedures for resolving disputes required by the parties' contract and was

---

15 [2002] EWCA Civ 303, [2002] 2 All ER 850.
16 [2002] EWHC 2059 (Comm), [2002] 2 All ER (Comm) 1041.

criticised by the court. The contract between C&W and IBM provided for any dispute to be resolved by negotiations between senior executives of the companies. If those negotiations failed to achieve a settlement, the contract required a further ADR procedure to be followed before court proceedings could commence.

C&W did not want to jump through the hoops provided by the contract – they wanted an enforceable judgment against IBM as quickly as possible. Colman J in the High Court decided that C&W had been too hasty – the contract provided for informal discussions followed by ADR before proceedings, and that is what C&W should have done.

The application in court by C&W was dismissed, to be heard again if the methods set out in the contract failed to produce a settlement.

The published judgment in C&W does not mention costs, but we consider it unlikely that C&W escaped without paying the costs of the abortive trip to court.

The Project Manager or his client, if they decide not to attempt ADR, may also miss out on an opportunity to settle their dispute amicably and without incurring large legal bills. ADR is also a good method of finding out exactly what the other party's case is and what you can expect to face in litigation or arbitration.

This judgment, together with that in *Dunnett v Railtrack*, shows that the English courts consider ADR to be a very important step in the dispute resolution process, and a step that can be expensive if an over-hasty litigant decides to miss it. It is possible to avoid ADR and proceed directly to litigation, but the party who refuses to adopt the ADR procedure must show that it was reasonable to do so, or that the delay before issuing formal proceedings would be harmful to their case.

Tiered dispute resolution clauses that require several stages of dispute resolution before litigation or arbitration can be commenced (as in C&W) are becoming increasingly popular in construction contracts, particularly on large PFI projects or in partnering contracts, where the emphasis is on minimising disputes and keeping the project on programme.

(d) Mediation

Mediation is the most popular form of ADR for domestic construction and commercial disputes, and that is what this section will concentrate on.

Mediation is a non-binding, without-prejudice process in which both parties attempt to negotiate the settlement of their dispute with the assistance of a neutral third party mediator who will try to find an acceptable middle ground for both parties. There are no strict rules of evidence or procedure, and the mediator does not have to impose a decision on the parties.

The mediator may hold separate discussions with each party and communicate one party's position to the other. The time spent in assessing what the other party wants to achieve in the mediation can be reduced by serving statements of case before the day of the mediation meeting.

1 THE MEDIATOR

Once the parties have agreed to refer the dispute to mediation they must find a mediator who is acceptable to them both and has the right characteristics to deal with the case. The mediator should be a creative problem-solver, a good listener and an effective communicator. His role is not to apportion blame or impose his views on the parties but to assist them in arriving at a mutually satisfactory solution to their problem.

The mediator will be appointed for his suitability to the particular dispute. In a dispute involving project management this may be a Project Manager, a construction professional or a construction lawyer. Mediators can be appointed directly or via a nominating body, the best known of which is the Centre for Effective Dispute Resolution (CEDR).

2 THE MEDIATION PROCESS

For the mediation process to commence, both parties must agree to mediate, as it is a voluntary process unless required by contract as in C&W. The process is usually started by both parties agreeing the identity of a mediator to whom they make a joint approach. Rarely, one party can approach a mediation organisation to invite them to ask the other party to attend a mediation.

The mediator, once appointed, will make directions for a meeting to be held between the parties. Statements of case may be served by the parties prior to the mediation. Under the CEDR procedure these are known as 'statements of position'.

The meeting itself can take various forms, depending on the individual mediator and the wishes of the parties. All mediations should allow for the mediator to meet with the parties individually, whereas some mediators may hear all parties together, perhaps at the start of the meeting before the parties separate. The mediator will attempt to facilitate a settlement by moving between the parties, conveying the views and positions of the other, until, hopefully, common ground can be found and a settlement achieved.

While there is no set procedure to follow in mediation, most mediations take a form similar to the one set out as follows.

1   The mediator convenes a joint meeting at which each party is given the opportunity to present its case, usually in a set period of time (15 minutes to 2 hours).

2   Each party goes into a private session. The mediator then moves from party to party, hearing more about their respective positions. If the mediator is told anything in these private sessions he needs the permission of that party to reveal that information to the other party.

3   The mediator should not impose his views on the parties – he may express opinions or pose questions to try to get the parties to truly assess the strengths and weaknesses of their case. The mediator will also move between the parties with information or offers from one party to the other.

4   When an agreement has been reached, the mediator will call the parties together and they will draw up the agreement that forms the settlement.

3 ENFORCEMENT

If the mediation is successful and the parties enter into an agreement, this will be a binding and enforceable contract, breaches of which can be enforced in the manner prescribed in the agreement.

6 Conclusion

The table on pp 292–294 below is designed to provide an at-a-glance comparison between the various forms of dispute resolution available.

Litigation and arbitration provide final and binding decisions, although arbitration is private and more flexible in terms of the tribunal and the procedure.

Adjudication is available automatically for parties to most construction contracts and parties often make it a contractual requirement. It is a quick method of resolving a dispute; however, if one party is dissatisfied litigation or arbitration may follow.

ADR is increasingly popular and has the backing of the courts as, if successful, it can lead to a considerable saving in costs and court time. If not successful, it is merely a hurdle for parties to negotiate before embarking on a finally binding procedure.

If a dispute does arise, a Project Manager will be in the best position to assist his client if he is aware of the contractual provisions and the duties of the parties (a requirement of the APM contract) and the procedure for the dispute resolution mechanism set out in the contract. In the event of a significant dispute developing, the Project Manager should advise the client to seek legal advice as a matter of urgency. In these circumstances the Project Manager will become a key member of the team and will be relied upon by the lawyers to provide relevant facts and figures, usually at very short notice.

If the Project Manager becomes involved in a dispute with the client, he should be aware of his contractual obligations in the first instance. Knowledge of the dispute resolution procedure set out in the contract with the client may help, but legal advice should be obtained if the dispute is anything other than very simple.

Bibliography

Boule, L and Nesic M *Mediation – Principles, Process, Practice* (2001) Butterworths.

Furst S and Ramsey V (eds) *Keating on Building Contracts* (7th edn, 2001) Sweet and Maxwell.

Redmond J *Adjudication in Construction Contracts* (2001) Blackwell Science.

St John Sutton D, Kendall J and Gill J (eds) *Russell on Arbitration* (21st edn, 1997) Sweet and Maxwell.

Uff J *Construction Law* (7th edn, 1999) Sweet and Maxwell.

COMPARISONS OF THE TYPES OF DISPUTE RESOLUTION PROCESS FOR CONSTRUCTION DISPUTES

	County Court	Technology and Construction Court (TCC)
Availability of the option:	Subject to limitation periods, most claims can be taken through the County Court. There is no lower limit on the value of a dispute. Complex cases worth over £25,000 are referred to the Technology and Construction Court.	Subject to limitation periods, most claims can be taken through the courts. The lower limit for claims in the High Court is £25,000. *Note: A pre-action protocol should be followed before proceedings are commenced.*
Who hears the dispute:	A judge with general experience.	A specialist TCC judge experienced in construction related matters.
Public or private?	Hearings are held in public but reports of judgments are rarely made available.	Hearings are held in public and reports of judgments are generally available.
Timetable:	This is decided at the first Case Management Conference ('CMC') based on standard case management criteria set out in the CPR. County Court matters should reach trial within 6–12 months, depending on how busy the court is and the length of trial required.	Decided at the first CMC. Depending on the complexity of the case and the number of parties, a TCC action can take anything between 12 and 30 months.
Cost:	The CPR requires the costs to be proportionate to the amount in dispute. A solicitor will be required and possibly a barrister. Court fees will also be payable at various stages in the proceedings.	The legal costs are likely to be significant; however, the CPR require costs to be proportionate to the amount in dispute. A solicitor and barrister will be necessary to conduct the litigation. Court fees will also be payable at various stages in the proceedings.

Arbitration	Adjudication	Mediation
Subject to limitation periods and the existence in the contract of an agreement to arbitrate, parties may refer a dispute to arbitration. Most construction contracts (e g JCT and ICE) contain arbitration clauses.	There is a statutory right under the Construction Act to refer disputes under a construction contract (subject to some exceptions) to adjudication. There is no limit on the value of the dispute.	Mediation is optional for parties to a dispute, unless required by the contract (unusual). Note the attitude of the courts under CPR such as in *Dunnett.*
An arbitrator can be named in the contract or be selected by the parties or a nominating body for their particular area of expertise.	An adjudicator can be named in the contract or be selected by the parties or by a nominating body for their particular area of expertise.	Qualified mediators appointed either by agreement of the parties or through nominating bodies such as CEDR.
Arbitration is held in private and the award is confidential.	Adjudication is held in private and the decision is confidential. If the decision is challenged, this procedure is public and the judgment will be made available.	Mediation is confidential and the meetings are held in private.
The timetable is likely to be comparable with litigation. As one arbitrator is usually appointed, problems will occur if he becomes unavailable through ill health or otherwise.	The main attraction of adjudication is its speed. A decision must be given within 28 days. This can be increased to 42 days if the referring party consents or longer if all parties agree.	The timetable is agreed between the parties and is usually short.
The legal costs are likely to be comparable to litigation. Note that a cost cap can be requested. A solicitor and barrister are not necessary. In addition to the costs of litigation, arbitrator's fees are payable, charged by the hour. A venue for the hearing will also have to be hired and paid for.	Most of the costs will be incurred by the referring party in preparing its case, although the shortened process will involve intensive work by both parties. Due to the speed of process it is likely to be less expensive than litigation and arbitration. A solicitor and barrister are not necessary.	Costs are not awarded in mediation, unless agreed by the parties.

	County Court	Technology and Construction Court (TCC)
Recoverability of costs:	Costs are at the discretion of the court. The normal rule is that the loser pays their own and the winner's costs. *Note: A party's costs position can be protected by a CPR Part 36 offer.*	Costs are at the discretion of the court. The normal rule is that the loser pays their own that the loser pays their own and the winner's costs. *Note: A party's costs position can be protected by a CPR Part 36 offer.*
Enforcement:	A judgment can be enforced through the courts.	A judgment can be enforced through the courts.

Arbitration	Adjudication	Mediation
Costs are at the discretion of the arbitrator. The normal rule is that the loser pays their own and the winner's costs. *Note: A party's costs position can be protected by a 'Calderbank offer'.*	An adjudicator does not have the power to order either party to pay the other party's legal costs. The adjudicator will decide which party pays his fees and may apportion payment of his fees between the parties.	If costs are part of a mediation agreement, this document is a contract that can be enforced as such.
An award can be enforced through the courts.	An adjudicator's decision can be enforced via an abridged process in court. *Note: The dispute may also be re-heard in court if a party disputes the adjudicator's decision.*	If the parties enter into a mediation agreement, this document is a contract that can be enforced as such.

.

Index